12/6

A PICTORIAL DICTIONARY of the Animal World

A

A PICTORIAL DICTIONARY of the Animal World

AN ILLUSTRATED DEMONSTRATION OF TERMS USED IN ANIMAL BIOLOGY

Michael Chinery, B.A.

WITH OVER 500 COLOUR PICTURES

PUBLISHED BY
Sampson Low, Marston & Co. Ltd: *LONDON*

Library of Congress Catalog Card
Number: 66- 14644

MADE AND PRINTED BY PURNELL & SONS LTD.
Filmset by Cox & Sharland Ltd.

THE DICTIONARY

A note on the finding of pictorial references

The main colour pictures have been grouped on to Plates which mostly alternate in facing pairs with pairs of text pages. Each picture is identified by a bold type subject name and a reference in the text under this subject name will be found on a fairly adjacent text page. Exact co-ordination of colour picture and text matter for each item has not been possible because of the necessarily varying lengths of text, but both the text items and the colour pictures are in alphabetical order. Monotone illustrations are normally alongside their text reference with the exception of Systematics and Classification, the pictures for which appear on pp.236–239.

There are however many references, duly labelled, to *parts* of pictures. It is suggested that readers will find these most easily by looking for the term in the text, where in most instances there will be a cross-reference to a Plate Number, or to another term which will have a reference to a Plate Number. Of course it is not claimed that every possible term is illustrated, but a vast number have been included in this small book.

The Orders of the Animal Kingdom have been brought together in the Plates numbered 106 to 123 and systematic notes are given on the back of each Plate. Cross references to additional articles on the Orders are also given there, and of course in these articles there are indications of the relevant colour Plates in the body of the book.

Deliberately the book has been kept as simple in plan as possible, and a comprehensive index has *not* been included because readers will probably require illustration of a term in a specific context, and many are illustrated on so many occasions as to destroy the usefulness of a conventional index. Most readers will probably find the pictorial reference that is relevant to their particular purpose more quickly by the methods suggested. It is greatly hoped that the book will prove of real and practical service.

Abdomen. In vertebrates the abdomen is the region of the body that contains the liver, the digestive organs, and the excretory and reproductive systems. It does not contain the heart and lungs which are contained in the thorax. In mammals, the thorax and abdomen are separated by the diaphragm. The abdomen of insects and other arthropods is the hind region of the body. (See Plate 62).

Abducens Nerve. The sixth *cranial nerve* (q.v.) of the vertebrate brain.

Absorption. The process whereby dissolved materials – e.g. food or oxygen – pass through a membrane – the gut or lung lining – and into the body.

Abyssal. Inhabiting or concerning the deep-sea region.

Acarina. An order of the class *Arachnida* (q.v.) containing the mites and ticks – small, generally rounded animals many of which are parasites and carriers of disease. (See Plate 112).

Accessorius Nerve. The eleventh *cranial nerve* (q.v.) of vertebrates. Present only in reptiles, birds, and mammals, it serves various parts of the neck.

Acetabulum. The socket in the pelvic (hip) girdle into which the head of the femur fits.

Acetylcholine. A substance that has been found in almost all animals possessing a nervous system. It is produced in minute amounts at many nerve-endings when a signal passes along the nerve cell. It appears to be responsible for passing the signal (impulse) on to the next nerve cell or for triggering off a reaction in a muscle when the signal arrives. Acetylcholine is destroyed almost immediately by cholinesterase. If this were not so, the acetylcholine would go on setting up impulses or reactions and the nervous system would be in chaos.

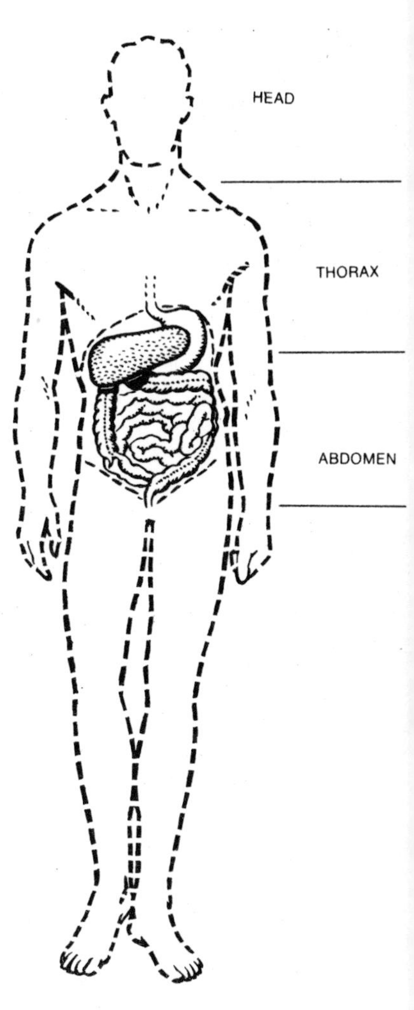

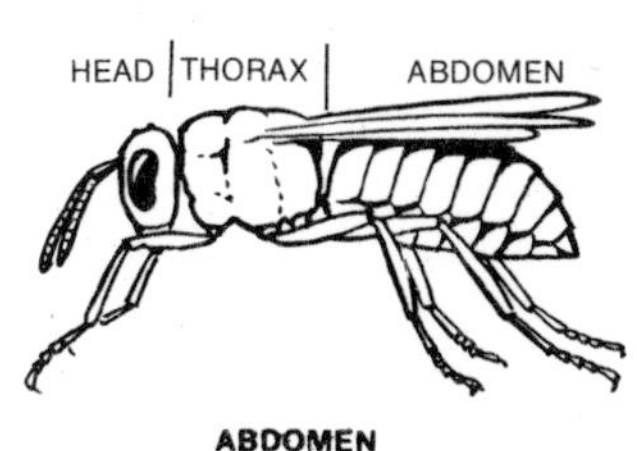

ABDOMEN

Acoelomate. Without a *coelom* (q.v.)—the body cavity found in most higher animals. Flat-worms, nematodes, and many other worm-like creatures are acoelomate animals. (See Plate 24).

Acoustic. Concerning hearing. The *Acoustic Nerve* is the eighth *cranial nerve* (q.v.) of vertebrates and supplies the ear.

Acrania. *(=Cephalochordata).*

Actinopterygii. A class of fishes that includes all the living bony fish other than the lung-fishes and the coelacanths. They are separated from the sharks and rays (Class *Elasmobranchii*) by virtue of their true bony skeleton (sharks and rays have cartilaginous skeltons and no true bone), and from the lung-fishes and coelacanths (Class *Crossopterygii*) by the fact that the paired fins have no central skeleton. Four orders are contained within the Actinopterygii — *Palaeoniscoidei, Chondrostei, Holostei,* and *Teleostei,* but all but a handful of living species are teleosts. (See Plates 28, 117).

Actinozoa *(=Anthozoa).* A class of coelenterate animals in which there is no free-living medusoid (jelly-fish) stage. Corals and sea-anemones belong to this class. Corals always have a chalky skeleton or cup around them and are often colonial, but the sea-anemones never have a skeleton and are usually solitary animals. Internally, they are very similar, having many vertical partitions in the food cavity. These give extra surface area for absorption and also contain thick bands of muscle that enable the animals to contract very rapidly. (See *Coelenterata*) and (Plate 1), and (Page 256).

Adaptation. Physiological adaptation is a change in the animal's body to counteract a change in the environment. For example, if a man used to living in London goes to live high up in the Himalayas, he will be subjected to the stress of lower temperatures and thinner air. His *adrenal glands* will react in such a way that he will be able to carry on quite normally. In other words he will adapt to the changed surroundings. The word adaptation is also used in connection with evolution to mean a characteristic that enables an animal to survive under certain conditions. As an example, during the evolution of amphibians millions of years ago, some of them developed shelled eggs and certain other features. These were of no great value at first but later, as the climate grew drier, these animals survived better than those without the adaptations. In other words they were adapted to the drier conditions.

Adaptive Radiation. The gradual spread of a type of animal into a number of different habitats with consequent changes in structure and appearance. The mammals, and the reptiles before them, radiated on land and into the air and water, producing from a basic stock such varied animals as gazelles, bats, and whales. A more recent example is that of Darwin's finches—a group of birds inhabiting the Galapagos Islands. There is a basic similarity between the various species but the beaks vary from the heavy seed-crushing type to the narrow insect-eating type. It is believed that a single ancestral type of bird arrived in the islands not too long ago and has since radiated into a number of distinct feeding types. The radiation was possible because variation in the original birds meant that some were adapted better to a diet of seeds and others to a diet of insects. (See *Natural Selection*) and (Plate 1).

Adrenal Gland. In man, the adrenal glands are loosely attached to the upper side of the kidneys. The combined weight of these tiny yellow glands is less than one ounce but they play an important part in the regulation of the body's activity. Each adrenal is actually composed of two distinct parts —a central medulla and an outer cortex. The origins and functions of the two parts are very different. The

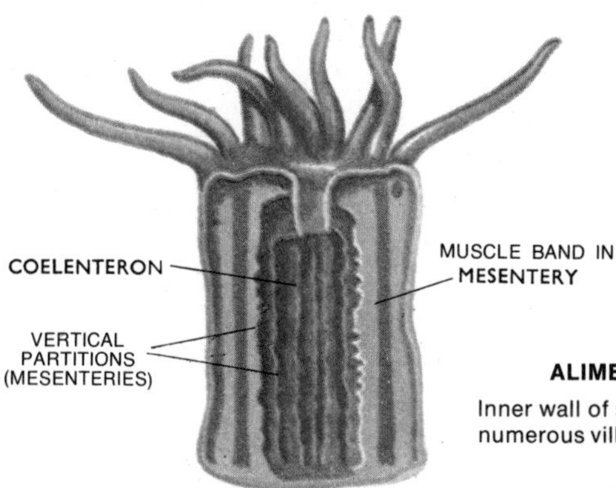

ACTINOZOA

Sea anemone showing the vertical partitions in the coelenteron.

ALIMENTARY CANAL

Inner wall of small intestine showing numerous villi.

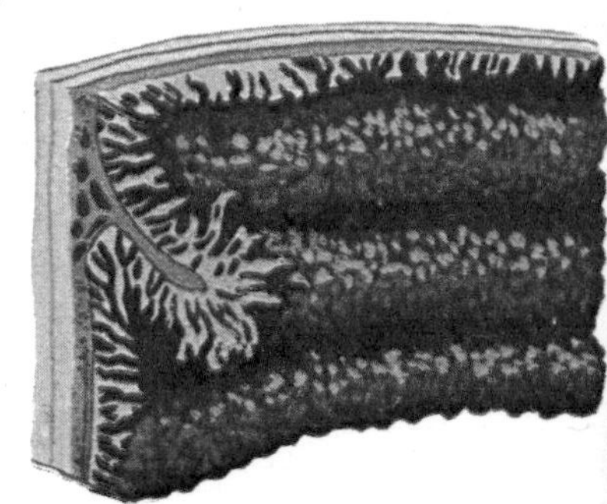

ADAPTIVE RADIATION

Isolated in the Galapagos Islands, the ancestors of Darwin's Finches evolved in several directions.

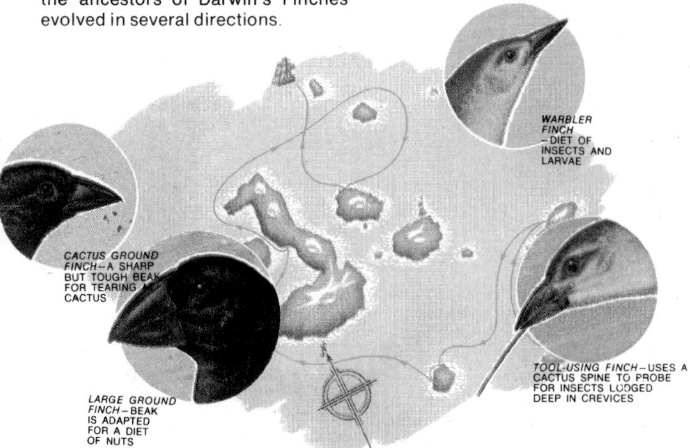

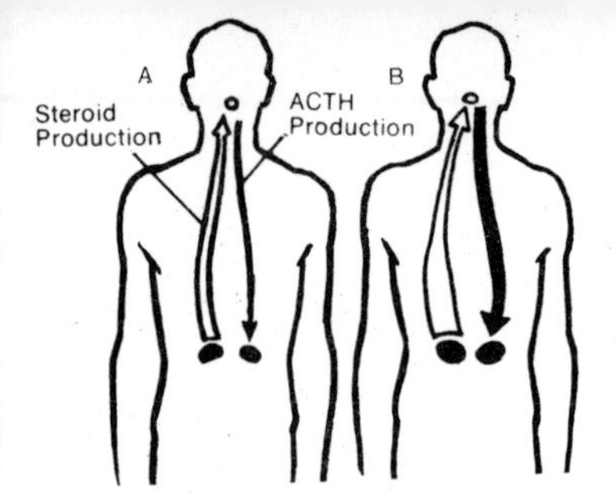

When the body is subject to stress (B) more steroids are used and less reach the brain: more ACTH is formed and causes the adrenals to grow and produce more steroids.

adrenal medulla resembles nervous tissue in its action: the nerves supplying it actually make contact with the medulla cells and control their secretion of *adrenaline*. This hormone is released in response to nervous signals when one experiences fright or mounting tension. Its action prepares the body for any sudden strain by increasing the blood supply to the brain and muscles. The heart-beat is accelerated and the skin pales. These symptoms can be experienced when someone steps out in front of your car or when you are about to sing your first solo in public. The bristling of a cat's fur when confronted by a dog is also due to the action of adrenaline.

The adrenal cortex also aids the body to prepare for or adapt to undue stress but the action in this case is not immediate. The secretions of the cortex are fatty substances called steroids and they are concerned with the production of energy in the cells of the body. Steroid production is triggered off by chemical messengers (hormones) from the pituitary gland.

The main hormone concerned is *adrenocorticotropic hormone* (ACTH). In a healthy person there is a delicate balance between the supply and demand of steroids from the cortex. The cells need more or less steroids according to the conditions. Prolonged cold, low air pressure, pregnancy, illness and many other features, all alter the demand for steroids.

If there is more than the necessary amount of steroids in the blood, they will not be used. Steroids returning in the blood to the pituitary will prevent the production of ACTH and thus the production of more steroids will be halted. Similarly, if not enough steriods are being produced, none, or only a low concentration, will reach the pituitary and ACTH will be released. This in turn causes increased production of steroids by the adrenal cortex. ACTH is also released by the action of adrenaline on the pituitary. Adrenaline therefore not only prepares the body for immediate action but also helps in the preparation for longer periods of stress.

Adrenaline. The secretion of the adrenal medulla. *(See Adrenal Gland).*

Adrenocorticotropic Hormone (ACTH). Hormone produced by the pituitary gland controlling secretion of the adrenal cortex. (See *Adrenal Gland).*

Aerobic. Requiring free oxygen for respiration. (See *Anaerobic*).

Aestivation. Animals in many of the drier parts of the world hide away in the summer or driest season and sleep, thereby avoiding the danger of drying up. This is known as aestivation. (See *Hibernation*).

Afferent. Leading towards. Used especially of arteries leading towards the gills of fishes.

Agnatha. Group of primitive vertebrates without jaws. Most of the group are extinct but the class *Cyclostomata* (q.v.) contains a few living forms – the lampreys and hagfishes. The extinct members – all fish-like – probably fed by sucking up mud and filtering out edible particles. (See Page 276).

Air Bladder (=*Swim Bladder*).

Albinism. Lack of pigment in the skin, resulting in pure white individuals.

Albinos have pink eyes because there is no pigment in the iris to mask the colour of the blood capillaries.

Alimentary Canal. The food canal or gut of an animal running from the mouth to the anus. The detailed structure varies enormously among the many groups of animals but is fairly constant within each group, with certain modifications according to diet. The mammalian alimentary canal follows a fairly standard pattern. The mouth opens into the *buccal cavity* which houses the tongue and teeth and leads back to the *pharynx* into which open the nasal cavity and the windpipe. From the pharynx a long muscular tube called the *oesophagus* runs down through the thorax and opens into the *stomach*. This is a muscular bag in which the food stays for a time and is thoroughly mixed up. Some chemical breakdown occurs in the stomach. The stomach of cows and other ruminants is divided into several compartments where cellulose is broken down by bacteria. Food is usually swallowed straight into the first compartment (the *rumen*) and later reguritated for mastication – chewing the cud. To return to the typical mammal, the stomach leads by way of a muscular valve into the *small intestine* – a long coiled tube where most of the digestion and absorption of food occurs. The inside wall of the small intestine is thrown into numerous folds and finger-like projections called *villi*. These increase the surface area for efficient absorption. (Sharks have only a short intestine but its effective length is increased by a 'spiral' valve. (See *Elasmobranchii*). The earthworm increases the surface area of its intestine by means of an infolding called the typhlosole. (See *Oligochaeta*). The small intestine passes into the *large intestine* which is concerned largely with the re-absorption of water from the undigested food. At the junction between the small and large intestines there is a blind sac called the *caecum*. In man and many other mammals the caecum is very small and at its blind end has an even smaller *appendix*, but in horses, rabbits, and some other animals the caecum is very large and is the site of cellulose digestion by bacteria. The large intestine leads to the *rectum* – a short tube that passes undigested matter (*faeces*) to the *anus*.

The alimentary canal of a bird is somewhat different from that of a mammal. The oesophagus leads to the *crop*, especially well developed in grain-eating birds, where food is stored and partially broken up. The stomach is in two parts – the *proventriculus* and the *gizzard*. The former produces enzymes and mixes them with the food which then passes to the gizzard, a very muscular region where the food is ground up. Many birds swallow stones which get trapped in the gizzard and help in the grinding work. Flesh-eating birds do not have such a muscular gizzard. (See *Digestion*), and (Plates 1, 2 and 3).

Allantois. A structure present in the embryos of amniote vertebrates. It is an outgrowth of the gut and contains many blood vessels. In the eggs of reptiles and birds the allantois grows near to the shell and oxygen can diffuse into its blood vessels and thus reach the embryo. The mammalian allantois mingles with the maternal tissues of the placenta and receives oxygen and food from the maternal blood vessels. (See *Placenta*).

Allele (See *Gene*).

All or Nothing Law. A feature of muscle and nerve cells. When such cells are stimulated they either react completely or not at all, depending on the intensity of the stimulus. There is no partial reaction.

ALLEN'S LAW

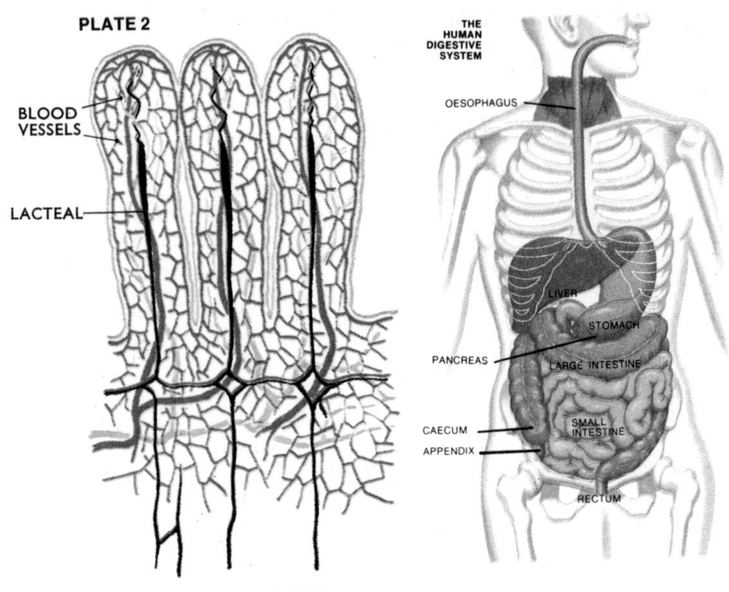

ALIMENTARY CANAL

Highly magnified villi showing blood vessels and fat-collecting lacteals.

The alimentary canals of animals with different diets.

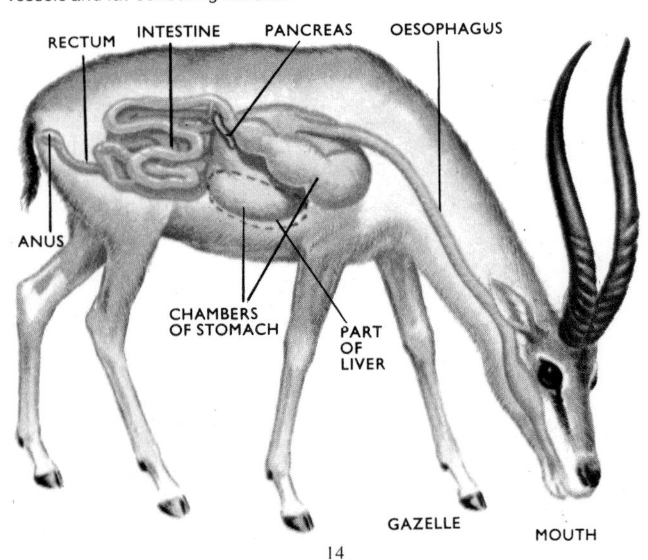

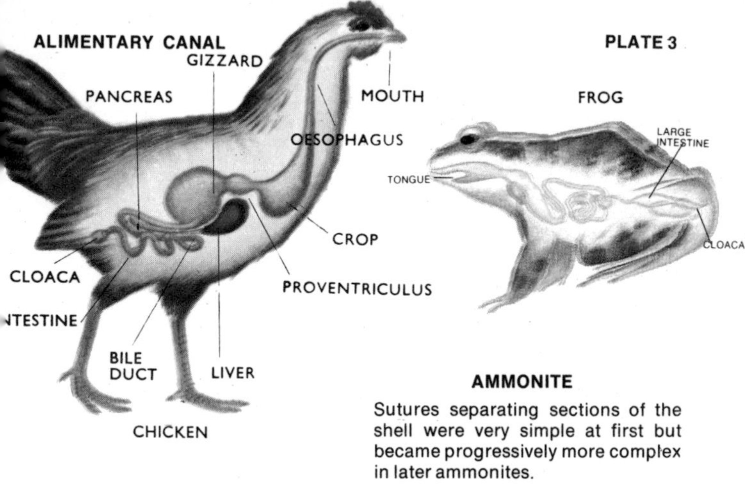

AMMONITE

Sutures separating sections of the shell were very simple at first but became progressively more complex in later ammonites.

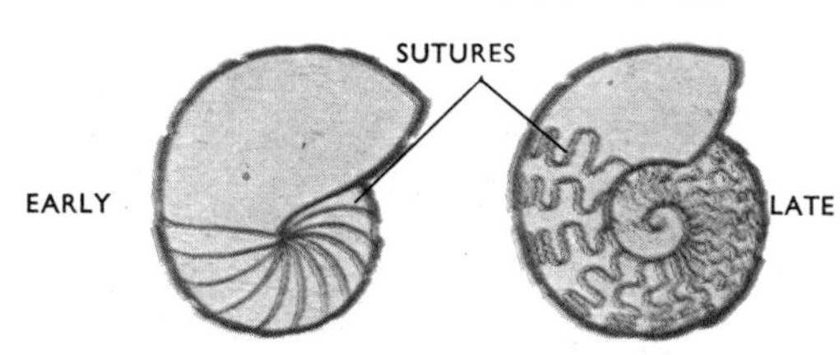

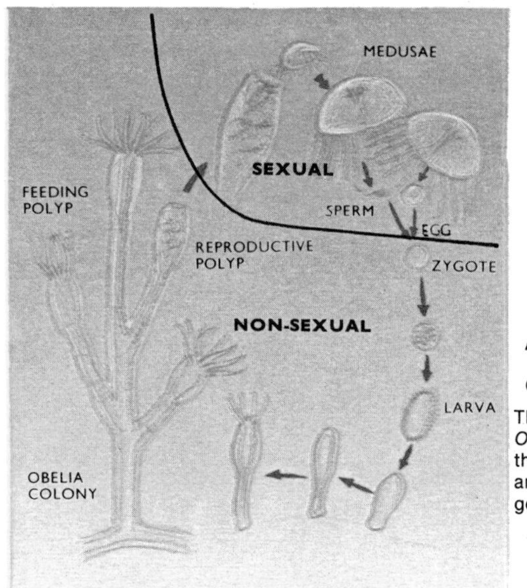

ALTERNATION OF GENERATIONS

The life-cycle of *Obelia* in which there is a sexual and a non-sexual generation.

Allen's Law. The recognised fact that animals living in cold climates have smaller ears, snouts, etc., than related animals in warmer lands. The reduction of these parts reduces heat loss and is therefore an advantage.

Alternation of Generations. The existence of two distinct forms in the life-cycle of an organism, both of which forms can reproduce. One form reproduces sexually and gives rise to the other form which in turn reproduces asexually to give the sexual form again. This phenomenon occurs in most plants but is less common in animals, being best shown by the coelenterates. *Obelia* is a colonial animal with a lot of Hydra-like polyps all joined together. Special reproductive polyps produce tiny jelly-fish (medusae) by budding and the medusae swim off into the water. Each medusa produces either male or female cells which are released and join together to grow into a new polyp colony. The polyps are the asexual generation and the medusae the sexual generation. (See Plate 3).

Alveolus. Name given to the millions of minute air-sacs that make up the *lung* (q.v.). The alveolus is the seat of gaseous exchange between the blood and the air. The term is also used to describe the socket into which teeth fit. (See Plate 72).

Amino-acid. An organic substance containing carbon, hydrogen, oxygen, and nitrogen (sulphur is also present in some amino-acids). About 25 amino-acids have been discovered and in various combinations they make up all the known proteins. During digestion, proteins in food are broken down into amino-acids which are absorbed and then built up into new proteins in the body. Animals can synthesise only some of the amino-acids: the others must be obtained from food.

Ammonite. An extinct creature related to the octopus and the *Nautilus*. Ammonite shells are very common as fossils in Jurassic rocks and are important aids for dating the rocks. (See *Geological Time Scale*) and (Plate 3).

Amnion. The embryos of reptiles, birds, and mammals grow in a sac of liquid. The inner wall of the sac is the amnion. (Plates 38, 39 and 88).

Amniote. An animal whose embryo develops within an amnion, in other words, reptiles, birds, and mammals are all amniotes.

Amoeba. Popularly regarded as one of the lowest forms of life *Amoeba* is one of the simplest protozoans and belongs to a group called the *Rhizopoda*. It lives in moist surroundings—ponds, ditches, seas and damp soils. Some specialized species even live as parasites inside other animals. Dysentery in Man is caused by one such type of amoeba.

To the naked eye, the largest amoeba is just visible as a whitish blob. Under the microscope, the blob can be seen to be a definite animal. But it is a very strange one. It has no shape, or rather the shape is permanently changing. And as the shape alters so does the animal's position. An arm-like projection (the pseudopodium or 'false leg') advances from a point on the surface and the living matter behind moves forward into it. The creature appears to flow across the microscope's field of view.

This curious method of locomotion depends upon alteration in structure of the living material. There is a thin, solid outer-layer (*ectoplasm*) and an inner fluid (*endoplasm*). Where a pseudopodium forms, the solid ectoplasm liquifies and flows forward by contraction of the solid ectoplasm elsewhere. The fluid in contact with the surface soon solidifies once more, but then the whole process is repeated.

The formation of pseudopodia also enables amoeba to feed. It engulfs microscopic organisms with cup-shaped pseudopodia. Inside the body, the food is surrounded by digestive enzymes. Undigested residues are easily lost: the amoeba simply flows away from them.

For respiration – the taking in of oxygen and removal of carbon dioxide – the gases simply diffuse through the whole of amoeba's permeable surface layer. Soluble nitrogen-containing wastes, produced by the amoeba's chemical activities, are excreted in the same way.

A bubble of liquid forms periodically inside an amoeba's body. The bubble grows until finally it bursts, releasing the water to the outside. This bubble is the *contractile vacuole* and its function is to remove the excess water passing by osmosis into the animal. Otherwise the animal itself would burst.

The nucleus can be clearly seen with the microscope as a darkish spot inside the body. It controls the whole course of life and an amoeba deprived of its nucleus soon dies. The nucleus is especially important during reproduction. This takes place when food is plentiful and amoeba can grow to its full size. Then the nucleus divides followed by division of the rest of the cell. The two new amoeba increase in size and may themselves divide.

During droughts or severe cold, amoeba withdraws all pseudopodia and secretes a tough coat or *cyst*. The cyst with its contents is called a *spore*. Each spore is very light and may be blown by the wind to new surroundings. Inside the cyst, the original animal divides to form numerous smaller individuals (*amoebulae*). In favourable conditions the cyst breaks down and releases them.

Amoeba has no special sense organs. Changes in the outside world are detected by all parts of the living material. In general, this sensitivity ensures favourable surroundings. For instance, amoeba quickly moves away from very bright light or strongly acidic or alkaline water. (See Plate 4).

Amoeboid. Moving and changing shape in the manner of *Amoeba*.

Amphibia. A class of vertebrate animals whose members are capable in general of life both in and out of water. The class contains the frogs and salamanders and a host of extinct forms very unlike any living amphibian. Amphibians are cold-blooded, that is their temperature varies with that of the surroundings and the majority have to return to the water to breed.

Amphibians were the first vertebrates to conquer the land, evolving from a type of lung-fish in the Devonian period some 300 million years ago. These early amphibians are grouped in the sub-class *Stegocephalia* which contains only extinct members such as *Ichthyostega* and *Eryops*. They were still fish-like in many ways with scaly skins, but they possessed the typical characteristic of land-living vertebrates – the five-fingered (*pentadactyl*) limb. The stegocephalians were very heavily boned, a feature that has been lost in modern amphibians.

Living amphibians fall into three sub-classes: – *Urodela*, the tailed newts and salamanders; *Anura*, the jumping frogs and toads; and the limbless *Apoda* – burrowing creatures resembling earthworms in outward appearance. Adult amphibians have lungs in most cases but many of them also breath through the moist skin. Eggs are normally laid in water where they hatch into larval forms known as tadpoles. But there are many variations in the life history. Some species lay eggs in damp soil and small adults emerge from the eggs: others give birth to active young resembling the parents in everything except size – the whole larval period is spent inside the mother. (See *Anura; Apoda; Urodela*). (See Plates 118 and 79).

Amphineura. A small class of *Mollusca* (q.v.). (See Page 272).

Anaerobic. Able to survive in the absence of free oxygen. Anaerobic

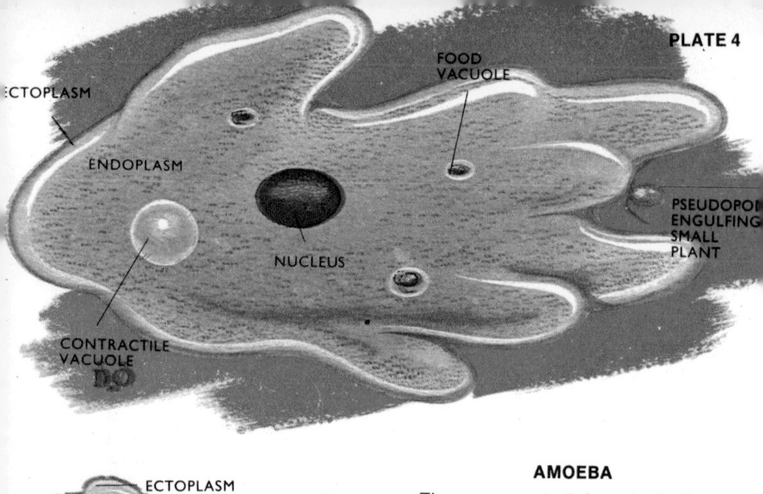

AMOEBA

The movement of *Amoeba* by flowing of the protoplasm.

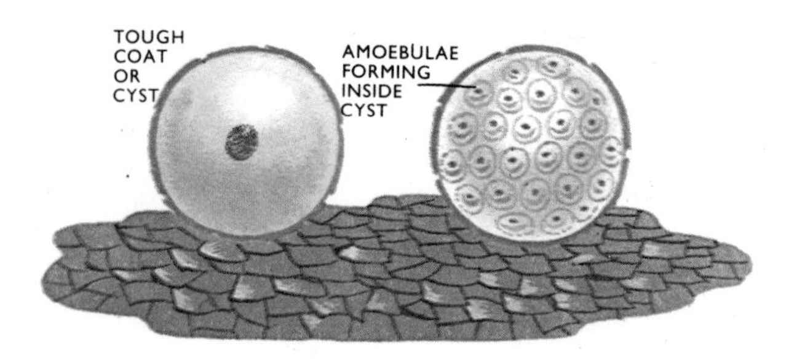

The encystment of *Amoeba* helps it to survive unfavourable conditions. Inside the cyst many tiny amoebulae may be formed and released when conditions are suitable.

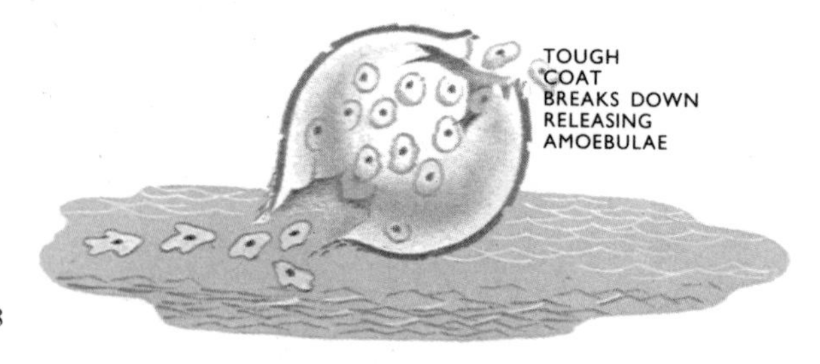

ANNELIDA

The two most important divisions of the phylum Annelida are the Oligochaeta (earthworms) and Polychaeta (rag-worms, tube-worms and other marine animals). The principal difference is in the development of moveable parapodia and many chaetae (bristles) in the polychaetes. Oligochaetes have only a few bristles. This is well seen in the cross sections. The parapodia of the tube-dwelling forms are reduced. Free-living polychaetes also have quite a well-developed head.

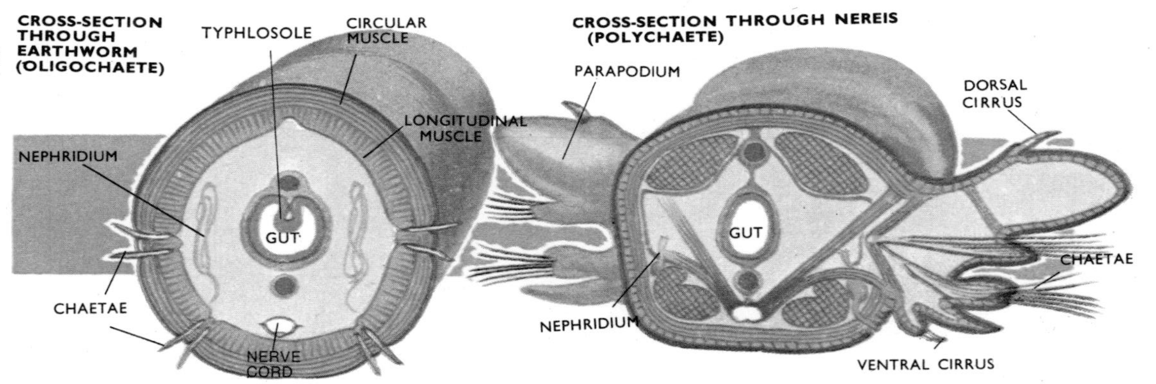

PLATE 5

respiration involves the liberation of energy from materials without using up oxygen. (See *Aerobic*).

Analogous Organs. Structures in different organisms which perform the same function but which develop in a different way. As an example, the wings of the humming bird and of the humming-bird hawk moth are used to hover in front of flowers, but they are structurally very different. (See *Convergent Evolution; Homologous Organs*).

Anapsida. A sub-class of the *Reptilia* (q.v.) including the tortoises. (See Page 280).

Anatomy. The study of the structure, both internal and external, of animals.

Androgen. Any substance that promotes the development of male sexual characteristics, such as the comb of a cockerel. Androgens are formed mainly in the testis.

Annelida. This phylum of animals contains the segmented worms – earthworms, bristle-worms, leeches, and others – whose bodies are normally well divided into segments or rings. There is a muscular body-wall covered in most members by a thin cuticle. The nervous system is well-developed and there is a blood system and a large coelom. Of the six classes of annelids the most important are: *Polychaeta* – mainly marine animals with many bristles (*chaetae*) arising in each segment; *Oligochaeta* – earthworms and various freshwater forms with few bristles per segment; and *Hirudinea* – the leeches – which have no bristles. (See *Polychaeta; Oligochaeta; Hirudinea*) and (Plates 5, 84, 85, 88, 89 and 110).

Ant. A member of the superfamily Formicoidea of the insect order *Hymenoptera* (q.v.). All ants are social insects living in large colonies and they are remarkable for the large number of different forms (castes) that exist – queens, workers, males, soldiers, etc. Ants can be recognised by the narrow pedicel or 'waist' joining thorax and abdomen and by the characteristically bent antennae.

Antagonism. Conflict between one organism and another, especially with reference to production of antibiotic substances by one organism that interfere with the other. Also used to refer to muscles with opposing actions. (See *Extensor; Flexor*).

Anteaters. (See *Edentata*).

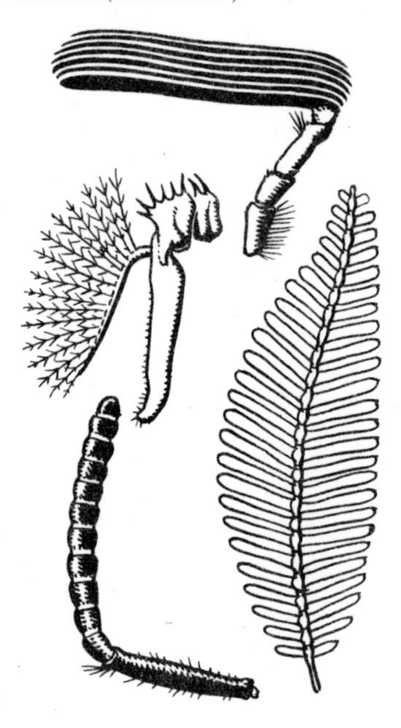

TYPES of ANTENNAE

Antenna. Sensory organ on the head of various arthropods. It is the first appendage of insects and myriapods, the second of crustaceans. There is great variation in shape. Antennae generally carry organs concerned with the senses of smell and touch but in some crustaceans they are used as 'oars' to propel the animal through the water.

Antennule. The first appendage of the crustacean head. Usually sensory.

Anthropoidea. Sub-order of the *Primates* (q.v.) containing monkeys, apes and man.

Antibody. A substance (normally a protein) which is produced in the body of an animal in response to certain foreign substances, such as bacteria that enter the body. Substances that can induce antibody formation are called antigens. Each antigen has one or more specific antibodies that are formed and combine with the antigen to render it harmless or more easily dealt with by the infected animal. Vaccination against a particular disease involves giving a weak dose of the disease, or an extract from the disease-causing organisms. Antibodies are then formed and remain in the blood. If the disease is picked up the antibodies destroy it before it does much harm.

Antigen. (See *Antibody*).

Anura. The order of Amphibia containing frogs and toads, all of which are modified in some degree for jumping. Toads tend to be more fully terrestrial than frogs but frogs of the genus *Rana* are perhaps the most successful of the amphibians. They have an almost world-wide distribution and live in a great variety of habitats. The common frog of Great Britain is *Rana temporaria* and shows the typical features of the group. The long hind legs are well adapted for jumping and for swimming. The moist, soft skin is well supplied with blood vessels and it is an important site of oxygen uptake for respiration (Some anurans have actually done away with their lungs and rely entirely on the skin for gaseous exchange). There are many glands in the skin, producing mucus which keeps the skin moist, and various poisonous substances. Poison glands are better developed in toads than in frogs. Internally, the skeleton is very reduced when compared with the early amphibians, especially in the skull.

Adult frogs spend the cold winter months in a state of inactivity – hidden under logs and stones, or buried in mud. They awaken in early spring and return to the water. As a rule, the males return first and, by their croaking, attract the females. Pairing takes place in the water without any courtship display. As the female discharges her eggs the male releases sperm over them and fertilisation follows. The eggs are covered with jelly which quickly swells on contact with the water. It keeps the eggs together and protects them.

After fertilisation, each egg-cell begins to divide and, within a few days, the black sphere elongates and develops a head and tail. The tadpole hatches in about ten days and attaches itself to a plant by means of a sticky gland. The mouth is not yet fully formed and the young tadpole exists on the yolk material from the egg. About three days after hatching, the mouth opens and the tadpole then begins to feed on algae. By this time three pairs of delicate external gills have developed.

During the next few weeks the tadpole grows rapidly and important changes take place both internally and externally. Internal gills are formed. These are respiratory openings connecting the mouth and the outside. A fold of skin (the operculum) covers them and opens at a single point (the spiracle) on the left hand side. The external gills disappear, and, apart from its large head the tadpole is like a fish. However, the legs soon begin to develop. The hind ones appear first because the front limbs are covered by the operculum. The left front limb appears through the spiracle, followed later by the right leg which breaks through the operculum. Lungs have formed by now and the tadpole begins to breathe air at the surface. It feeds on animal material now, insect larve for example – and the mouth enlarges.

As the legs grow, the tail shortens

PLATE 6

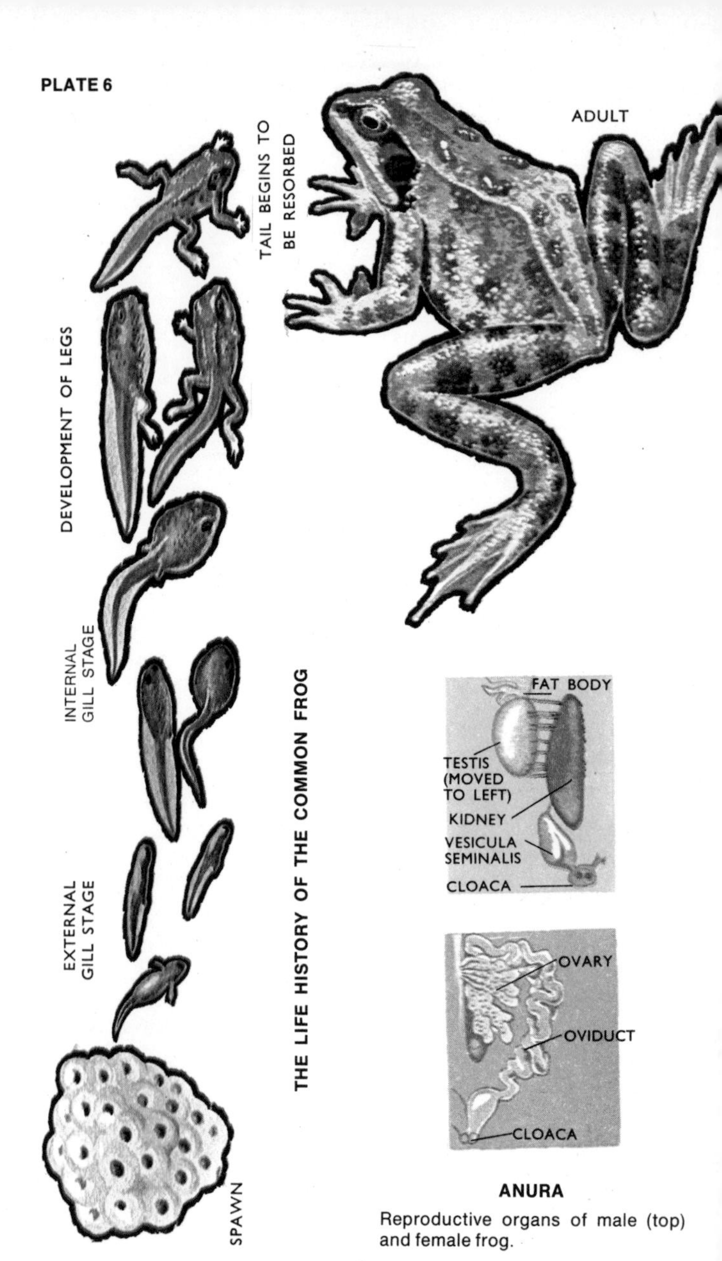

ANURA

Reproductive organs of male (top) and female frog.

PLATE 7

AORTIC ARCHES

Diagrams showing the evolution in the higher vertebrates of the blood vessels (aortic arches) that originally served the gills of fishes.

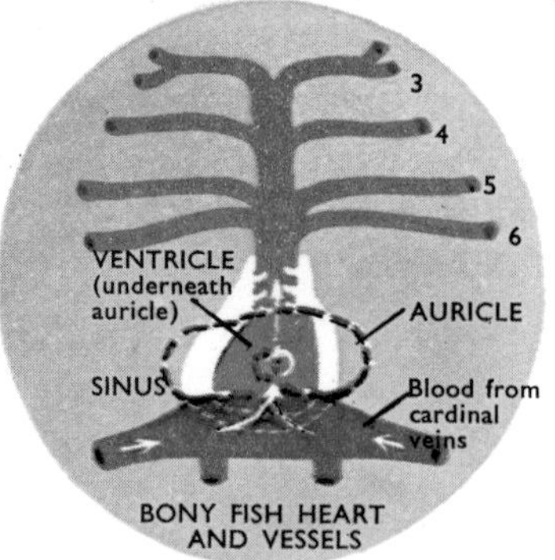

BONY FISH

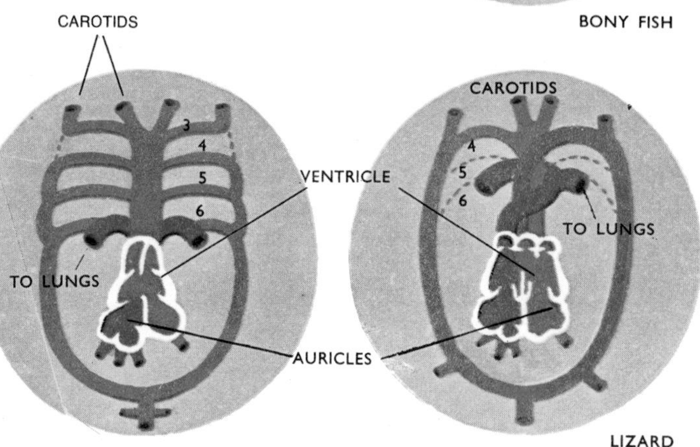

SALAMANDER

LIZARD

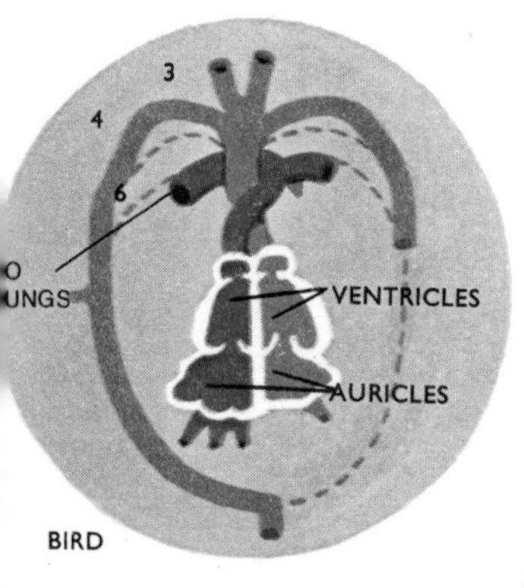

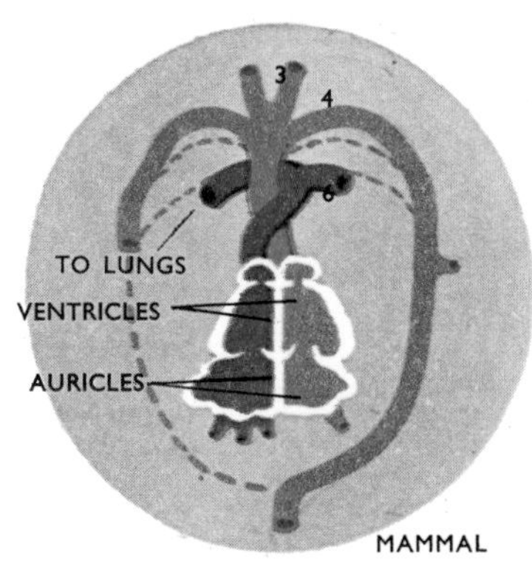

BIRD

MAMMAL

and the typical frog shape becomes obvious. The frog has now metamorphosed or changed into the adult form. It leaves the water and lives in damp vegetation feeding on insects, slugs and worms. The whole process from egg to metamorphosis takes about three months but the small frog requires another three or four years to become mature and able to breed. (See Plates 3, 6, 41 and 71) and (Page 277).

Aorta. Major artery of the body. (See *Aortic Arches*) and (Plates 7, 16 and 17).

Aortic Arches. Fishes extract oxygen from the water by means of their gills. Each gill is supplied by an artery branching off from the main artery (ventral aorta) leaving the heart. The branches are the afferent branchial arteries. In the gills the arteries break up into capillaries which join up again on leaving the gills to form the efferent branchial arteries leading to the dorsal aorta. These blood vessels joining the ventral and dorsal aortas are the aortic arches. They are seen not only in fishes but also in most vertebrate embryos where there are six pairs of arches. In fishes and in larval amphibians the arches continue to supply the gills but in adult amphibians and other vertebrates the aortic arches undergo a remarkable series of changes.

Only the efferent part of the first arch remains in adult fishes. Most fishes lose the second arch altogether while all higher vertebrates lose the first and second. These higher vertebrates do not have gills and the arches have become modified for other functions. The third pair of arches form the beginning of the carotid arteries leading to the head and the fourth pair curve backwards as the systemic arches which join up and supply blood to most of the body. The fifth pair of arches join the systemics in amphibians but are lost in higher forms. Both parts of the systemics remain in most reptiles; in birds only the right arch remains; and in mammals, only the left. The sixth pair of aortic arches form the pulmonary arteries leading to the lungs. There are corresponding changes in the structure of the heart. (See *Heart*) and (Plate 7).

Apoda. Order of *Amphibia* (q.v.) whose members have no limbs and have scales in the skin. They are tropical and live in burrows. *Ichthyophis* is a typical example. (See *Amphibia*) and (Plate 118).

Aposematic Coloration. (=*Warning Coloration*) Conspicuous colours or patterns are exhibited by many poisonous or distasteful creatures. It is thought that the striking colours warn potential predators and enable them to learn more quickly that these creatures are distasteful. Yellow-and-black and red-and-black are the commonest combinations of warning colours. (See *Mimicry*) and (Plate 8).

Appendix. Blind sac in the alimentary canal of mammals. It is important in rabbits and some other herbivorous animals as a reservoir of cellulose-digesting bacteria. In man and many other mammals the appendix is functionless. (See *Alimentary Canal*).

Apterygota. Sub-class of *Insecta* (q.v.) with many primitive characters. No wings. (See Page 268).

Aqueous Humour. Liquid filling the front chamber of the *eye* (q.v.).

Arachnida. A class of *Arthropoda* (q.v.). The front part of the body (*prosoma*) has six segments but it is never divided into head and thorax. Unlike all other arthropods, the arachnids have a pair of clawed pincers (*chelicerae*) as the first appendage on the head. The next pair are either sensory palps or large pincers (*pedipalps*), while the remaining four pairs are walking legs. The hind part of the body (*opisthosoma*) does not normally bear limbs. Best known of the arachnids are the spiders (Order *Araneida*), scorpions (*Scorpionidea*), and mites (*Acarina*) but there are several other orders. (See Plate 112) and (Page 265).

Araneida. Order of *Arachnida* (q.v.) containing the spiders. The prosoma is separated from the soft opisthosoma by a distinct waist. Spiders are carnivorous, feeding largely on insects. The clawed chelicerae contain poison glands and are used to paralyse the prey, caught usually in some sort of trap made from silk. Digestive enzymes are then poured over or into the prey and the spider then sucks up the resulting liquid, leaving only the hard skeleton of the insect. Most spiders possess tracheae resembling those of insects but they also breathe by means of *lung books*. The silk glands of spiders open at the hind end on to small projections called spinnerets. The eyes, although well developed, are simple: there is no trace of the compound eye found in insects. (See Plate 112).

Archaeopteryx. The earliest known fossil bird. Apart from feathers it looked very like a reptile, with claws on its wings, and teeth. It also had a long, feathered tail. The fossils are about 150 million years old (Jurassic age). (See Plate 120).

Aristotle's Lantern. Jaw apparatus of sea-urchins. It is made up of a series of chalky plates which rasp seaweed from the rocks.

Arteriole. A small artery.

Artery. A vessel leading blood away from the heart and into the tissues. Arteries have thick muscular fibrous walls which withstand the high pressure set up by the pumping of the heart. As they get further from the heart, the arteries branch and get smaller, becoming arterioles, and finally capillaries. The latter join up after passing through the tissues and form veins which return the blood to the heart. Veins do not have such thick walls as arteries, and capillaries have no wall at all other than a single layer of cells. This layer is continuous with the inner lining of the arteries and veins. (See Plates 15, 16 and 17).

Arthropoda. A very large phylum of animals all of which have jointed limbs and are normally covered by a stout cuticle. The latter is usually impregnated with a horny protein called chitin and often with other materials such as lime. Like the annelid worms from which they are probably descended, the arthropods show definite segmentation. *Peripatus*—a strange animal belonging to the class Onychophora—shows several characteristics intermediate between annelids and arthropods. *Peripatus* is the only arthropod that has cilia. The head is more marked in arthropods than in annelids and the nervous system more advanced. The limbs of the head are modified for feeding and for sensory functions. The large body cavity of most annelids is reduced and largely replaced by a haemocoel in arthropods. (See *Crustacea; Trilobita; Insecta; Onychophora; Myriapoda; Arachnida*). (See Page 264).

Artiodactyla. An order of hoofed mammals (ungulates) including pigs, hippopotamuses, deer, cattle, camels, and sheep. The animals walk on the tips of their digits, toes three and four being equally developed and the rest reduced. Compare with *Perissodactyla* in which toe three is most developed. Apart from pigs and hippos, all artiodactyls chew the cud and their stomachs are specially modified. (See *Perissodactyla; Ruminant*) and (Plate 123).

Ascidian. A sea-squirt. (See *Urochordata*).

PLATE 8

APOSEMATIC COLORATION

Warning coloration of the Cinnabar moth and its caterpillar, both of which are unpleasant to taste.

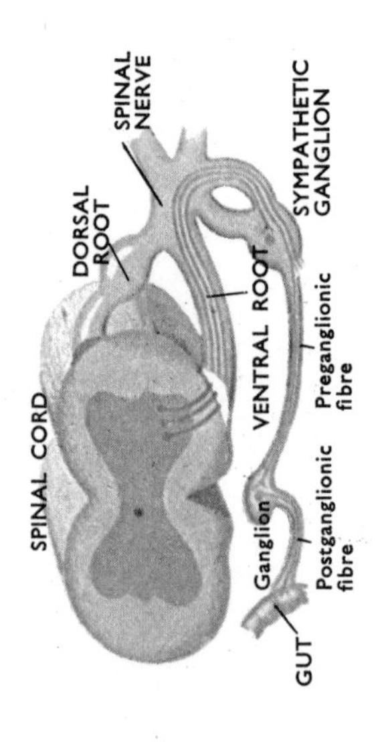

The path of the sympathetic fibres out of the spinal cord.

AUTONOMIC NERVOUS SYSTEM

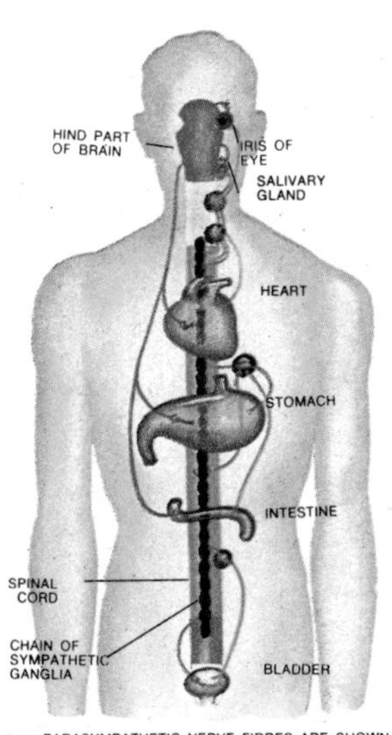

PARASYMPATHETIC NERVE FIBRES ARE SHOWN RED
SYMPATHETIC NERVE FIBRES ARE SHOWN BLUE

A simplified diagram of the human system.

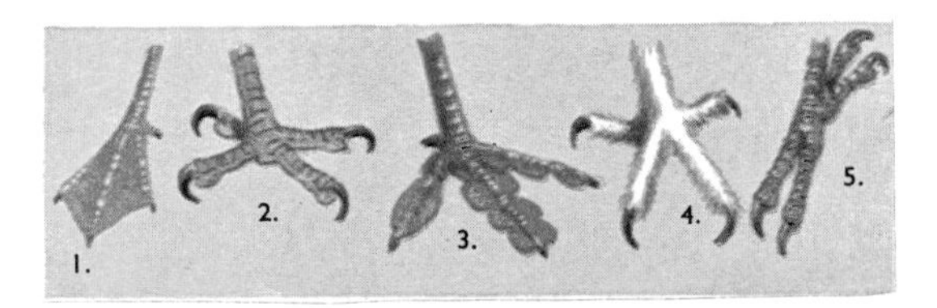

AVES

The beaks and feet of various birds modified according to feeding and other habits (See also Plates 120 and 121)

1. GULL 2. EAGLE 3. COOT 4. OWL

5. CUCKOO 6. HERON 7. CROSSBILL 8. SKIMMER

9. VULTURE 10. DUCK

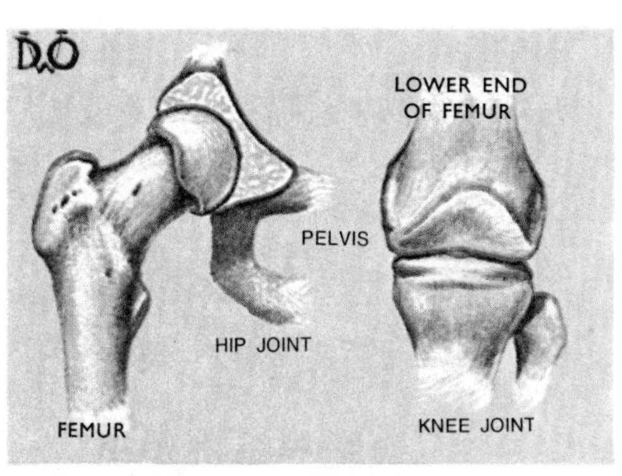

BALL AND SOCKET JOINT

Ball and socket joint (left), giving movement in several directions, and HINGE JOINT giving movement in one plane only.

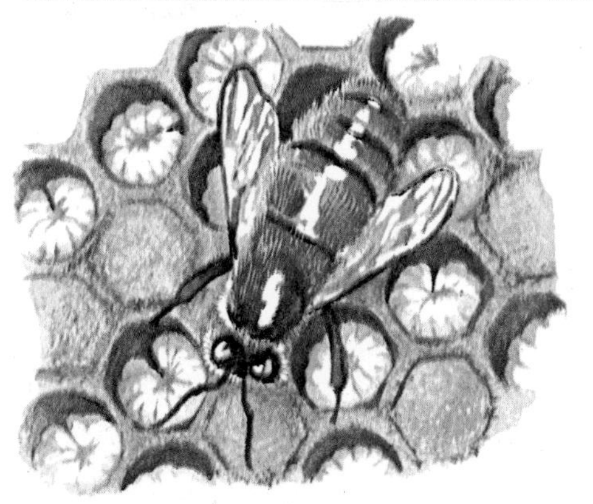

BEE

Worker honey bee tending the brood.

Assimilation. The taking in and building up of simple materials into the complex proteins and other constituents of the body.

Association. The method by which animals 'remember'. An encounter leading to an unpleasant experience is avoided at a future date. An encounter which ended in a reward will be repeated. In this manner animals can be trained. (See *Instinct*).

Atlas. The first vertebra (q.v.) of the spine specially adapted to carry the skull. A nod of the head involves movement between skull and atlas.

Atrium. The chamber surrounding the gill-slits of *Amphioxus* and of sea-squirts. Water passes in through the mouth of the animal, through the gill-slits which extract food particles, and into the atrium. It then passes out through the atrial pore. (See *Cephalochordata; Urochordata*).

Auditory. (=*Acoustic*). Concerning hearing. The auditory capsule of the skull encloses the inner ear.

Auricle. A chamber of the vertebrate heart. There is only one in fishes but two in tetrapods, receiving blood returning from the body and from the lungs. (See *Heart*).

Autolysis. The destruction of cells by their own enzymes.

Autonomic Nervous System. The system of nerves spreading through the body is referred to as the peripheral nervous system. The outer or somatic part links up the sense organs that provide the animal with a 'picture' of the outside world, with the effectors that move the animal towards food or away from danger. But in order that these sense organs and effectors function, the inner machinery of the body must be functioning smoothly and the rate at which it works must be adjustable so that the varying demands of the outer structures may be satisfied. When an animal is moving, its muscles require a greater supply of oxygen than when it is lying down. The heart must beat faster to supply more blood and this blood must be supplied with sufficient food and oxygen. The lungs must be filled with air and emptied more frequently, the blood vessels to the muscles must be expanded and more channels opened up there to cope with the increasing supply of blood.

The nerves that co-ordinate the inner workings (e.g. smooth muscle of the gut and blood vessels, and the glands) form the visceral part of the peripheral nervous system. The visceral motor nerves are usually called the autonomic nervous system although they are controlled by the central nervous system just as the somatic motor system is. The autonomic nervous system is often referred to as the involuntary nervous system since we have very little conscious control of its activities, but with training it is possible to change the size of the pupil of one's eye or to increase the speed of one's heartbeat.

The cell bodies of somatic motor nerve cells are inside the spinal cord but a characteristic of the visceral motor system is that the cell bodies of the final motor nerve cells (those that are in contact with the organ that they supply) are outside the spinal cord. These cell bodies are grouped together to form ganglia that lie either close to the spinal cord along nerves or actually in contact with the organs that they supply. Thus, whereas the axon of a somatic motor neuron is long and carries impulses out from the spinal cord to the structure concerned, the typical visceral motor nerve is composed of two parts. One runs from the spinal cord to a ganglion and is called a preganglionic neuron; the other links with the preganglionic neuron in the ganglion and passes to the organ that it supplies. It is called a postganglionic neuron. In mammals the preganglionic neurons usually have a fatty myelin sheath (they are myelinated), but the postganglionic neurons have no sheath and are said to be unmyelinated.

The autonomic nervous system may be divided into two parts, sympathetic and parasympathetic. Generally their actions are opposite and their positions in relation to the spinal cord are different. Sympathetic nerves arise from the spinal cord between the neck and waist region. Parasympathetic nerves arise from the head and from the sacral region (between the waist and tail). Sympathetic preganglionic fibres leave the nerve cord by ventral roots as do somatic motor nerves, but para-sympathetic fibres leave by both dorsal and ventral roots. Each preganglionic fibre is connected with many postganglionic fibres.

Though the two parts of the autonomic system arise in different parts of the spinal cord their branches spread nearly everywhere within the body. Most organs receive both sympathetic and parasympathetic neurons, though some (e.g. sweat glands) receive only one (in this case the sympathetic). The gut, for example (apart from the sphincter muscules), relaxes when it receives signals through sympathetic neurons. Signals through parasympathetic fibres cause it to contract. The sphincter muscles are affected in the opposite way, contracting on the receipt of impulses from the sympathetic and relaxing on receipt of signals from the parasympathetic. On the other hand the actions of the two systems may not strictly be opposite. The salivary glands produce a thick slime (mucus) when stimulated by the sympathetic system, but they produce the more watery saliva when stimulated through parasympathetic fibres.

Some of the Actions of Autonomic Nerves in Man

Organ	**Sympathetic causes**	**Parasympathetic causes**
Heart	increase in rate and strength of beat	reduction in rate and strength of beat
Skin blood vessels	constriction	no supply
Blood vessels to muscle	usually constriction	no supply
Gut blood vessels	constriction	no supply
Muscles of alimentary canal (except sphincters)	relaxation	contraction
Sphincter muscles of gut	contraction	relaxation
Salivary glands	production of mucus	production of saliva
Pancreas	no supply	production of pancreatic juice
Hair muscles	contraction	no supply
Sweat glands	release of sweat	no supply

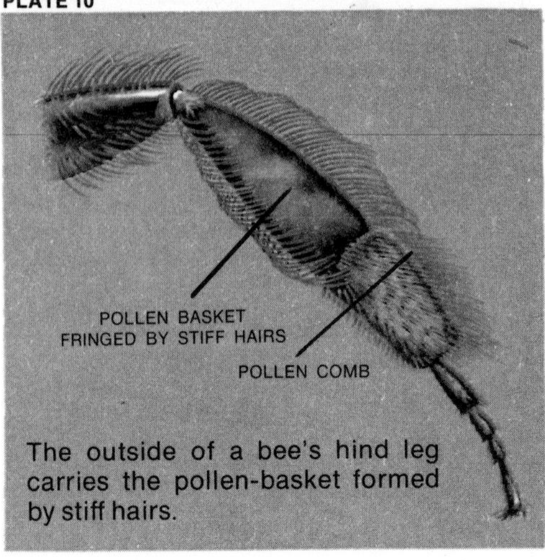

The outside of a bee's hind leg carries the pollen-basket formed by stiff hairs.

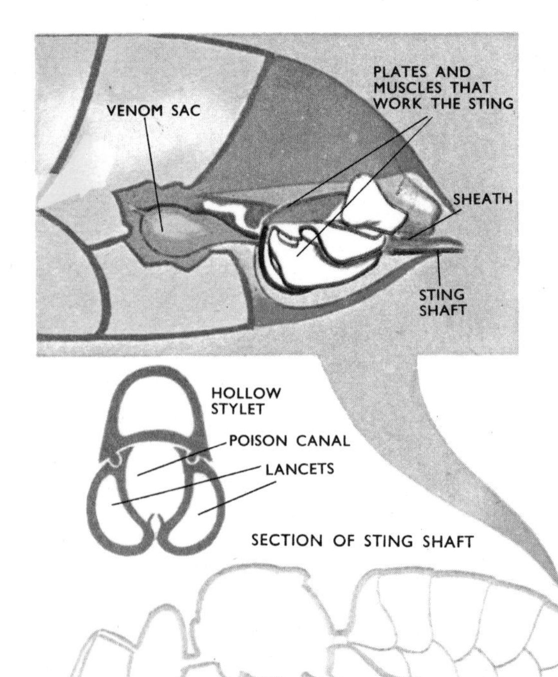

THE STIN
APPARATU

PLATE 11

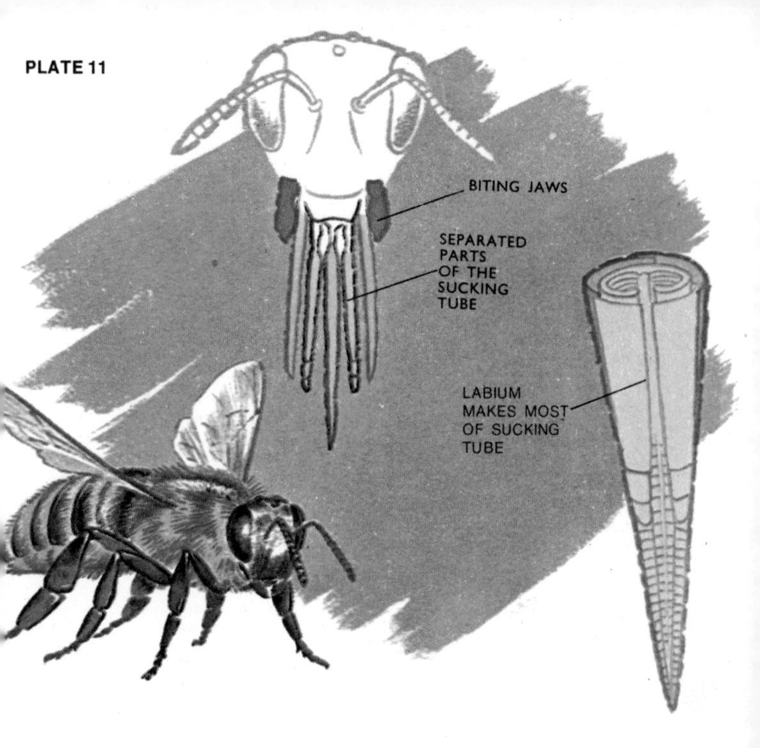

BEE

As well as sucking mouth-parts, the bee has functional jaws which are used in nest-building.

The Honey-bee's sting is barbed and cannot be withdrawn from human skin. The whole sting apparatus is left behind as the bee wrenches herself free.

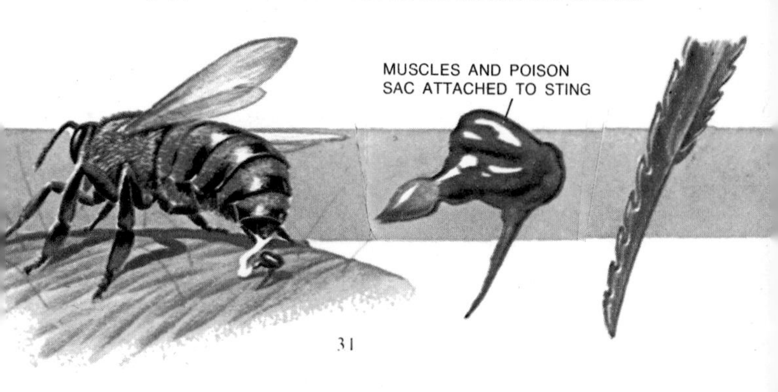

The action of one system on different parts of an organ system may vary considerably. Signals from sympathetic nerves increase the strength and rate of the heartbeat, but the main arteries leaving the heart relax, so allowing an increased flow of blood. Sympathetic nerves usually cause the musculature of the rest of the blood system to constrict. During digestion the blood flow to the gut is increased by the gut blood vessels relaxing. At the same time the blood supply to the muscles is reduced to allow for this.

The actions of the autonomic nervous system are many and varied. Experiments indicate that the sympathetic part is concerned with preparing the animal for violent action and for withstanding abnormal conditions. The parasympathetic system is more concerned with re-establishing normal conditions in the animal once it has been involved in strenuous actions, so that it is ready once more to expend large amounts of energy if necessary. Parasympathetic nerves initiate peristalsis (contraction of the gut) and stimulate the production of digestive juices by the associated glands. Parasympathetic fibres also supply the heart, lowering the frequency and strength of the heartbeat. (See Plate 8).

Autotomy. 'Deliberate' shedding of part of a limb or tail when seized by an enemy. A lizard can part with its tail by snapping a vertebra by muscular action. Many arthropod limbs have a weak spot where they may break off. Limbs shed in this way usually grow again. (See *Regeneration*).

Aves. This class of chordates contains the birds. Their main features are the possession of feathers, a constant body temperature, and the egg-laying habit. The front limbs are modified as wings and the majority of birds can fly. All living birds are toothless.

Birds show traces of their reptilian ancestry in the scales on their legs and in their egg-laying habit. The fossil bird *Archaeopteryx,* with teeth, clawed wings, and a long, feathered tail, shows a number of features intermediate between reptiles and birds and it is thought that modern birds developed from creatures like this. All birds rely largely on sight to find food and to protect themselves and consequently we find that the

AVES: TYPICAL BIRD WING STRUCTURE

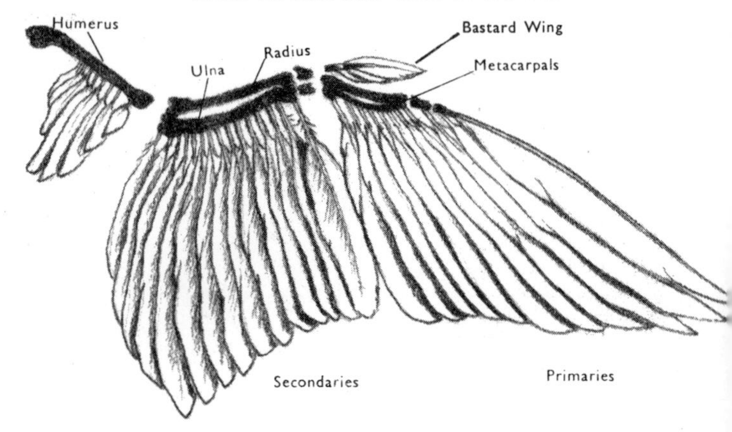

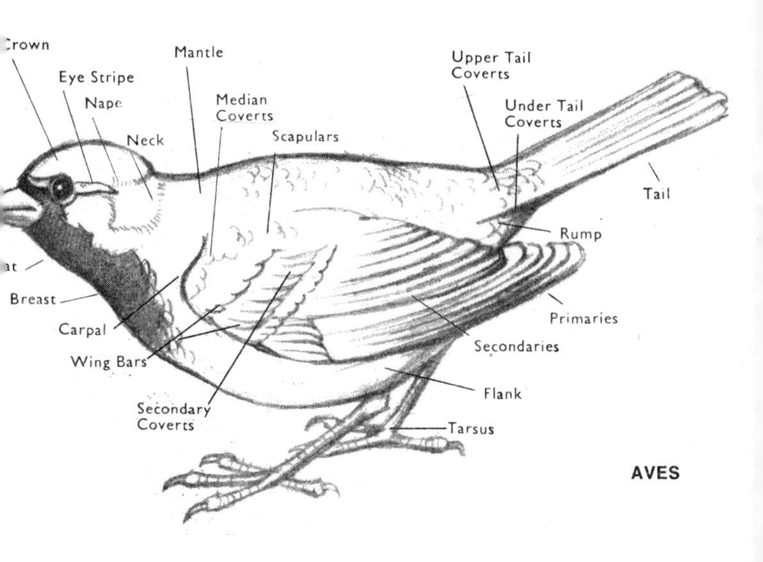

optic lobe of the brain is well-developed. The olfactory region (dealing with the sense of smell) is tiny in most birds. The jaws are extended beyond the head into beaks which vary considerably according to the diet of the bird. Feet are also varied according to the habits.

The classification of the class is described at the end of the book. (See *Alimentary Canal*; *Feathers*; *Archaeopteryx*) and (Plates 2, 9, 48, 49, 120 and 121).

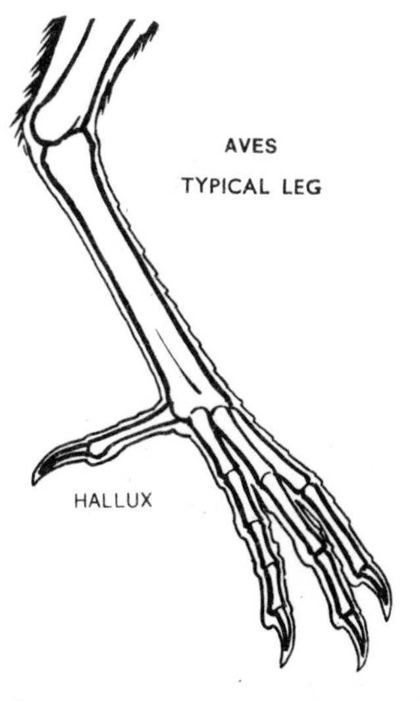

Axis. The second vertebra (q.v.) of the tetrapod spine.

Axon. The long, narrow part of a nerve cell. (See *Nerve Cell*).

Balance. A function of the inner *ear* (q.v.).

Baleen. (=*Whalebone*) Name given to the plates of keratin that hang from the upper jaws of the toothless whales. The plates filter out the small crustaceans on which the whales feed. (See *Cetacea*) and (Plate 21).

Ball-and-Socket Joint. A joint such as the hip or shoulder joint that allows movement in any direction. (See *Hinge Joint*) and (Plate 9).

PLATE 12

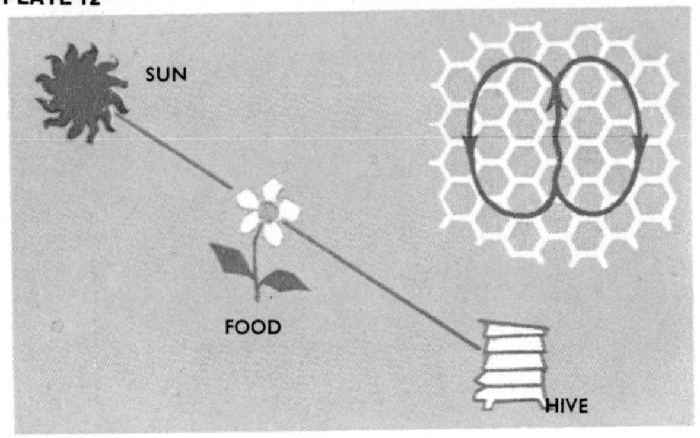

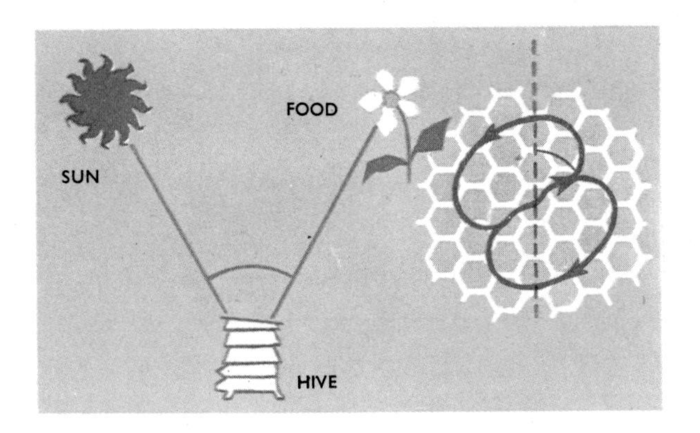

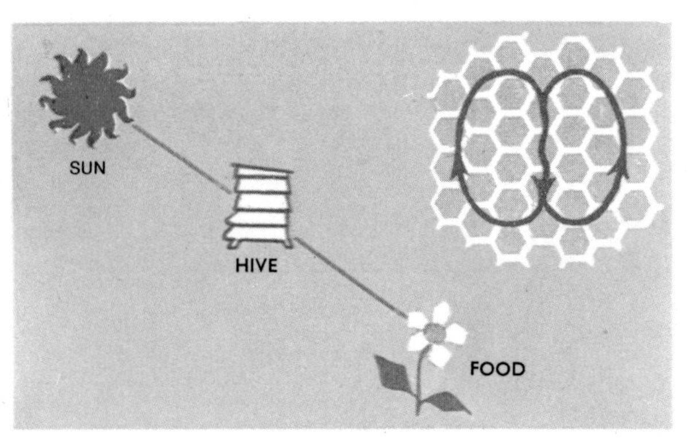

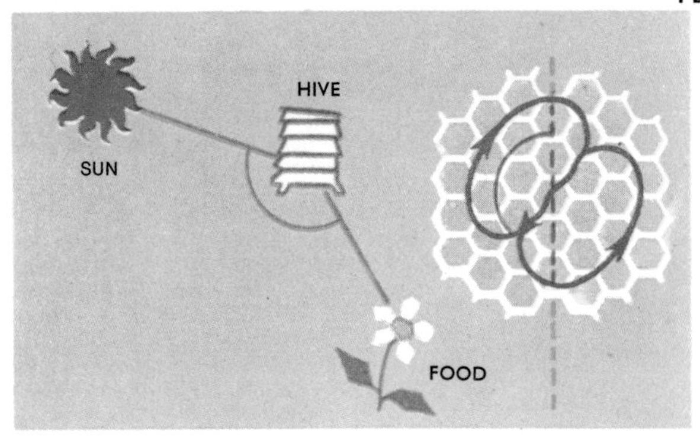

BEE

The 'waggle dance' on the comb indicates the direction (relative to the sun) and the distance of a source of nectar. The direction of the sun is represented by a vertical line and the angle between this and the direction of the dance indicates the direction of the food.

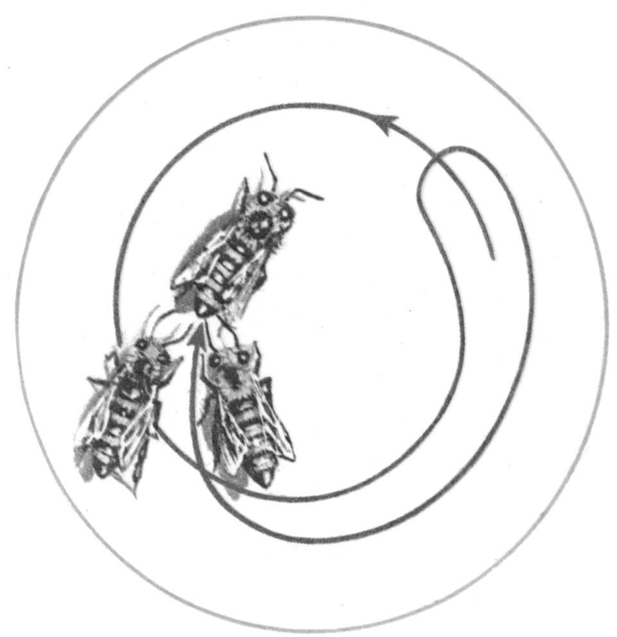

The 'round dance' indicates a nearby source of food and bees fly out in all directions to search.

Barnacles (See *Cirripedia*).

Basement Membrane. The thin, usually structureless membrane on which epithelial cells rest. (See *Epithelium*) and (Plate 41).

Bastard Wing. That part of a bird's wing formed by the first finger. It plays an important part in the flight of some birds. (See *Aves*).

Bats. (See *Chiroptera*).

Bee. An insect of the super-family Apoidea of the order *Hymenoptera* (q.v.). Most species are solitary but some – the familiar bumblebees and honeybees – are social and live in large colonies. There is normally only one mated female – the queen – in each colony and she is tended by workers who are all sterile females. The queen does nothing but lay eggs. Bees feed on pollen and nectar and they are very important pollinating agents. Their mouthparts are finely adapted to sucking up nectar from flowers but they also have biting jaws which they use in constructing the combs. Other parts of the body are specialised for collecting pollen: the hairs on the body are feathery and collect the pollen grains which are then combed off by the legs and transferred to 'pollen baskets' on the hind legs.

Honeybee workers construct sheets or combs of cells made of wax and these combs hang vertically in the nesting space which is often a hollow tree, although with domestic bees of course, it is the hive. There are two main types of cell – worker cells about 1/5th inch across and slightly large drone cells. Worker cells predominate and the eggs that the queen lays in them develop into worker bees. The queen lays special unfertilised eggs in the drone cells and these develop into male bees or drones. There are usually a few hundred drones in a colony, compared with thousands of workers. Every now and then the workers construct large flask-shaped cells. Fertilised eggs are laid in them, the larvae are given special treatment by the workers. They develop into fertile females of which one will take over the colony after mating with a drone. The original queen dies or, if she is young she goes off with a swarm of workers to found a new colony. Pollen and honey are also stored in the cells of the combs. Honey is nectar that has been acted upon by certain enzymes produced by the bees and from which much of the water has been removed. Both honey and pollen are used to feed the young bees and as a reserve food supply for when the weather is too bad to go out.

The workers perform a number of different tasks in the colony, usually graduating from looking after the young to comb-building and other domestic work and then to foraging for food. The honeybees have developed a wonderful way of telling each other where there is a good source of food. When a bee has found a rich source of nectar it returns to the colony and 'dances' either outside, or inside the nest on the combs. The Austrian biologist Karl von Frisch was the first to study the dances and to discover how they convey information. If the nectar source is within about 100 yards of the nest the returning bees perform what is known as the 'round dance', running round in circles, first one way and then the other. Other bees follow the dance and then set out from the hive in all directions searching for the nectar.

When the nectar source is more than about 100 yards from the nest the bees perform the 'waggle dance' which takes the form of a figure-of-eight. If the dance is performed on a flat surface in the open, the 'straight run' of the dance points towards the food. Other bees note the angle between the run and the sun and then fly off in the right direction. More often, however, the dance is performed on the vertical combs inside the hive. In this case, the angle between the vertical and the straight run of the dance equals the angle between the sun and the food and the bees can still fly in the right direction. The waggle dance – so called from the way in which the bee waggles her abdomen while performing it – also tells the other bees how far the food is. The further the food, the slower the dance. The bees thus know how far to fly and in what direction. Having arrived in the indicated area, their sight and sense of smell help them to locate the nectar. An inborn sense of time enables the bees to allow for the change in the position of the sun during the day and so they can always find their way about.

The bee's sting is actually a modified egg-laying apparatus. The actual sting is barbed and although it can be withdrawn from other insects, it cannot be withdrawn from human skin. After stinging the bee can free herself only by leaving the whole stinging apparatus behind and this normally results in her death. Because the sting is a modified egg-layer, only the females can sting.

Although the honeybee colony described here is perennial, going on from year to year, bumblebee colonies are annual affairs. Only the mated queens survive the winter and they have to build the first cells of the new nest in Spring. (See *Insecta; Caste*) and (Plates 9, 10, 11, 12 and 13).

Beetle. Insect of the order *Coleoptera* (q.v.).

Benthos. Term used to cover organisms living on the sea floor as opposed to those swimming and floating in the water. Includes sea-anemones, starfishes, molluscs, and many others. (See *Nekton; Plankton*).

Bilateral Symmetry. The arrangment of an organism in such a way that there is only one plane of division that will give two similar halves. Most free-living animals are bilaterally symmetrical, with the plane of symmetry running from front to back and from dorsal side to ventral side. (See *Radial Symmetry*) and (Plate 14).

Bile. Secretion of the vertebrate liver which is passed to the intestine where it aids in the digestion of fats. It also contains various waste products which are ejected with the faeces. (See *Digestion*).

Binary Fission. Simple division into two.

Binocular Vision. In many animals the eyes are in the side of the head. Each eye has a distinct field of view, and vision is said to be monocular. But others (birds such as owls, and primates, for example) have binocular vision. The eyes are in the front of the head and their fields of view overlap. The brain interprets the two slightly different sets of signals that it receives from the eyes as one composite picture. The nerve fibres from the right half of each retina pass to the right side of the brain. Those from the left halves pass to the left side of the brain. Presumably fibres from corresponding parts of each retina pass to the same part of the brain. The stimulation of two corresponding parts of each retina results in a single sensation. Thus the combination of the two retinal images produces a single picture. When we 'look cross-eyed' at something the images of an object do not fall on corresponding parts of each retina. We thus see everything in duplicate.

It is possible to judge distance when using only one eye, but it can easily be shown that the use of two eyes together increases the speed and accuracy of this operation if a pencil is held vertically in one hand at arm's length. After closing one eye attempts are made to bring the tip of the index finger quickly from the side of the body to the tip of the pencil. If the experiment is then repeated with both eyes open it can be seen how much greater is the precision with which the tip of the pencil can be located. The eyes of man lie about

PLATE 14

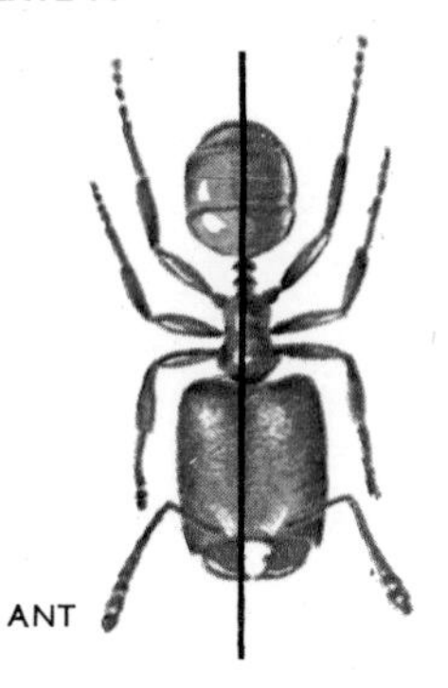

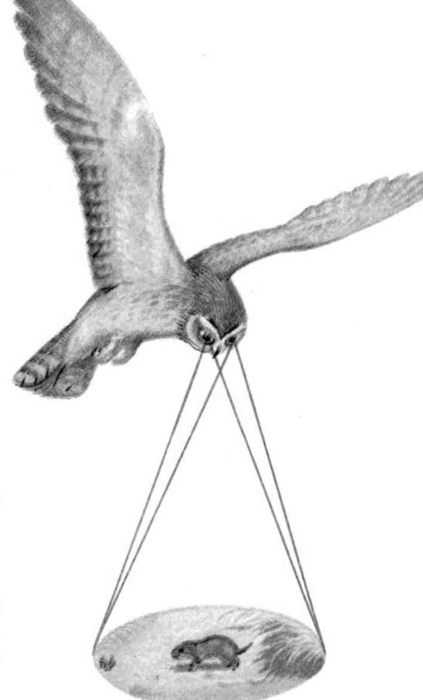

BILATERAL SYMMETRY

Only the line shown will divide the animal into two similar halves.

BINOCULAR VISION

The owl's binocular vision allows it to judge distance accurately. Without it, the bird would have difficulty in catching its food.

BIOLOGICAL CONTROL

Guppies are frequently used to keep down mosquito larvae.

FIREFLY

BIOLUMINESCENCE

BLOOD CELLS

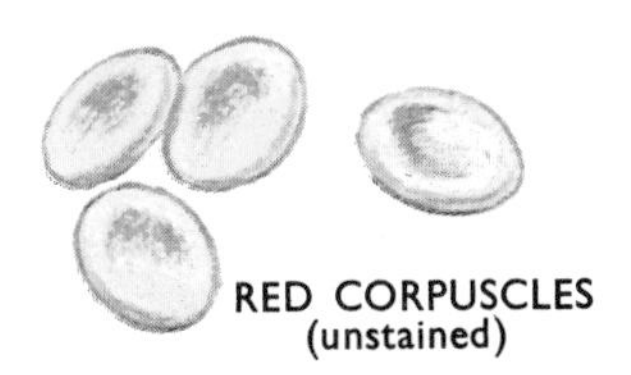
RED CORPUSCLES
(unstained)

PLATELETS

WHITE
CORPUSCLES
(stained)

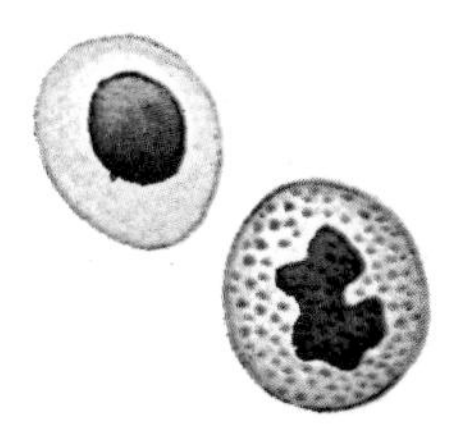

BLOOD SYSTEM

Diagrams showing the thick muscles around an artery, thinner ones of a vein and the thin walls of a capillary.

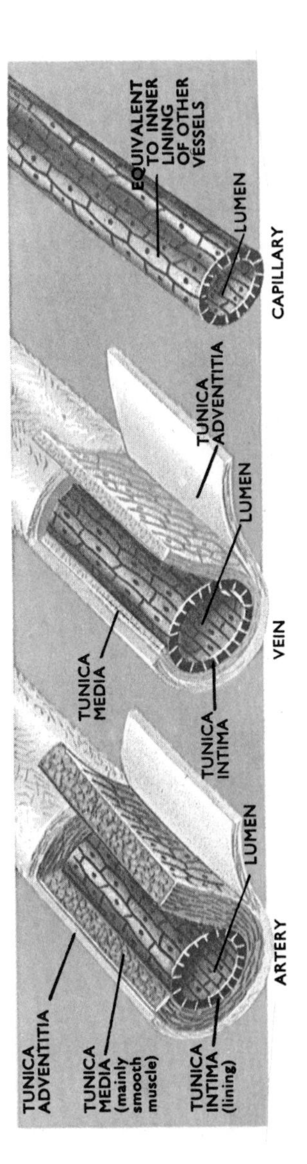

an inch and a half to two inches apart so that a pencil tip (or any other object for that matter) is seen from two slightly different angles. This enables the position of an object to be judged with accuracy.

Many animals with their eyes placed at the sides of the head judge distance by continually moving the head from side to side so that an object is viewed first with one eye and then with the other. A hen, for example, does this when pecking in the grass for grit or edible food material. (See Plate 14).

Binomial System of Nomenclature. The system of naming animals and plants whereby each type of organism has two latin names. The first is the generic name and is spelt with a captial letter. The second is the specific name, spelt with a small letter. The great Swedish naturalist Linnaeus was the first to use this system on a wide scale. Each species has its own specific name but several closely related species may be grouped in one genus and share one generic name. E.g., the large white butterfly is *Pieris brassicae* and the related small white is *Pieris rapae*. It is normal procedure to write scientific names in italics. (See *Classification*).

Biochemistry. Study of the chemical processes going on in the cells and tissues.

Biological Control. The use of one organism to control the numbers of another – usually a pest. Guppies, for example, are used to keep down mosquitoes by feeding on their larvae. (See Plate 14).

Bioluminescence. Light production by living organisms. Nearly all the main groups of animals contain light-producers – protozoans, sponges, corals, jellyfish, worms, clams, snails, squids, shrimps, centipedes, insects, and fishes provide examples. Perhaps the most familiar are the fireflies and glow-worms.

Several species of protozoans are brightly luminous and so numerous that, when disturbed, they light up the surface of the sea. *Noctiluca* often occurs near the shore in the surface of the sea. At night, as the breakers crash on to the beach, they appear to burst into flame. In a similar way the wake of a boat may be marked out as a ribbon of sparkling light.

Several bristle worms are luminous. *Odontosyllis,* swarms prior to spawning. Males and females are attracted to each other by the exchange of light signals. They begin to swarm at the surface between two and three days after a full moon. The males are attracted to the surface by the strong and continuous greenish glow produced along the entire length of the female worms. The males emit short flashes of light. Sperms and eggs are discharged into the water amidst this illuminated confusion.

Many shrimps and prawns have lantern-like photophores. A few can also release clouds of luminous slime from special glands. This lighted 'smoke-screen' no doubt baffles pursuers in much the same way as the wriggling cast-off tail of a lizard. The photophores of shrimps and prawns occur on some of the legs and on parts of the body. Perhaps the pattern they make serves for recognition purposes.

Photophores are best developed in the squids and their relatives, and in fishes. Each photophore consists of a number of light-producing cells, a reflector, a lens, and an on-off 'switch'. The light emitted is of varying colour. It is possible that the differing arrangements of the photophores distinguish between the sexes or indicate the stage of maturity that the squids have reached.

Heteroteuthis, a small deep-water squid living in the Mediterranean, instead of shooting out a cloud of ink, as do most other squids when escaping from enemies, produces a luminous cloud round itself.

Most of the luminous fishes live in moderately deep water, a few in the abyss. The photophores are usually arranged in rows. A deep-sea angler fish has on top of its head a long lure, the luminous tip of which hangs just above its mouth. Prey are attracted by the light and so fall victim to the fish. Certain East Indian fishes have special organs beneath the eye. They are pockets containing bacteria. Bacteria and other light-producing plants release their light continuously, but the fishes have a shutter mechanism whereby they can either conceal the light or display it.

Famous luminous insects are the glow-worms and fireflies. In New Zealand the larvae of a certain fly live on the ceilings of caves. Each glows and spins a web of luminous silk with which to trap food. The ceilings glow as though covered in thousands of tiny hanging chandeliers. The glow-worm of Europe is a wingless female beetle (not a worm!) that lives in grass and in hedgerows. Pale green light emitted by photophores on the lower hind part of the abdomen attracts males flying nearby.

Pairing in fireflies depends on the exchange of light signals. The pattern of the signals differs from one species to another. In one species the male emits short flashes at regular intervals. After a pause of about two seconds the female replies with a short flash. The male then flashes again, followed after the pause by a response from the female. There are several such exchanges of signals prior to pairing.

The light produced by living organisms is often referred to as cold light, for very little heat is evolved during its production. Measurements indicate that nearly one hundred per cent of the energy produced is released as light (an ordinary electric light bulb is only about 10% efficient!).

The chemical reaction involved is a modification or sidebranch of the reactions that proceed in every living cell. It is essentially the same in all cases so far investigated and, like other 'living' reactions, it is promoted by an enzyme. This enzyme is called luciferase. In the presence of oxygen and an organic compound rich in phosphate (adenosine triphosphate or A.T.P.), luciferase promotes the oxidation of luciferin. This causes the production of light. For each molecule of luciferin that is oxidized, one packet or quantum of light energy is released. The chemical structure of luciferin has been established and it has been synthesized. The luciferase molecule is thought to be a protein chain made up of about one thousand amino acid molecules. (See Plate 15).

Biotic Factors. The influences of other living organisms on an animal or a community.

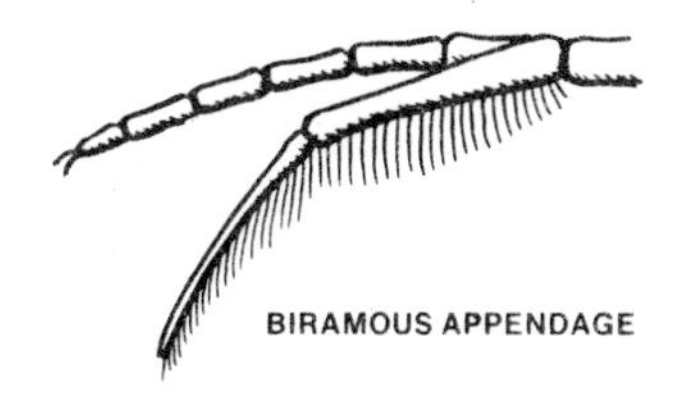
BIRAMOUS APPENDAGE

Biramous Appendage. Limb or other appendage (e.g. antenna) with two branches, often different in appearance and differing in function (e.g. one branch used for swimming, the other for food catching). Typical of many crustaceans and of the extinct trilobites.

Birds. (=Aves).

Bivalve. A mollusc with a shell of two valves. (See *Lamellibranchiata*). Also applied to *Brachiopoda*.

Bladder. The urinary bladder where urine is stored is usually referred to as *the* bladder but, strictly, any thin walled sac is a bladder (e.g. gall bladder, swim bladder). (See Plate 42).

Blind Spot. Point on the retina where the optic nerve leaves. It lacks light-sensitive cells and is therefore blind. (See *Eye*).

Blood. A fluid that circulates in the body of all higher animals carrying food and oxygen to the tissues and

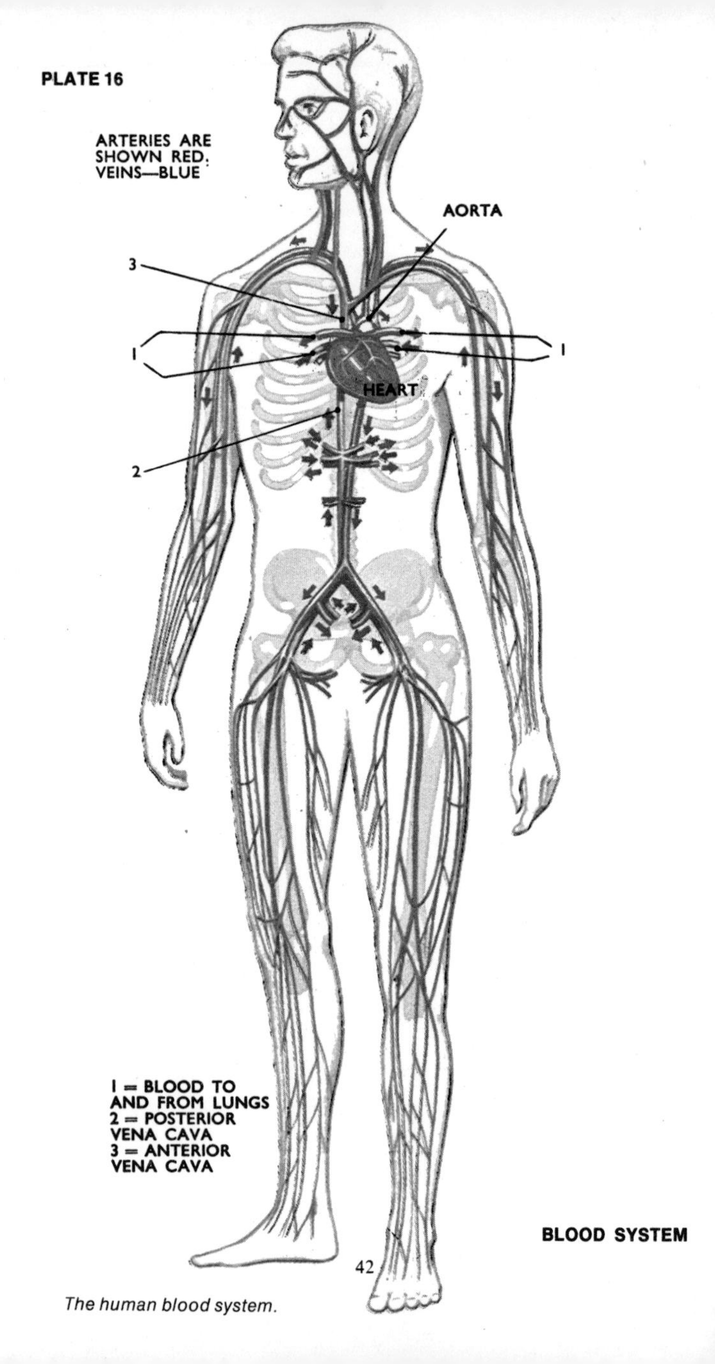

The human blood system.

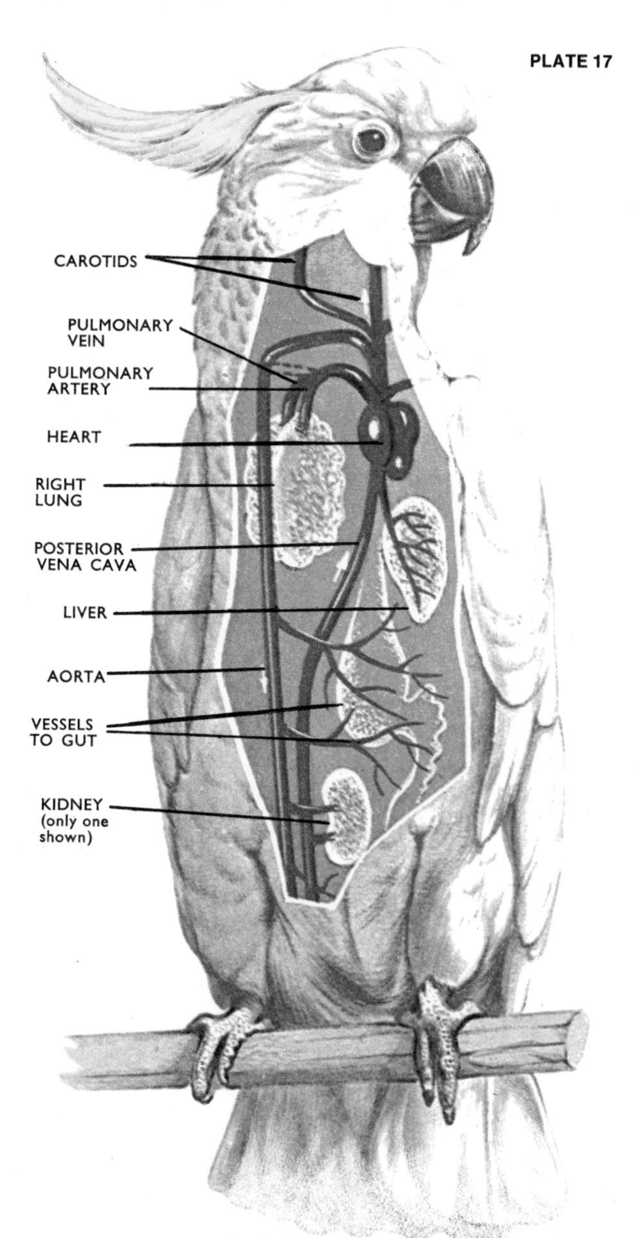

The main blood vessels of a bird (veins from the head not shown)

removing waste products from them. Protozoans, coelenterates, and other small animals have no need of blood for the tissues are not thick enough to hinder the diffusion of food and other materials throughout the body. Blood is circulated through a series of vessels and spaces by the pumping action of the heart. Its composition varies among the groups of animals. Vertebrate blood consists of a liquid plasma in which there are millions of tiny cells, the chief ones being the red corpuscles. These are tiny discs containing haemoglobin, the pigment that gives blood its red colour. Haemoglobin is a respiratory pigment (q.v.) that increases the oxygen-carrying capacity of the blood. Haemoglobin of invertebrate animals is carried in the plasma. Blood also contains large numbers of white cells which are amoeboid in nature and which are important in the destruction of bacteria and dead cells in the body. Mammalian blood contains many tiny bodies called platelets. These are probably fragments of corpuscles and they play a part in the clotting of blood when the blood vessels are damaged.

Blood plasma contains food materials, carbon dioxide and other waste products from the tissues, hormones from the various glands of the body, and all the antibodies that have been produced to combat infections. It also contains the necessary substances for blood-clotting. The composition is precisely regulated by the kidneys and liver which remove wastes and excesses so that the tissues are not subjected to varying concentrations of substances which would affect their working. On its journey round the body, plasma seeps out from the blood vessels and bathes the tissues. It returns to the main blood stream via the *lymphatic system* (q.v.). (See Plate 15).

Blood System. The system of vessels and spaces in which blood moves round the body. Its structure and complexity varies enormously. (See *Heart; Artery; Aortic Arches; Haemocoel*) and (Plates 7, 16 and 17).

Body Cavity. Internal cavity possessed by all higher animals (annelids, molluscs, arthropods, chordates, and others) in which the gut and other organs are suspended. (See *Coelom; Haemocoel*).

Bone. The skeletal material of vertebrates. It is hard and able to stand up to all kinds of stress. The mineral which gives bone its hardness and its resistance to decay is a complex calcium salt which contains both phosphate and carbonate radicals. But, however solid bone may appear, organic substances make up between 30% and 40% of its weight. There are in fact living cells within the bone supplied with minute blood vessels and nerves. The bones, of course, must be 'alive' for they could not otherwise mend after breakage.

Two different types of bone are distinguished by their mode of formation – the membrane bones and the cartilage bones. The membrane bones have the simpler formation. They commonly develop in the dermis – the lower layer of the skin. For this reason they have an alternative name – dermal bones. In fishes the membrane bones form scales; in some crocodiles, plates covered by horny skin, while lizards often have dermal bone underlying their horny scales. The armour of turtles and their relatives is mainly of bone and many of the extinct dinosaurs were protected by outside bony plates.

The armadillo is one of the few mammals with outside membrane bones. The bones cover the whole of the back and the top of the head. In most mammals and birds the only dermal bones are found incorporated into the skull, shoulder girdle and jaw.

Membrane bones develop (or ossify) when certain cells (*osteoblasts*) become bone-secreting. The osteoblasts, with numerous fibres of connective tissue cells, form an organic network. Layers of calcium salts (lamellae) are deposited into this network, and slowly a plate is built up. The plate can grow about its margins and also can be thickened on either its inner or outer surface. Some of the osteoblasts remain alive and actually become incorporated into the growing bone. They are then known as osteocytes and come to have very irregular shapes. The spaces (lacunae) in which the osteocytes are situated are also irregular with long branching processes (canaliculi) extending in all directions. The canaliculi of neighbouring spaces link up and provide a network through which blood containing food and oxygen can filter.

Cartilage bones are not formed directly; they are replacement structures. In the developing embryo most of the skeletal structure is first laid down as cartilage. This softer material is only gradually replaced by bone – a process which is not completed until the animal is full grown. In Man the ossification of the cartilage continues until the age of 25 or 26.

In shape the embryonic cartilage structures are miniatures of the final adult bones. They begin their transformation into bone soon after formation. First, the cartilage becomes calcified (impregnated with calcium salt) and many of its cells die. Then large amoeboid cells called osteoclasts penetrate into the calcified cartilage and begin to destroy it. They soon create a series of channels and blood vessels break in. With the blood come osteoblast cells and bone begins to be laid down.

The cartilage of many vertebrates ossifies from one centre only. For instance the limb bones start to ossify in the middle and the process continues towards either end of the structure. The zone of ossification is called the diaphysis. In mammals, in addition to the diaphysis, other points of ossification may be set up. Each accessory point is called an epiphysis. Epiphyses are especially to be found on bony projections for muscle attachment or places which articulate with other bones. Thus, though ossification is incomplete as a whole, those parts which must particularly stand up to strain are already reinforced.

If the original cartilage did not grow, bone would soon replace all of it. But growth does continue. In the limb bones for instance, as fast as ossification takes place towards their middles, so new cartilage is formed towards the extremities. Only when the adult skeleton is completely grown does cartilage stop developing; ossification is at last able to catch up.

The advantage of cartilage as an early skeletal tissue is that though less rigid than bone it can increase its volume from the inside. Bone, on the other hand, grows only by additions at its surface. Parts of the bone surface are attached to muscles or are delicately articulated with neighbouring bones. Additional bone forming at the surface would disrupt these connections.

But nevertheless, the larger cartilage bones making the limbs are not entirely formed by replacement of cartilage. When ossification begins at at early stage, the cartilage structures are still very small in diameter. But later, the cartilage forming towards the extremities will be expanded in width. Bone replacing the cartilage produces a shaft that tapers towards the middle.

A bone shaped like an hour-glass would be very weak at its middle. The problem is solved by additions of bone to parts of the cartilage surface. The bone is particularly thick in the original, thin middle part of the structure. This coating of bone is, strictly speaking, membrane bone for it does not replace earlier cartilage. It forms on top of the cartilage and for this reason is called perichondral bone.

Throughout the life of an animal, bone is continuously being re-worked. Old material is resorped by the osteoclasts and new material deposited by osteoblasts. Bones which have been remodelled can be recognized in thin section under the microscope by the

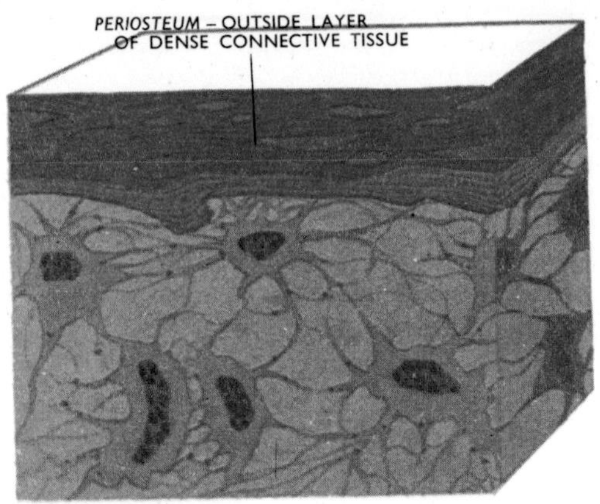

PLATE 18

OSTEOBLASTS BECOME OSTEOCYTES WHEN THEY ARE FINALLY SURROUNDED BY BONE. THE CAVITIES WHICH CONTAIN THE OSTEOCYTES ARE CALLED LACUNAE

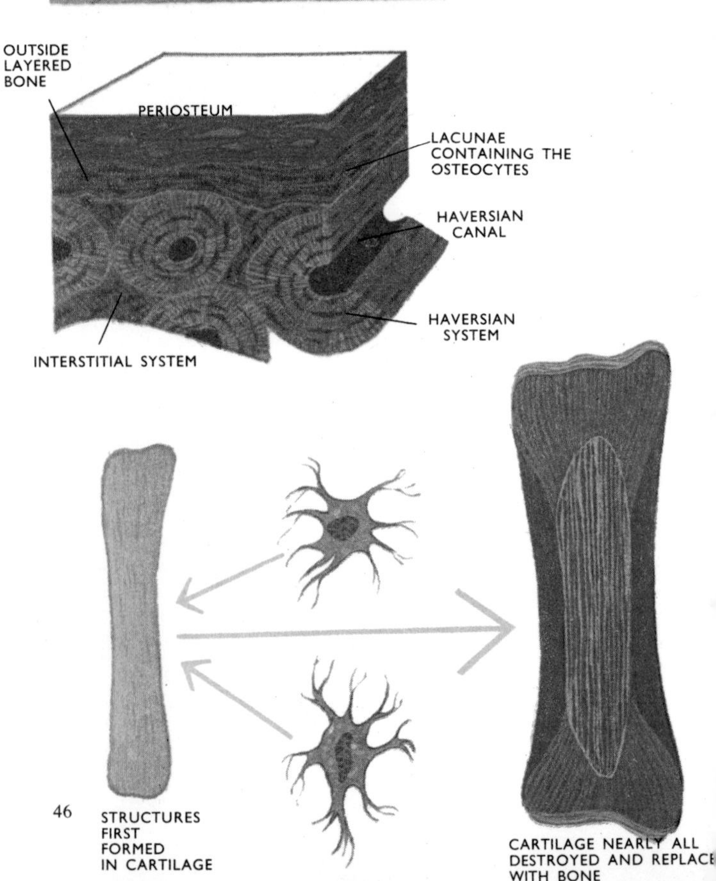

PLATE 19

BONE

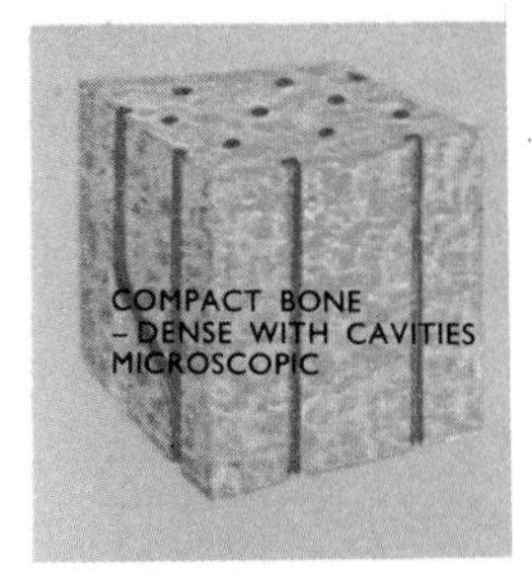

(Far left) When bone first forms, the osteoblasts become linked together into a network. (Left centre) Re-working of bone forms the *Haversian* systems. Some of the first formed bone (the interstial systems) remains within the Haversian systems. (bottom left) Bone may form when osteoblast cells invade structures already laid down in the embryo as cartilage. The result is *cartilage* or *endochrondral* bones. Most bones in the human skeleton form in this way.

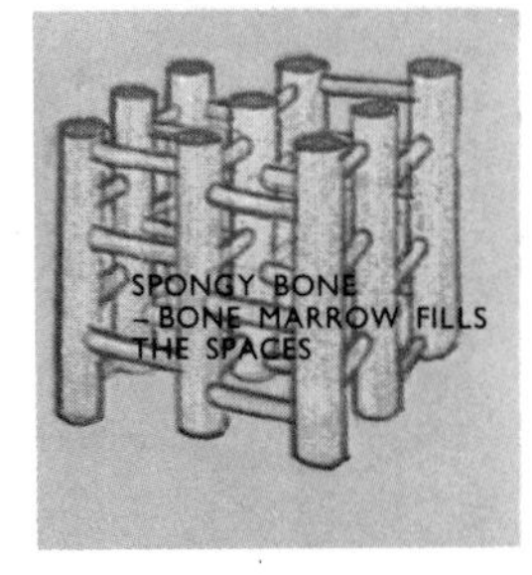

(Left) Bone varies in density, strength and hardness. The outer portions of bony structures usually consist of *compact* bone in which the percentage of living cells and organic substances is small. The inner surface of larger bones is made of *spongy* bone, a framework of rigid bony bars between which are fatty, vascular and other tissues forming bone marrow. The ossification of a mammal limb bone is shown below right.

(Below) Cartilage is destroyed by osteoclasts. Osteoblasts invade and lay down bone.

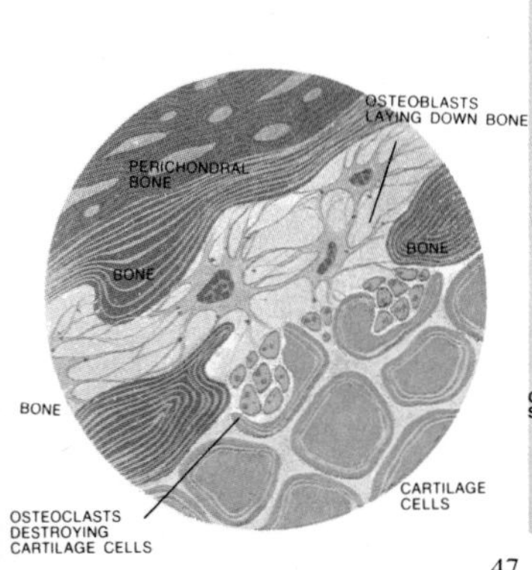

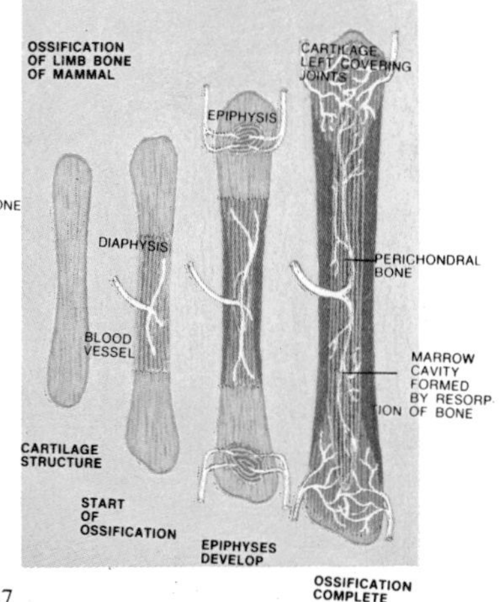

development of Haversian canals. The canals which usually run parallel to one another, carry blood vessels and nerves. The blood vessels carrying food, pass out into the surrounding bone. Osteoblasts become arranged in a series of concentric circles about each canal. They rely upon the blood vessels in the canal for a supply of nourishment. Each canal with its dependent series of osteoblasts constitutes an Haversian system.

Bone varies in density, strength and hardness. The outer portions of bony structures usually consist of compact bone in which the percentage of living cells and organic substances is small. The inner surface of the larger bones is made of spongy bone. This consists of just a framework of bony bars giving rigidity; in between are fatty, vascular, and other tissues forming part of the bone marrow. Spongy bone is light and lowers the overall weight of the skeleton without losing much of its strength. The very centre of the larger bones may become hollow. Replacing the bone are the soft, fatty tissues of the bone marrow where fats are stored and blood corpuscles made. (See Plates 18–19).

Bowman's Capsule. A chamber in the vertebrate kidney, one connected to each renal tubule. Inside is the glomerulus – a knot of blood vessels where waste is removed from the blood. The capsule and glomerulus make up the Malpighian body. (See *Kidney*).

Brachial. Concerning the arms.

Brachiation. Method of movement, practised especially by apes, involving swinging from hand to hand in the trees.

Brachiopoda. A phylum of animals with a very long fossil history but relatively few living forms. They are shelled animals, the shell having two valves which may or may not be hinged. The characteristic feature

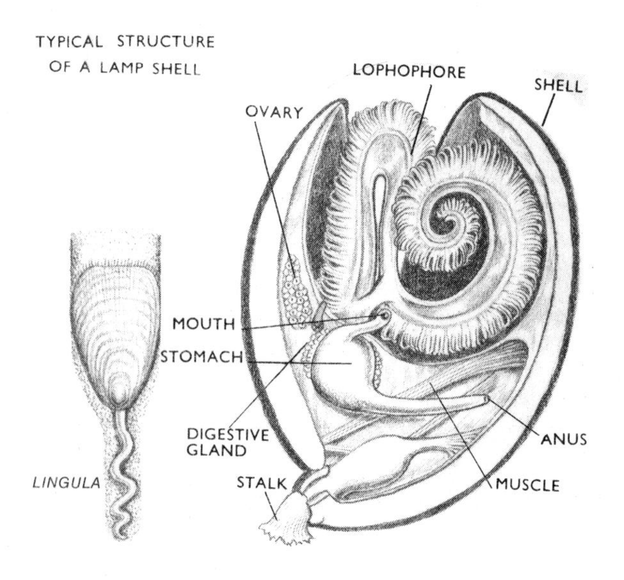

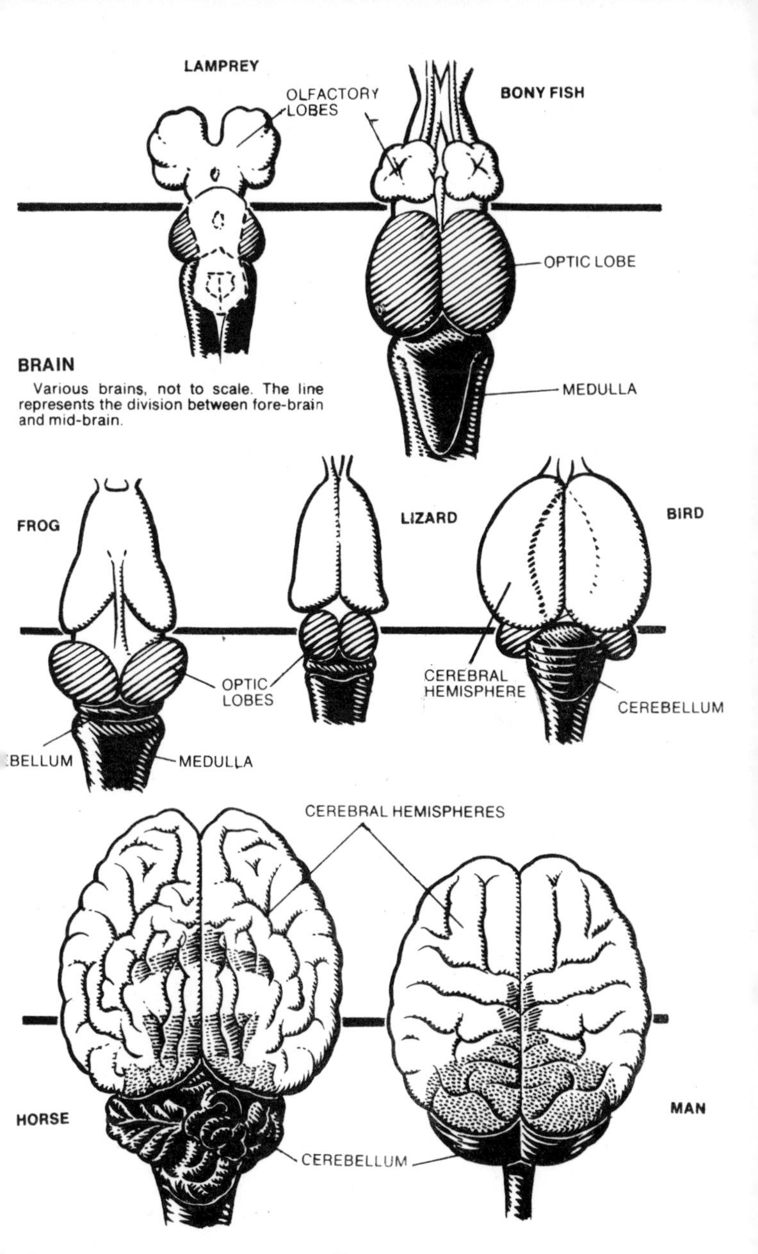

BRAIN

Various brains, not to scale. The line represents the division between fore-brain and mid-brain.

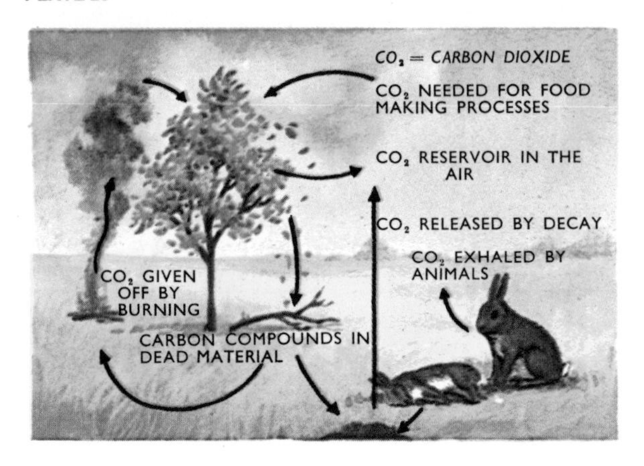

CARBON CYCLE

A simplified diagram of the circulation of carbon between air, earth and living things.

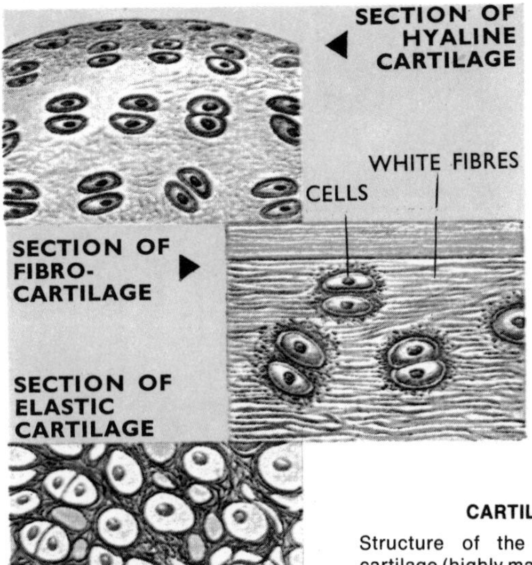

CARTILAGE

Structure of the main types of cartilage (highly magnified).

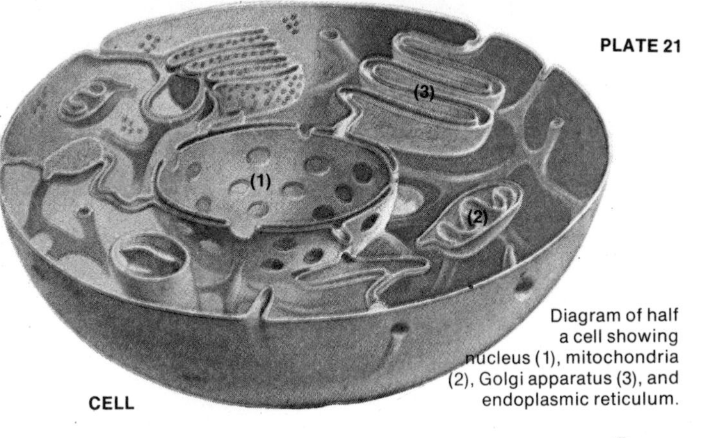

CELL

Diagram of half a cell showing nucleus (1), mitochondria (2), Golgi apparatus (3), and endoplasmic reticulum.

CEPHALOPODA

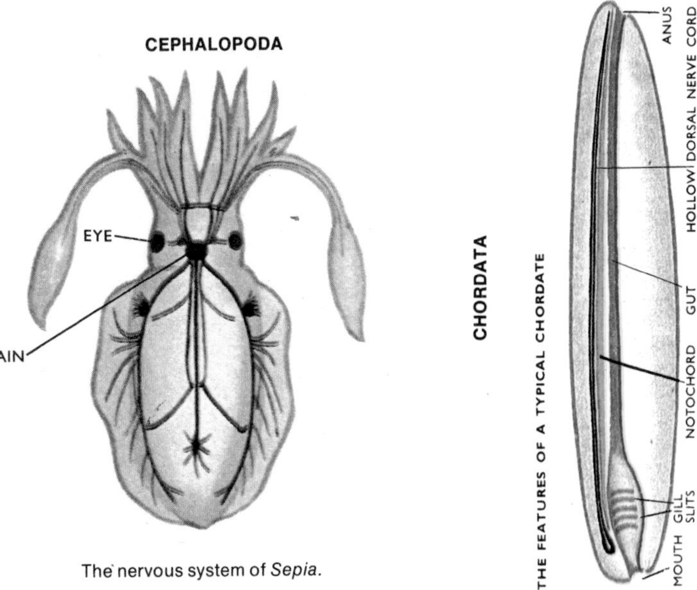

The nervous system of *Sepia*.

CHORDATA

CETACEA

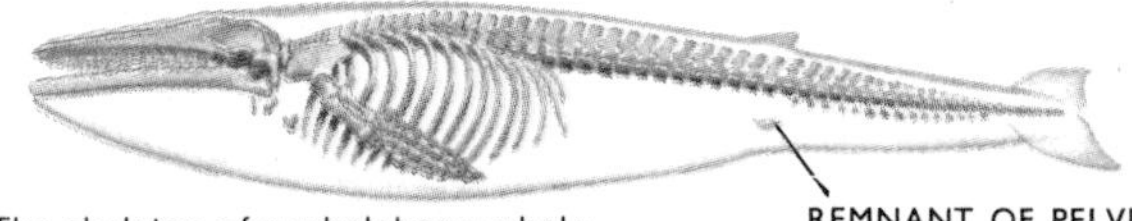

The skeleton of a whalebone whale. Note the great length of the head, modified fore-limbs and the absence of hind-limbs.

is a pair of coiled ciliated arms which are used for feeding. The cilia draw a current of water towards the mouth which collects any food particles from the water. Brachiopods are commonly called lamp shells. (See Plate 110).

Brain. The co-ordinating centre of the nervous system. It is the front part of the central nervous system and as well as its general co-ordinating function it is specially concerned with the sense organs of the head and the special senses. Coelenterates, star-fishes, and other animals without well-defined heads do not have the concentration of nervous tissue called the brain but all animals that are bilaterally symmetrical have some sort of brain, even if it is merely a slight swelling of the nerves in that area.

The brain is most highly developed in cephalopods and in vertebrates. Three main regions can be detected in the primitive vertebrate brain: the fore-brain, consisting mainly of the olfactory lobes; the mid-brain, made up largely of the optic lobes controlling the sense of sight; and the hind-brain which is composed of the cerebellum and the medulla oblongata. The cerebellum is concerned largely with balance and movement while the medulla is the centre for the senses of taste and hearing among other things.

These three regions can be detected in all vertebrate brains but their relative sizes differ a great deal according to the habits of the animals. Sharks rely largely on their sense of smell and the olfactory lobes are correspondingly large. Most bony fishes rely mainly on sight and so the optic region is large. The basic pattern is similar in amphibians and reptiles but there is a marked change in the fore-brain: it is roofed over and developed as the cerebral hemispheres. These receive nerve tracts from other parts of the brain and nervous system. The fore-brain is developing into the main 'association centre' controlling the actions of the animals. This development of the cerebral hemispheres is carried further in the birds and mammals and they come to dominate the whole brain. The roof of the cerebral hemispheres is known as the cerebral cortex and in man it spreads back so as to almost cover the rest of the brain. The cortex is made up of millions of cells known as 'grey matter' and overlies the 'white matter' made up of the nerve axons that conduct messages to and from other parts of the brain. The cortex controls the behaviour of the animals and it has been found that each region of the cortex controls certain aspects. In man, for example, there are definite regions for speech, memory, sight, etc. (See Page 49).

Branchial. Concerning the gills – e.g. branchial arteries.

Branchiopoda. Sub-class of the *Crustacea* (q.v.) including the fairy shrimp and the water fleas. (See Page 264).

Bristle-worm. (See *Polychaeta*).

Brittle-star. (See *Echinodermata*).

Bronchus (plural bronchi). The vertebrate trachea divides into two bronchi, one leading to each *lung* (q.v.). (See Plate 73).

Bronchiole. One of the branches of a bronchus within the lung.

Bryozoa. (=*Polyzoa*) Sea-mats, a group of largely marine animals often found encrusting rocks and seaweeds. Now split into two phyla: – *Endoprocta* and *Ectoprocta* (q.v.).

Buccal Cavity. The mouth cavity which in vertebrates contains the teeth and tongue.

Bug. Popularly used for any insect, this term should strictly be applied only to members of the order *Hemiptera* (q.v.).

Butterfly. (See *Lepidoptera*).

Caddis Fly. (See *Trichoptera*).

Caecum. Blind sac in the mammalian alimentary canal. Important as the site of cellulose digestion in some herbivores. (See *Alimentary Canal*).

Cambrian Period. First period of the Palaeozoic era which began some 500 million years ago. (See *Geological Time Scale*).

Canine. 1) Concerning dogs. 2) The stabbing 'eye tooth' of mammals.

Capillary. Tiny blood vessel whose wall is only one cell thick. Capillaries arise from the repeated branching of arteries and run through all the tissues of the body, later joining up to form veins. (See *Artery*) and (Plate 15).

Carapace. The hard, protective shell covering the head and thorax of many arthropods. Also the dorsal part of a turtle shell. (See Plate 97).

Carbon Cycle. Carbon is an essential component of all living matter. Plants remove it from the air in the form of carbon dioxide and use it to make sugars, proteins, and other materials. Animals obtain their carbon from the food they eat (derived ultimately from plants). But carbon is also returned to the atmosphere in many ways. Both plants and animals 'burn up' food materials to provide energy. This process (respiration) releases carbon dioxide back into the air. Bacterial decay of dead organisms also releases carbon dioxide. Coal and oil are organic deposits rich in carbon and when they are burnt they too return carbon dioxide to the air. This interchange of carbon between the atmosphere and living organisms is called the carbon cycle. (See Plate 20).

Carboniferous Period. Period of geological time when the important coal seams were formed. Began about 280 million years ago. (See *Geological Time Scale*).

Cardiac. Concerning the heart. Cardiac muscle is a special type found only in the heart. (See *Muscle*).

Carnassial Teeth. The cutting cheek teeth of carnivores. They are specially adapted for shearing through meat and even bones.

Carnivora. The order of flesh-eating mammals including the dogs, cats, and seals. (See Plates 123 and 86).

Carnivore. Any meat-eating animal, but the term is frequently restricted to mean members of the order Carnivora.

Carotid Artery. Major artery leading to the head.

Carpal Bones. Bones of the wrist region of the fore-limb.

Cartilage. A skeletal tissue of vertebrates. It is not so hard or rigid as bone but is extremely tough and resistant to both compression and extension. Except in sharks, rays, and a few other fishes whose skeletons are composed entirely of cartilage, it is found only in certain parts, such as the joints, of adult vertebrates.

Under the microscope, cartilage shows up as a clear matrix in which are embedded numerous small groups of cells. These cells (chondroblasts) lie in fluid-filled spaces (lacunae) and secrete the matrix which is called chondrin. Compression forces are resisted mainly by the fluids in the cell spaces. The chondrin itself is slightly compressible and elastic and it absorbs shocks such as would be transmitted through the leg bones when a person is running.

Cartilage surrounding the ends of bones at their joints and lining the wind-pipe is known as hyaline cartilage. There are relatively few fibres in it. Fibrous cartilage, however, contains lots of collagen fibres. They help it to resist extension. The intervertebral discs of the back-bone are composed

PLATE 22

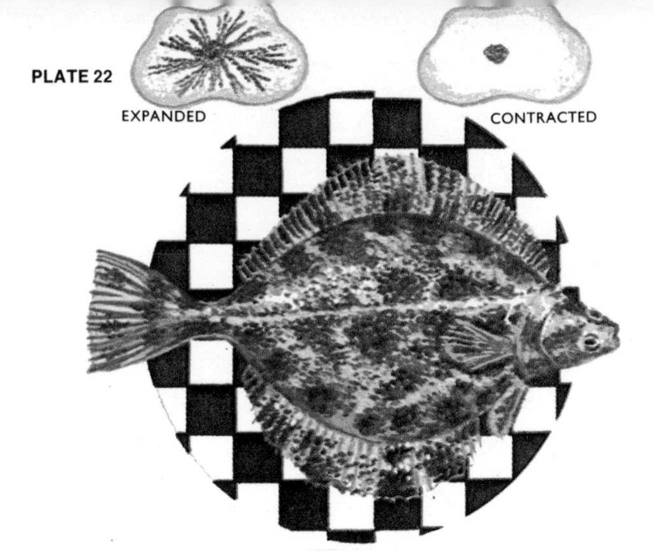

CHROMATOPHORE

The pigment cells are under nervous control and by expanding some and contracting others, the plaice can produce this blotched effect to match the background.

COELENTERATA

Diagrammatic structure of the double-layered body wall.

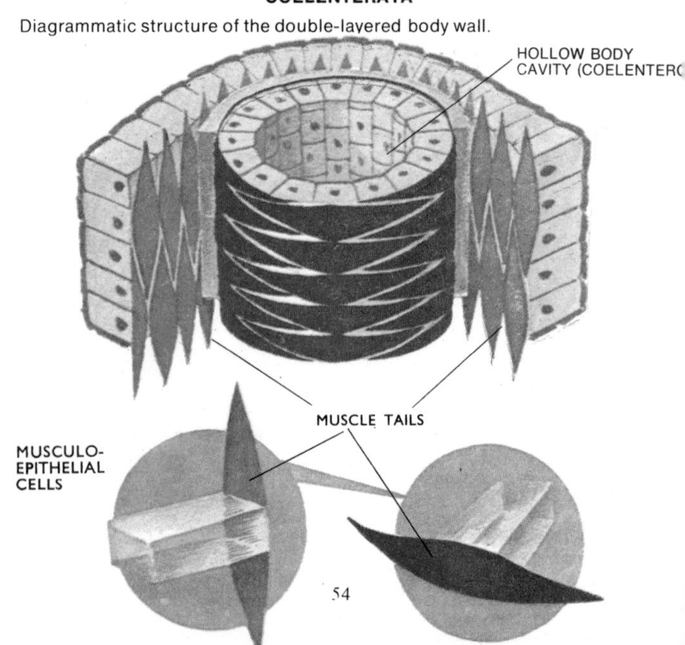

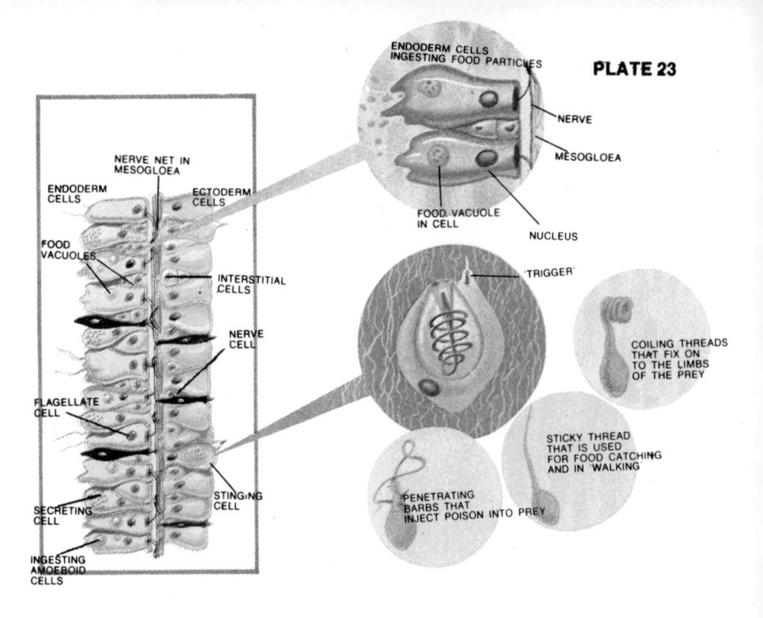

Detailed structure of the body wall and the stinging cells.

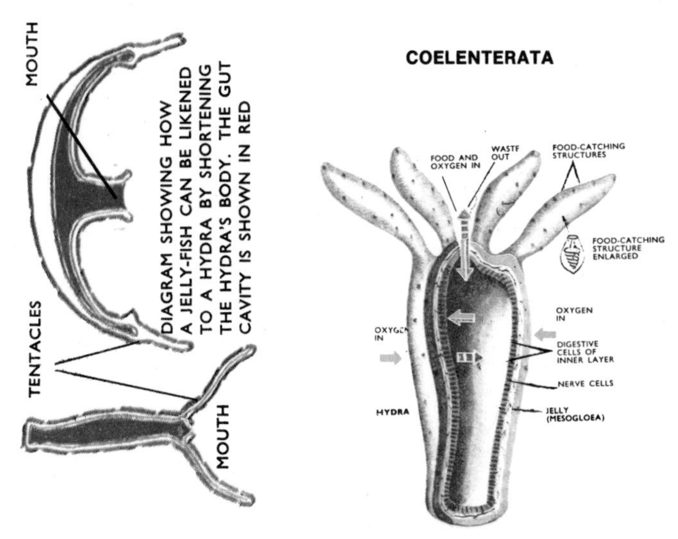

of fibrous cartilage and it is also found where tendons and ligaments join bones—especially at the joints.

Elastic fibres are found in some cartilage—for example that at the tip of the nose and that forming the outer ear. This type of cartilage is flexible and is called elastic cartilage.

Each mass of cartilage (except at the ends of bones) is surrounded by a sheath of tough connective tissue called the perichondrium. This sheath contains blood vessels from which food materials diffuse out to the cartilage cells. New cartilage cells are built up from the cells of the perichondrium. Cells on the inside of this layer break away and gradually turn into cartilage cells. They begin to secrete chondrin and each group of cells becomes separated by the accumulating matrix. A section through the cartilage shows that the cells near the edge are much closer together and less specialized than the older cells near the centre. (See Plate 20).

Caste. Social insects normally have a number of structurally and functionally different forms: honeybees have queens, workers, and drones: ants have various types of worker such as soldiers and foragers: termites have kings as well as queens and working forms. All the various forms are called castes. (See *Isoptera*) and (Plate 67).

Catabolism. Part of *metabolism* (q.v.) involving the breakdown of material with release of energy.

Caterpillar. Young stage of various insects (especially Lepidoptera). The soft body carries three pairs of jointed legs on the thorax and a number of stumpy legs behind.

Caudal. Concerning the tail.

Cell. All living organisms are composed of one or more cells—tiny compartments normally invisible to the naked eye—within which the vital processes of life go on. In protozoans the body consists of only one cell and all the processes have to go on in that one cell. In many-celled animals, however, there are several different types of cell each specialised for a different function. Examples are muscle-cells, nerve-cells, bone-cells, blood-cells, and many others. Their shapes and the processes that go on within them differ according to function.

The basis of all living cells is protoplasm. It is important to realise that this is not a single substance; it is a very complicated mixture of organic and inorganic substances in which chemical changes are continuously taking place. The chemical composition of protoplasm therefore varies not only between species and between cells performing different functions but also in individual cells at different times. The main component is water in which there are suspended or dissolved numerous proteins, lipids (fatty substances) and inorganic salts. The electron microscope shows that there is an elaborate structure—of fibres and channels—within the protoplasm.

Every cell is bounded by a cell-membrane. This is not an external structure but a living part of the cell. The membrane can be seen with the aid of the electron microscope and much other evidence points to its importance. Cells placed in liquid surroundings do not mix with the liquid unless they are pierced with a very fine needle. This suggests some sort of envelope for the protoplasm. Research indicates that the surface layer of the protoplasm consists of a network of protein and lipid material which prevents loss of the cell contents and also allows some flexibility. The thickness of this cell membrane layer is less than one thousandth of a millimetre.

Apart from the protoplasm almost all living cells have one structure in common—the nucleus. This structure controls the activity of the whole cell and as a rule there is only one nucleus in each cell. It consists largely of nucleoproteins. These regulate the manufacture of the proteins of the rest of the cell protoplasm (cytoplasm). Surrounding the nucleus is a membrane similar to that around the whole cell. There is a darker region within the nucleus called the nucleolus. The nucleus also contains the *chromosomes*—thread-like structures that play an important part in cell-division and heredity. (See *Chromosome, Heredity*).

It must not be thought that cells consist merely of a nucleus suspended in a bag of protoplasm. There are many other structures to be found in a cell, depending on its function. Most cells are permeated by a system of canals (the *endoplasmic reticulum*) which probably serves to carry materials to various parts of the cell. The *Golgi apparatus* is a collection of fatty and protein material which forms tubular bodies, normally in the region of the nucleus. It is found in almost all animal cells but its function is not understood. The *centrosome* is a region of clear protoplasm near the nucleus. In its centre is a dark body—the *centriole*—which seems to be connected with cell-division. Throughout the cell protoplasm there are numerous tiny bodies called *mitochondria*. They are concerned with the respiratory mechanisms of the cell and are most numerous when the cell is most active. Gland cells and some others contain secretory granules which produce hormones or enzymes that are passed out to other parts of the body. Every cell in the body originates from another by division for every creature starts life originally as a single cell. (See Plate 21).

Central Nervous System. (C.N.S.). The brain and spinal cord or main nerve cord of the body. The central nervous system co-ordinates the activity of the whole body because all stimuli are transmitted to it and the appropriate responses originate from it. (See *Peripheral Nervous System*).

Centrum. The central part or 'body' of a vertebra. It replaces the notochord during development in most vertebrates. (See *Vertebra*).

Cephalochordata. (=*Acrania*) A subphylum of the Chordata (q.v.) containing *Amphioxus* and a few related animals. These animals have a dorsal, hollow nerve cord, a notochord, and gill-slits—all typical features of chordates. Although they have no

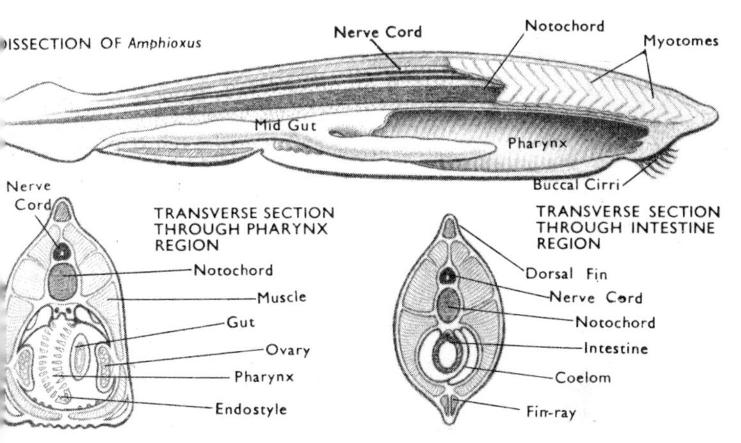

PLATE 24

COELOM

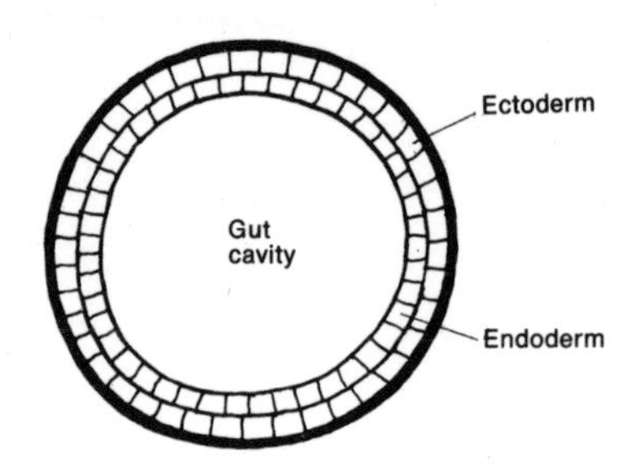

Section through a generalised diploblastic animal with only two layers of cells.

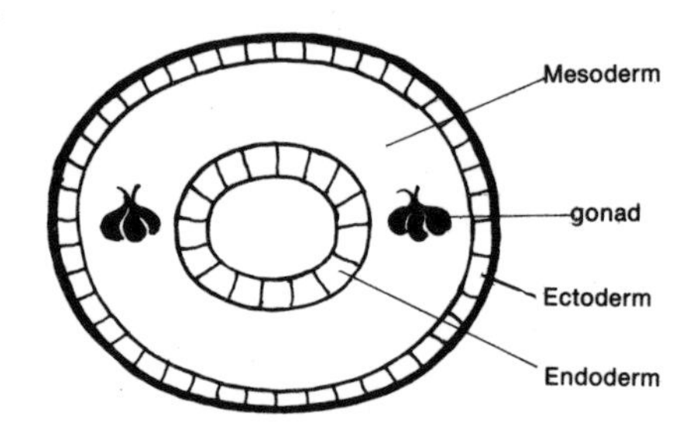

Simplified section through a generalised acoelomate triploblastic animal where the mesoderm fills the space between ecto- and endoderm.

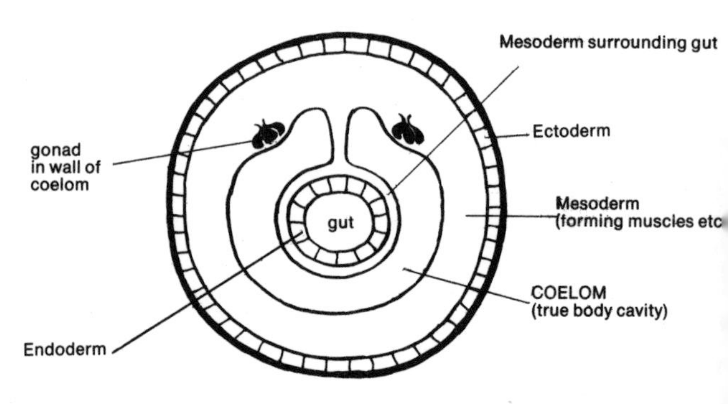

Simplified section through a coelomate animal. A cavity—the coelom—develops in the mesoderm which thus becomes split into two regions.

PLATE 25

COLEOPTERA

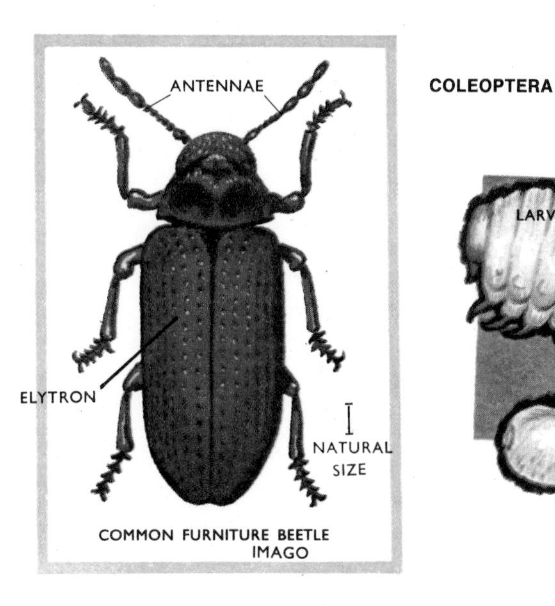

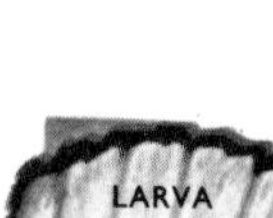

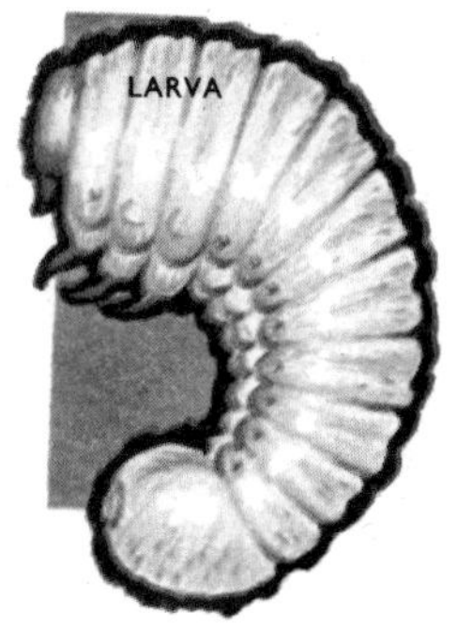

CONNECTIVE TISSUE

(Left) Areolar tissue – the commonest packing tissue, (Right) Fat or adipose tissue.

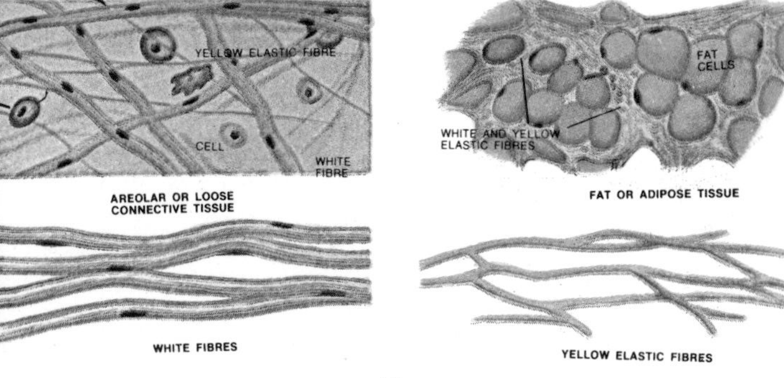

brain as such and no skull or skeleton, these creatures probably represent the early ancestors of the fishes. *Amphioxus* lives around the coasts of all the seas where it burrows in the sand. It draws a current of water in through its mouth and passes it to the pharynx which has numerous gill-slits. The gill-bars hold back any small particles of food and let the water pass out into the atrium. From there it passes through a small pore and out to the sea again. The trapped food particles, mixed with slime, are swept by ciliary action into the mid-gut for digestion. (See Page 273).

Cephalopoda. A class of the phylum *Mollusca* (q.v.) containing the squids, octopuses, and cuttlefish, all of which are marine. There are many extinct members–ammonites, belemnites, and others – typically with a chambered shell. Modern forms, however, except for the Pearly Nautilus have a very reduced shell. In size they vary from a few inches to 60 feet – the length of a giant squid including tentacles.

At first inspection, the relationship between these animals and the slugs, snails and mussels is not very obvious. But it is made clearer by considering a cephalopod in an upside-down position. (See Plate 78).

As in all molluscs a thick layer of skin (the mantle) surrounds the internal organs. The shell is usually secreted inside the mantle. In octopuses it is represented by a pair of small rods or a thin plate. In cuttlefish it is better developed, and forms a calcareous, shield-shaped object familiar as the canary's cuttlebone or sea-biscuit. Squid shells (called pens) are slender and are made of chitin.

Cephalopods differ from other molluscs in having a distinct head, marked off from the rest of the body by a narrower 'neck'. The mantle does not cover the head: it stops at the neck and there forms a loose fold called the collar. The mantle is muscular and alternately expands and contracts. When it expands water is drawn in around the collar. The water fills a space between the inside

VENTRAL VIEW OF *Sepia officinali*

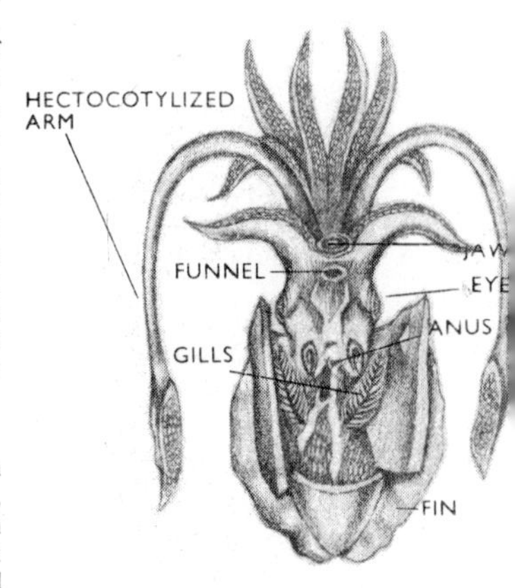

structures of the creature and the mantle. This space is the mantle cavity and projecting into it are two delicate filaments of tissue – the gills. The gills absorb oxygen from the water.

The water does not pass out the same way as it came in. When the mantle cavity is full, the entrances at the collar are closed and the cavity becomes a compression chamber. As the muscular mantle contracts, the water is forced out through a single narrow outlet, the siphon, situated on the underside of the head. When necessary, the water may be pumped out with great force which gives the creature jet propulsion in the opposite direction to which the siphon is pointing.

The most conspicuous structures of all cephalopods are the arms surrounding the head. The arms (together with the siphon) really correspond to the foot of the snail and mussel. The name cephalopod means in fact head-footed (Greek, kephale, a head; podos, a foot). The octopuses have eight arms while the squids and cuttlefish have ten, two of them longer than the rest and called tentacles.

The arms are equipped with numerous suckers. There may be a single or a double row according to the species. Each sucker is a remarkable structure. In the octopus it consists of a flat muscular disc supported on a cushion of tissue. When the octopus grabs hold of an object, the outer thickened rim of the sucker firmly presses against the surface, giving it a water-tight contact. Then the centre of the disc is raised like a piston by muscular contraction. A partial vacuum is created inside the sucker and gives the octopus a strong grip. The suckers are very sensitive to mechanical and chemical sensation, and are also used as organs for exploration. The suckers of squids and cuttlefish are toothed.

The mouth is armed with a horny beak made of chitin. The beak consists of two hard, pointed plates which work against one another. Inside the mouth is a tongue strengthened with cartilage and covered by the radula —a strip of tissue covered with rows of curved rasping teeth.

Compared with other molluscs, cephalopods lead a very active life and have a correspondingly better developed nervous system with a large brain. The animals feed on crabs, prawns, fish, and other molluscs. They find their food by sight and their eyes are very good, in fact, they show remarkable similarities to vertebrate eyes. (See *Mollusca*) and (Plates 21, 78 and 115).

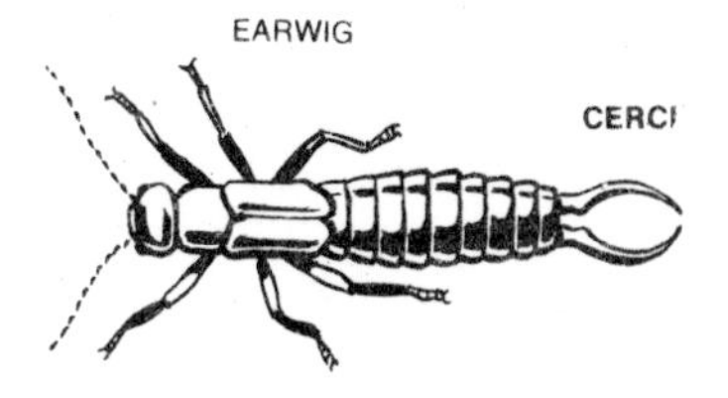

Cerci. Paired structures found at the end of the abdomen of various insects. They may be long and thin as in mayflies or more robust as in cockroaches or the pincers of earwigs.

Cerebellum. Part of the vertebrate brain (q.v.) concerned with balance and the co-ordination of movement. Best developed in fast-moving animals.

Cerebral Cortex. The outer layer of nerve cells (grey matter) covering the cerebral hemispheres (fore-brain)

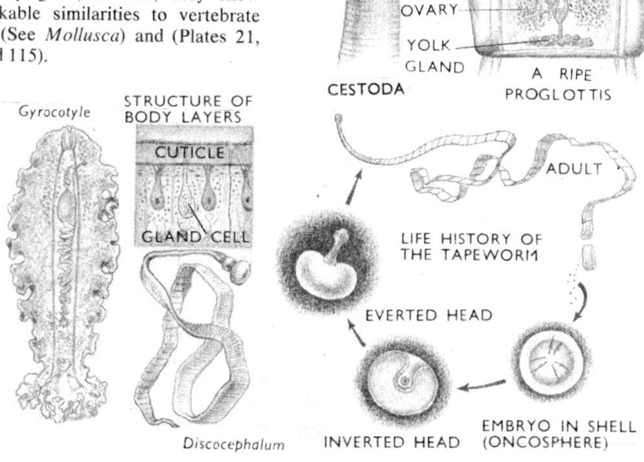

PLATE 26

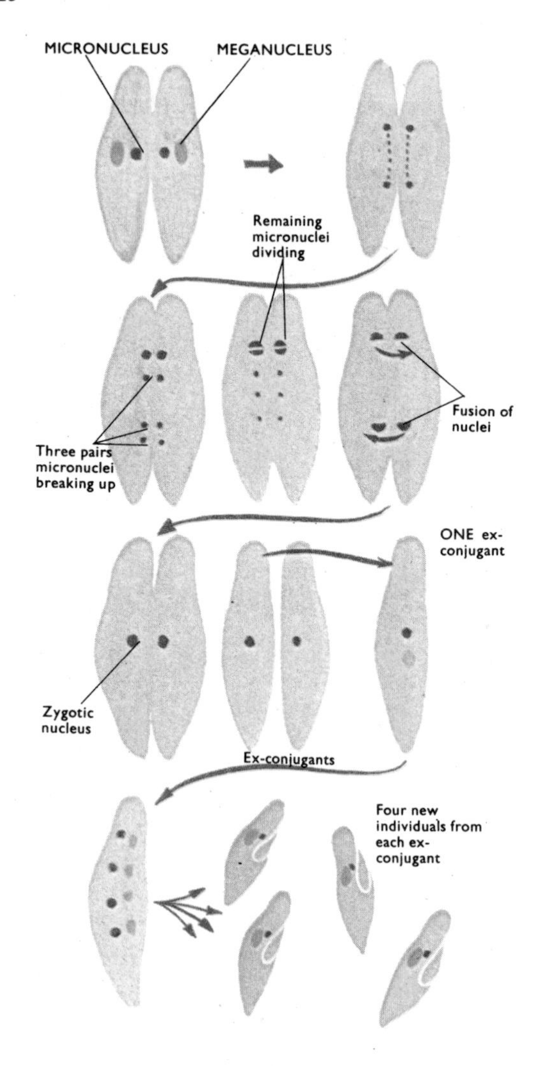

CONJUGATION

A form of reproduction found in *Paramoecium* and some other protozoans, in which two individuals come together and exchange nuclear material before dividing into several new animals.

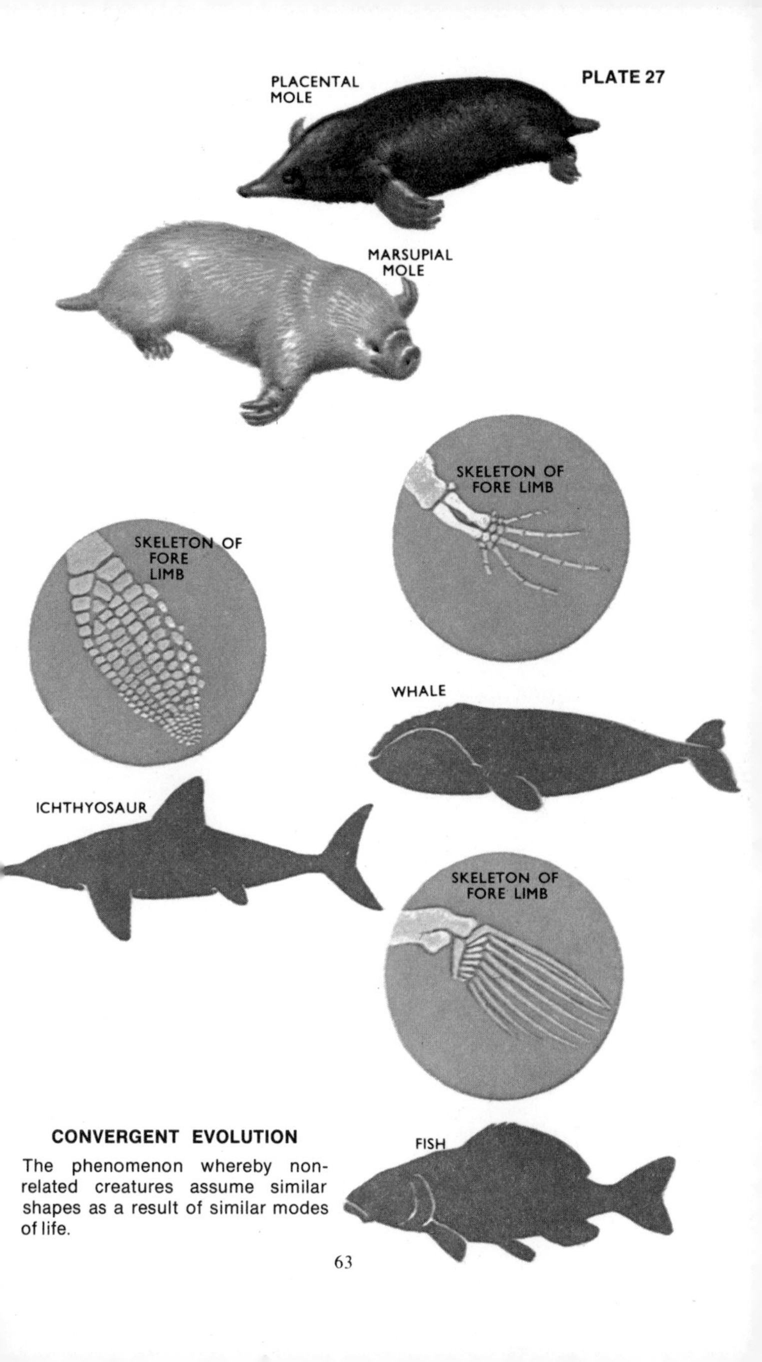

CONVERGENT EVOLUTION

The phenomenon whereby non-related creatures assume similar shapes as a result of similar modes of life.

of vertebrates. It is very extensive in mammals and in man covers most of the brain. (See *Brain*).

Cerebrospinal. Concerning the brain and spinal cord – e.g. cerebro – spinal fluid inside the nerve cord.

Cervical. Concerning the neck – e.g. cervical vertebrae. (See *Vertebra*).

Cestoda. Class of flatworms all of which are parasitic in the food canals of other animals. They have no gut of their own. Commonly known as tape-worms, they have a rounded head provided with hooks and suckers, and the body is normally ribbon-like, consisting of numerous segments called proglottides. The head is attached to the gut wall of the host and food is absorbed through the cuticle of the body. The tape-worm grows by forming new segments just behind the head. Older segments are pushed further from the head. Each segment contains both male and female sex organs and when these are mature the eggs are fertilised. Most of the organs then disappear, leaving a mass of eggs in each segment. The segments eventually break off from the worm and pass out of the host with the faeces. The eggs develop but do not normally hatch until they are swallowed by another animal. The full life history often involves two or three separate species of host animal, such as a waterflea, a fish, and a bird. Not all cestodes have such a complicated life story: *Gyrocotyle* lives in the gut of certain fishes and does not produce proglottides. It resembles a trematode except that it has no gut. (See *Platyhelminthes*). (See Page 257).

Cetacea. Order of mammals containing the whales, extremely specialised aquatic mammals. The fore-limbs are paddle-like and there is no trace externally of the hind limbs. The tail has two large horizontal flukes which propel the body through the water. Except for a few bristles round the snout whales have no hair but, like all other mammals, they are warm-blooded and they suckle their young. There are two groups of whales: Odontoceti, the toothed whales, and Mysticeti, the whale-bone whales. Toothed whales (sperm whale, porpoise, dolphin and others) have a number of peg-like teeth suited to their diet of fish and squids. The whale-bone whales, including the largest of all animals, the blue whale, feed on tiny planktonic crustaceans which they strain from the water with plates of *baleen* that hang from the upper jaws. Teeth are present only in the embryos of these whales. (See Plates 21, 123).

Chaeta (plural chaetae). Bristle, especially of annelid worms. (See *Annelida*) and (Plate 5).

ARROW WORM

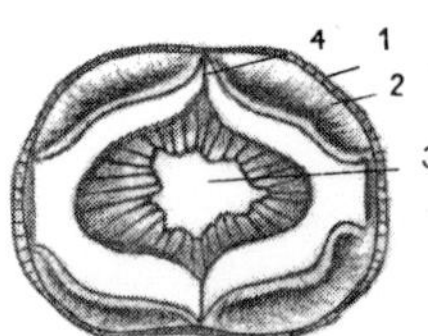

SECTION THROUGH TRUNK OF *Sagitta*

1. EPIDERMIS
2. MUSCLE
3. INTESTINE
4. MESENTERY
5. MOUTH
6. JAW
7. VENTRAL GANGLION
8. FINS
9. OVARY
10. TESTIS

5

Chaetognatha. A small phylum of marine, coelomate animals including *Sagitta,* the common planktonic arrow worm. The relationships of this group are not clear. (See Plate 110).

Chaetopoda. A name sometimes used to refer to those annelid worms possessing chaetae (Polychaetes and Oligochaetes).

Chela. Claw or pincer of crabs, lobsters and some other arthropods.

Chelicerae. The 'jaws' of spiders and other Arachnida (q.v.).

Chelonia. Order of reptiles with the body enclosed in bony plates—the turtles and tortoises. The bony casing protects the animals and has probably allowed them to survive with relatively little change since the days of the earliest reptiles. Chelonians are all toothless. (See *Reptilia*) and (Plate 119–2, 3).

Chemoreceptor. Sense organ reacting to chemical stimulation—e.g. organs of taste and smell.

Chemotaxis. Movement of an organism in response to chemical stimulation. Flatworms and many other creatures move instinctively towards food but away from acids and other harmful substances. (See *Irritability*).

Chilopoda. Centipedes; sub-class of *Myriapoda* (q.v.).

Chiroptera. Order of mammals containing the bats—the only truly flying mammals and the limbs are modified accordingly. The wings are elaborate folds of skin supported by the enormously elongated finger bones (other than that of the first digit or thumb), the rest of the arms, the sides of the body, and the legs and tail. Compare this arrangement with the wings of the birds and the pterosaurs—the only other vertebrates to have taken to the air. The most amazing thing about bats is their 'radar' system of echo-location. A bat's eyes are almost useless and it finds its way about by sending out series of high-pitched sounds (much too high for human ears to detect). These sound waves bounce back from nearby objects and the echoes are picked up by the bat's large ears. This all happens so quickly that the bat can detect and avoid an obstacle even when flying at high speed. The 'radar' is so sensitive that the bats can use it to detect and catch the flying insects on which they feed. Apart from their modifications for life in the air, the bats closely resemble the insectivores. (See Plate 122).

Chitin. Horny, nitrogen-containing material which makes up most of the external skeleton (cuticle) of arthropods and also the chaetae of annelid worms. It is very tough and resistant to a wide range of chemicals.

Chitons. (See *Mollusca*).

Choanae (=Internal Nares). The internal openings of the nasal cavity possessed by all land-living vertebrates. Lung-fishes have internal nares but other fishes do not: their organs of smell are situated in pits at the front of the head but the pits do not open into the mouth cavity.

Choanichthyes (=*Crossopterygii*).

Cholinesterase. A very important enzyme that destroys acetylcholine in the nervous system. (See *Acetylcholine*).

Chondrichthyes (=*Elasmobranchii*).

Chondrostei. Order of fishes of the class *Actinopterygii* (q.v.) in which there is a reduction of bone so that most of the skeleton is of cartilage. Bony plates on the head, and other features, however, show that they are descended from bony ancestors and are not related to the cartilaginous sharks and rays. The order contains the sturgeons and the strange paddle-fish *Polyodon*. (See Plate 117–6).

Chordata. Large phylum including all the back-boned animals (sub-phylum *Vertebrata*) and a number of other creatures: the sea-squirts (sub-phylum *Urochordata*); acorn-worms and their relatives (*Hemichordata*); and *Amphioxus* and its relatives (*Cephalochor-*

data). The diagnostic characteristics of the phylum are the possession at some stage in the life history of gill-slits, a flexible skeletal rod called the notochord, and a hollow, dorsal nerve cord. These features are present in the embryos of all vertebrates but in the higher forms the gill slits disappear and the notochord is replaced by the vertebral column, leaving the hollow, dorsal nerve cord as the only connection between the vertebrates and the invertebrate chordates. (See Plate 21).

Chorion. An embryonic structure; the outer wall of the sac containing the embryo of reptiles, birds, and mammals. The amnion is the inner wall.

Choroid. Pigmented layer outside the retina of vertebrate eye (q.v.). Contains blood supply for retina.

Chromatid. One of the two strands of a *chromosome* (q.v.).

Chromatophore. Cell containing pigment. In many animals the cells, or the pigments within them, can expand and contract and thus bring about a colour change in the animal. The chromatophores are controlled by nerves or hormones. (See Plate 22).

Chromosome. Double thread-like structure which can be seen in cell-nuclei when the cells are undergoing division. In normal body cells the chromosomes occur in pairs, the number of pairs depending on the species. The members of each pair (except *sex-chromosomes* (q.v.)), look exactly alike and are said to be homologous. Chromosomes are composed mainly of nucleo-proteins and they carry the genes that control the features of the cell and, indeed, of the whole body. When, for example, a skin-cell divides, it is essential that the new daughter cells are identical with the parent. During the division of the nucleus the chromosomes all divide along their length, each producing two identical daughter-chromosomes. One daughter from each pair goes to each new cell, carrying identical instructions, so that the new cells will be exactly alike. This process is called *mitosis* (q.v.).

Although the body cells contain pairs of chromosomes (*diploid* condition), the sex-cells, i.e. sperms and ova, contain only half the normal number, one of each pair—(*haploid* condition). A special form of cell division known as *meiosis* (q.v.), gives rise to the sex-cells: the homologous chromosomes come together and they separate, one going to each new cell. At fertilisation, a sperm and an egg-cell join and so produce the diploid number of chromosomes again. (See *Heredity*).

Chrysalis. Pupa or resting stage between larva and adult insect of butterflies, moths and some other insects. (See *Insecta; Lepidoptera*).

Chyme. Partly digested food in stomach. (See *Digestion*).

Ciliary Body. Outer part of iris of vertebrate *eye* (q.v.).

Ciliated. Covered with minute hairs (cilia) e.g. ciliated *epithelium* (q.v.).

Ciliophora. A class of protozoans all of which possess cilia at some stage in their lives. Most of them (e.g. *Paramoecium*) retain the cilia but some such as *Acineta* lose them as adults and replace them by suction pads on small tentacles. (See Plate 26 and page 253).

Cilium (plural cilia). Very short, fine 'hair' projecting from the cell surface of certain types of cell. There are always many and they beat with a definite rhythm. They are found in most animal groups and their function is to move the animal through the water (e.g. *Paramoecium*) or to move liquids along inside the animal. The lining of man's nose is covered with cilia which beat and sweep out mucus and any dust that it traps.

Cirripedia. Barnacles – a sub-class of the *Crustacea* (q.v.), although, because of their fixed mode of life they are very unlike typical crustaceans. (See Page 264).

Class. A category used in the *classification* (q.v.), of living organisms.

Classification. There are over a million known kinds or species of animals and zoologists must be able to refer to any of these by a definite name so they will be understood by other zoologists no matter what language they speak. For this reason living things are named in Latin. 'Seven-spotted ladybird' means nothing to a Russian zoologist but if he reads *Coccinella septempunctata,* he knows exactly what creature is being referred to. All organisms are given two names: the first is the generic name, indicating the genus to which the creature belongs, and the second is the specific name indicating the exact species within the genus – a genus being a group of closely related species. The double name therefore gives a better idea of the relationships of a creature than a single name could do. Linnaeus was the first to use this binomial system on any wide scale. Classification, however, means more than merely dividing creatures into genera and the genera into species; these are merely the finest divisions. The animal kingdom is in fact divided into about twenty major groups called phyla. Each phylum contains animals with certain basic similarities. Within each phylum some animals are more alike than others and these are separated into classes. Classes may be subdivided into sub-classes, these into orders, orders into sub-orders, sub-orders into families, families into genera and genera into species.

The members of a large division, therefore, have fewer characters in common than those in a sub-division. For example, mammals and bony fishes are vertebrates, that is they have a backbone and a hollow dorsal nervous system, part of which forms a brain that is protected by a brain-case. However, mammals have hair, suckle their young, have limbs and are warm-blooded. Fishes lack hair and have a scale-covered body, they have fins and not limbs, the young generally hatch from eggs which are laid, and they are cold-blooded. Both are placed in separate sub-groups of the Vertebrata.

If we classify man starting with his mammal grouping (Class: Mammalia) we can see how his genus and species rankings are arrived at. He is a placental mammal (sub-class: Placentalia) which is based on a number of characters. He belongs to the Order Primates along with the tarsiers, lemurs, apes and monkeys – all animals with binocular vision, similar skeletons, etc. Only the apes and monkeys are included with man in the sub-order Anthropoidea and only fossil man is in the same family, Hominidae. His genus *Homo* is the same for Neanderthal man, but the latter's species is *neanderthalensis,* while man's is *sapiens*.

Man's classification as described here may be summarised as:

Class:	Mammalia
Subclass:	Placentalia
Order:	Primates
Suborder:	Anthropoidea
Family:	Hominidae
Genus:	*Homo*
Species:	*sapiens*

Man is a backboned animal (i.e. a vertebrate) which places him in the sub-phylum Vertebrata. Above this, his phylum ranking is the Chordata (all animals that at some stage in their life possess gill slits and an elastic supporting rod or notochord and always have a hollow dorsal nervous system, i.e. one in the back). Vertebrata and Chordata would be placed above class Mammalia in a fuller classification. (See *Binomial System*). (See Pages 253 and 236).

Clavicle. Bone of the pectoral girdle (q.v.). (See Page 217).

Cleavage. After fertilisation an egg cell undergoes many divisions to produce many small cells. The process is called cleavage. (See *Embryology*).

Clitellum. The 'saddle' – a thickened region of skin in earthworms and some other annelids. Concerned with reproduction, it is conspicuous only in mature animals. (See *Oligochaeta*).

Cloaca. Posterior opening of the body of most vertebrates into which open the gut, the excretory ducts and the reproductive system. Only the placental mammals have a separate anus. (See Plates 41 and 42).

Cnidoblast. Stinging cell of jellyfish and other *Coelenterata* (q.v.). (See Plate 23).

Cnidocil. 'Trigger' of coelenterate stinging cell. (See *Coelenterata*) and (Plate 23).

Coccyx. Rudimentary tail skeleton consisting of fused vertebrae.

Cochlea. That part of the ear (q.v.) which is concerned with the 'sorting out' of the sounds received.

Cockroach. Insect of the order *Dictyoptera* (q.v.). (See Plate 64).

Cocoon. A protective covering. Earthworms and many spiders wrap their eggs in cocoons. Many caterpillars spin silken cocoons around themselves as a protection when they are about to pupate.

Coelenterata. A phylum of animals which are radially symmetrical and whose body wall is composed of only two layers of cells – ectoderm and endoderm – separated by a layer of jelly-like material – the *mesogloea.* The body has a single cavity – the coelenteron – which has a single opening – the mouth – surrounded by a ring of tentacles. All coelenterates live in water and the majority are marine but a few, such as *Hydra,* live in fresh water.

Coelenterates are carnivorous animals, feeding on a variety of animals which they catch by means of stinging cells found on the arms or tentacles. These stinging cells are called *nematoblasts* or *cnidoblasts* and each contains a small capsule called a *nematocyst.* Inside the nematocyst there is a hollow thread that is inverted like the finger of a glove that has been pulled into the hand part. A passing animal – perhaps a water flea in the case of *Hydra* or a small fish in the case of a sea-anemone – stimulates the tiny 'trigger' (*cnidocil*) of the stinging cell and the thread is shot out from its capsule. Some threads have poison barbs, others are coiled or sticky, and they all help to capture the prey. When an animal is caught the tentacles concerned curve towards the mouth,their movement being controlled by a network of nerves that spreads throughout the coelenterate body.

The food is taken into the mouth and digestion begins. Some of the cells of the endoderm secrete enzymes that act upon the food and break it down: other cells possess whip-like flagella that keep the liquid moving around. Digestion is completed within certain cells which engulf small particles just as *Amoeba* does.

Most of the cells of the body and arms are called musculo-epithelial cells because they possess muscular processes running through the mesogloea. These 'muscle tails' produce movement in the animals by contraction. The tails of the ectoderm cells run along the body while those of the endoderm run around the body. Contraction of the outer muscle tails shortens the body and contraction of the inner ones makes the body long and thin. The arms and body bend by contraction of the outer muscle tails of one side only.

Many coelenterates possess two distinct forms in their life-history – a fixed, tubular polyp and a free-swimming, disc-shaped medusa – but some groups have either polyp or medusa only. When both stages are present the polyp reproduces asexually by budding off mudusae and the medusae produce sex cells which fuse in pairs and develop into new polyps (See *Alternation of Generations*). The polyp stage often develops into large branching colonies by budding.

There are three classes within the phylum: (1) *Hydrozoa*—coelenterates normally forming branched colonies and having both polyp and medusa (e.g. *Obelia*). There is, however, great variation in the life history. *Hydra* itself is very atypical of the group as it is solitary and has no medusoid stage. (2) *Scyphozoa*—coelenterates with an inconspicuous or absent polyp stage. The medusa may be very large. These are the typical jellyfishes. (3) *Actinozoa*—solitary and colonial forms with no medusae. The coelenteron contains vertical partitions (*mesenteries*). Corals have a calcareous skeleton secreted by the ectoderm and are frequently colonial. Sea anemones are usually solitary and never have a skeleton but they are nevertheless basically similar to corals and are included in the same class. (See Plates 1, 3, 22, 23 and 107).

Coelom. Coelenterate animals like *Hydra* have a body wall with only two cell layers—ectoderm and endoderm. Higher animals have another layer—the mesoderm—between these layers and, because they have three layers, they are called *triploblastic* animals. The mesoderm forms the muscles, reproductive organs, etc. In flatworms and other simple creatures it also forms a sort of packing tissue that separates the internal organs from the body wall and from each other. In more advanced animals, however, the mesoderm becomes split into two regions—one surrounding the gut and other internal organs, the other lining the body wall. The fluid-filled cavity between the two layers is the coelom. It is well developed in vertebrates, echinoderms, and many worms, but in arthropods and molluscs it is reduced and the main body cavity in these animals is really part of the blood system (*a haemocoel*). Animals with a coelom are said to be coelomate. (See Plate 24).

Coelomoduct. A duct of mesodermal origin connecting the coelom to the outside of the body e.g. the vertebrate oviduct. Eggs are shed into the coelom and then carried to the outside in the coelomoduct.

Coleoptera. Beetles. This order of *Insecta* (q.v.), is characterised by the possession of horny front wings (*elytra*) that meet in the mid line and normally cover all of the abdomen. All have biting jaws but they feed on a wide range of materials: some are fiercely carnivorous. Metamorphosis is complete, there being a larval stage very unlike the adult. (See Plate 25) and (Page 268).

Collagen. A tough, fibrous protein which binds various tissues together and also forms tendons and ligaments where high tensile strength is required.

Collembola. Order of primitive insects—springtails. (See *Insecta*). (See Page 268).

Colon. Large intestine of vertebrates. (See *Alimentary Canal*).

Comb Jellies. (See *Ctenophora*).

Commensalism. A state where two or more species of an animal live in fairly close association but without having much influence on each other. One species may benefit but not both. (See *Symbiosis*) and (Plate 95).

Commissure. Bundle of nerve fibres joining two parts of the central nervous system. E.g. circum-oesophageal commissure joining the ganglia above and below the oesophagus of the earthworm. (See *Oligochaeta*) and (Plates 84, 85).

Conditioned Reflex. The smell or taste of food makes a dog's saliva flow. This is a normal reflex action involving no learning by the dog, but it can be conditioned so that it occurs with a different stimulus. If a bell is sounded every time food is given the dog will associate the bell with food and soon the bell alone will cause saliva to flow. This is the conditioned reflex.

Condyle. Rounded projection of bone, especially on the skull, that fits into a socket on another bone to allow limited movement. The occipital condyles at the back of the skull articulate with the atlas vertebra and allow the head to be nodded.

Cone. Colour-sensitive cell of the vertebrate retina. (See *Eye*).

Conjugation. A type of reproduction found in some protozoans such as *Paramoecium*. It involves partial fusion of two individuals and the exchange of nuclear material. (See Plate 26).

Conjunctiva. Thin layer of tissue covering the front of the *eye* (q.v.), and lining the eyelids of vertebrates.

Connective Tissue. This term is applied to various body tissues all of which bind cells and organs together. Connective tissue underlies the skin, surrounds nerves and muscles, joins bones and muscles to each other, and often stores fat in its cells. Connective tissue cells are normally well-spaced in a matrix of fluid in which there are numbers of collagen and other fibres. Tendons which join muscles to bones have to be very resistant to stretching and are made almost entirely of collagen, whereas other connective tissues may have very few collagen fibres. (See Plate 25).

Contractile Vacuole. Feature of many protozoans, especially fresh-water species. There may be more than one in each organism and they gradually swell as they extract water from the surrounding protoplasm. Suddenly the vacuoles burst and force the water out of the body. They then begin to fill up again. This may be a means of discharging waste from the body but the main function appears to be the removal of water which continually passes into the body because of *osmosis* (q.v.). (See also *Amoeba*).

Conus Arteriosus. Muscular chamber of primitive vertebrate heart at beginning of ventral aorta. (See *Heart*) and (Plate 57).

Convergent Evolution. Hermann Melville, in his great sea story 'Moby Dick', wrote, "To be short, then, a whale is a spouting fish with a horizontal tail'. Whales do of course resemble fish. They are streamlined; they have a fluked tail, a pair of flippers as fore limbs, and they may even have a dorsal fin on the back. But whales are mammals; they have warm blood and the females suckle their young with milk. Thus, despite all appearances, they are far more closely related to dogs, rabbits and Man himself than any fish.

One hundred and fifty million years ago another fish-like creature swam the seas. Though it became extinct 70 million years ago, fossils of its bones enable its appearance to be reconstructed. But, far from being a fish, the preserved skeletons show beyond all doubt that the creature was a reptile. Because of its remarkable resemblance to a fish it was called ichthyosaur or fish-lizard (Greek, ichthys, a fish; sauros, a lizard).

The connecting link between whale, fish and ichthyosaur is: all have lived in the sea and during their evolution became adapted to an aquatic life. This evolutionary development, which often leads to apparent likenesses between stocks that have diverged a long way from an original ancestor, is called convergent evolution or simply convergence.

Convergence is a common phenomenon found in organisms living on land, in water and in the air. It provides powerful support for the theory of evolution by natural selection: under the same selective pressures different groups will respond with apparently similar adaptations. Care must be taken in classifying animals and plants; superficial resemblances between two organisms do not necessarily mean that they are closely related.

Cut off in the continent of Australia, the marsupials or pouched mammals have flourished for 150 million years. In most other parts of the world they have disappeared, for competition from the placental mammals proved too much.

Australia offers a wealth of environments, and many different marsupials evolved, filling the niches.

The similarity in appearance between the various marsupials and placental mammals elsewhere provides striking examples of convergence.

Thus Australia has its wolf – the Tasmanian wolf, it has its native 'cat' (*Dasyurus*) and its native 'mouse' (*Dasycercus*). There are 'ant-eaters' and there are 'sloths'. The flying phalanger is comparable with the flying squirrels and Australia even has its own marsupial mole.

Marsupials and placentals are all mammals and do possess a common ancestry in the not-too-remote past. Convergence can, however, produce similarity between completely unrelated creatures. Thus insects and birds are far removed from one another, yet at a glance it is very difficult to tell the difference between a humming bird and a humming bird hawk moth in flight. Both are similar in size, and both live off nectar in flowers and have converged in their hovering flight and their feeding procedures. (See *Analogous Organs; Homologous Organs*) and (Plate 27).

Copepoda. Sub-class of *Crustacea* (q.v.), including *Cyclops* and many planktonic forms. They often swim by means of their antennae. There are also a number of parasitic forms.

Coprophagous. Dung-feeding.

Coracoid. Bone of the *pectoral girdle* (q.v.). (See Plate 66).

Coral. A colonial coelenterate with a chalky skeleton (See *Actinozoa*).

Cornea. Transparent layer of tissue in front of iris and lens of vertebrate *eye* (q.v.).

Coronary. Concerning the heart.

Corpora Allata. Glands in insect head secreting hormones concerned with development, especially with moulting and pupation.

Corpus Luteum. Temporary hormone-producing body in mammalian ovary formed in Graafian follicle after ovum is released. Goes on secreting throughout pregnancy but if pregnancy does not follow release of ovum the corpus luteum breaks up. (See Plate 86).

Cortex. Outer layer e.g. of adrenal gland or of brain.

Cosmoid Scale. Thick, bony scale of many primitive fish.

Costal. Concerning the ribs.

Cranial. Concerning the head and skull.

Cranial Nerves. Nerves that arise from the brain, not the spinal cord, and emerge through holes in the skull. There are ten pairs in fishes and in amphibians, twelve pairs in higher vertebrates. The nerves supply the special sense organs of the head, the general musculature of the head and neck, and the gills and the lateral line in fishes. A branch of the 10th nerve also serves the internal organs of the body. It has been shown that some cranial nerves correspond to dorsal roots of *spinal nerves* (q.v.), others to ventral roots, while some consist of both dorsal and ventral roots. The cranial nerves have been numbered and named for easy reference.

Cranial Nerves (cont).

No.	*Name*	*Serves*
1	Olfactory	Organs of smell
2	Optic	Retina of eye
3	Oculomotor	Inferior oblique, anterior, posterior, and internal rectus eye muscles
4	Trochlear	Superior oblique eye muscle
5	Trigeminal	Sensory regions and some muscles of jaws and face
6	Abducens	External rectus eye muscle.
7	Facial	Muscles of face and jaws; also taste buds at front of tongue
8	Acoustic	Ear
9	Glossopharyngeal	Gills of fishes: throat and tongue of mammals
10	Vagus	Heart, lungs, stomach, etc. Also gills and lateral line of fishes.
11	Accessorius	Neck region
12	Hypoglossal	Muscles of tongue.

(See Plate 37).

Craniata (=*Vertebrata*).

Cranium. The skull, especially that part surrounding the brain.

Cretaceous Period. Geological period during which the chalk was formed. Began about 135 million years ago. (See *Geological Time Scale*).

Crinoidea. Class of *Echinodermata* (q.v.) which are usually stalked and fixed to the sea floor. These are the sea-lilies and feather stars. They have a long fossil history and some carboniferous rocks are composed largely of their remains. (See Plates 28 and 116).

Crop. Part of the *alimentary canal* (q.v.) where food is stored prior to completion of digestion. Not all animals have a crop, but it is well developed in grain feeding birds such as the pigeon. (See Plate 2).

Crossing Over. Term used to describe the breaking and rejoining of *chromosomes* (q.v.) that sometimes occurs during cell reproduction. (See *Heredity*).

Crossopterygii (=*Choanichthyes*) Class of fishes including the coelacanth (*Latimeria*), the modern lung fishes, and many fossil forms. They are bony fishes but they differ from the typical modern fishes in that the paired fins contain a fleshy lobe and a bony skeleton. Most of the crossopterygians also have internal nasal openings (choanae)—a feature leading to the alternative name of Choanichthyes. The possession of internal nares suggests that the ancient crossopterygians could breathe air and it seems certain that the land-living vertebrates evolved from this group of fishes. (See *Dipnoi*) and (Plates 28, 117).

Crustacea. A large class of the phylum Arthropoda including crabs, water-fleas, and woodlice. All have, at least at some stage in their life, two pairs of antennae, the first pair of which are called antennules. The majority of crustaceans live in water and breathe by means of gills which are modified limbs or parts of limbs. The cuticle is often strengthened by a deposit of calcium carbonate and it may be developed as a large shield (*carapace*) covering the front part of the body. The most primitive members of the class have many pairs of similar limbs but there is a tendency in the more advanced forms to specialisation of the limbs and a reduction in the number of body segments. Most of the limbs are biramous, the two branches often performing different functions.

There are six sub-classes. The *Branchiopoda* are free-living and normally have many pairs of broad, bristle-fringed limbs on the body. The limbs act as gills and also filter food particles from the water. In many cases they also propel the animal through the water but when, as in *Daphnia,* the water-flea, the trunk limbs are enclosed by the shell, the head limbs are used for movement. Sub-class *Ostracoda* contains tiny animals whose carapace develops into a bivalve shell round the whole body. The feathery antennae and antennules move the animal through the water and also sweep food particles into the mouth. Sub-class *Copepoda* contains both free and parasitic forms, the latter often without limbs. A typical example is *Cyclops* found in almost any stretch of fresh water. There is no carapace and no limbs on the abdomen. Swimming is performed by the antennae and antennules and also by the thoracic limbs. Members of the sub-class *Branchiura* are parasites on fish but they are able to swim from one fish to another by means of the four pairs of thoracic limbs. Sub-class *Cirripedia* includes the barnacles – sessile, somtimes parasitic creatures very unlike typical crustaceans. The trunk limbs of barnacles are used to 'comb' food particles from the water. The sub-class *Malacostraca* is a large one containing a wide range of forms. Typically there are six head segments, eight thoracic segments, and six abdominal ones. A carapace encloses the sides of the thorax and the limbs are modified for walking, swimming, food-catching, etc. Unlike those of all other crustaceans, the antennules are biramous. Members of the sub-class include crabs, lobsters, shrimps, woodlice (the only truly land-living crustaceans), and sand hoppers. (See Plate 111).

Cryptic Coloration. Colouring or patterning that renders its owner less visible against its natural background. There are several ways in which this is achieved. (See Plate 29).

Cryptozoic. (1) Living in secluded places. (2) A division of geological time. (See *Geological Time Scale*).

Ctenophora. A phylum of free-living, solitary animals, probably related to the coelenterates, although there is neither polyp nor medusa. Known as sea-gooseberries or comb jellies, the ctenophores swim in the surface layers of the sea by means of cilia. There are two classes – Tentaculata, with tentacles, and Nuda, without tentacles. None has stinging cells. (See Plate 108).

Cuticle. Non-cellular covering layer found in most invertebrates. It is secreted by the epidermis and is mainly protein – e.g. chitin – although frequently hardened by calcium salts and other substances.

Cyclostomata. Class of vertebrates containing the lampreys and hagfishes – the only living jawless vertebrates. They are eel-like creatures without paired fins and with circular gill-slits. They feed on living or dead fish by rasping away the flesh with their mouths. The alimentary canal is very simple. Hagfishes are entirely marine but some lampreys live in fresh water. (See *Agnatha*) and (Plate 117 – 1).

Cytology. The study of cells.

Cytoplasm. The fluid contents of cells other than that contained in the nucleus. (See *Cell*).

Darwinism. The theory of evolution based on the idea of natural selection, first put forward by Charles Darwin and, independently, by Wallace. (See *Evolution; Natural Selection*).

Daughter Cells (or Nuclei). Two cells or nuclei resulting from the division of a single parent cell or nucleus.

Decapoda. (1) Group of malacostracan crustaceans to which crabs and

PLATE 28

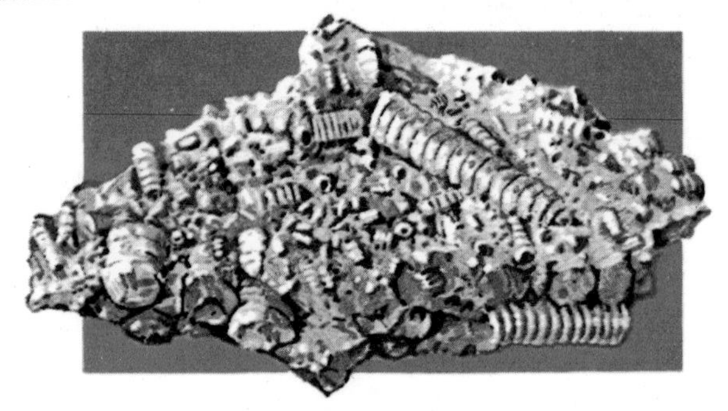

CRINOIDEA

Limestone composed of fossilised Crinoid stalks.

CROSSOPTERYGII

Diagrams showing the fundamental differences between lobe-fins and ray-fins in fishes.

LOBE FINS

RAY FINS

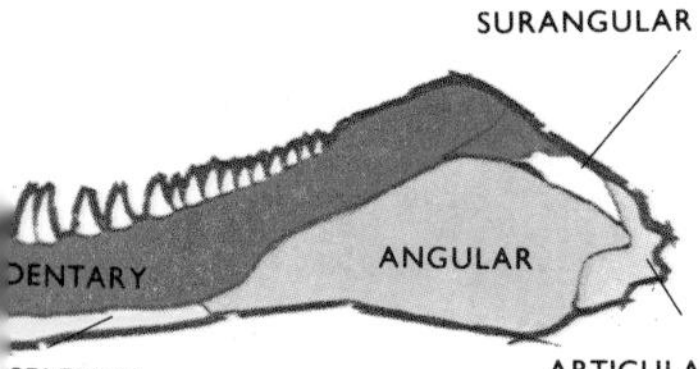

EARLY MAMMAL-LIKE REPTILE

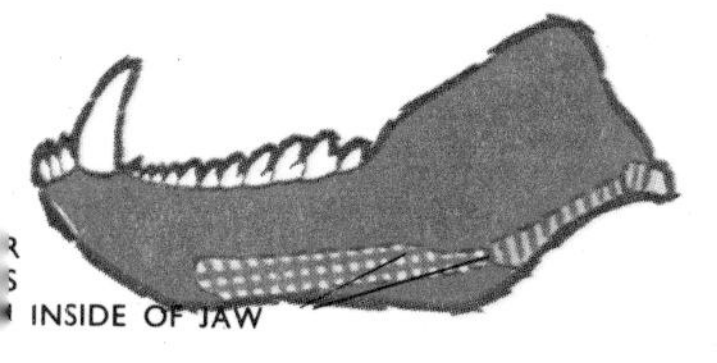

LATER MAMMAL-LIKE REPTILE

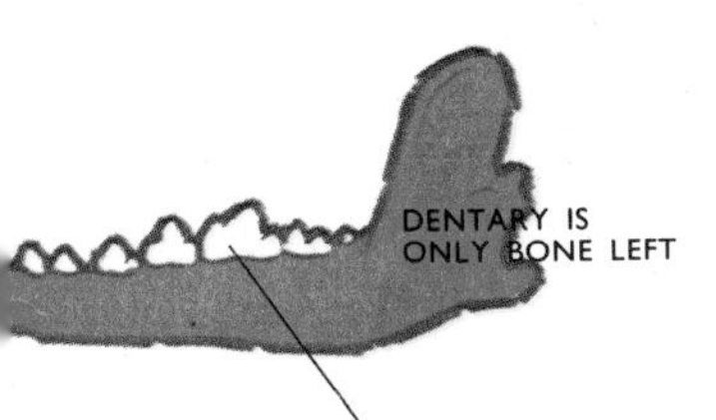

DENTARY

Three lower jaws showing the gradual increase in size of the dentary bone until, in the mammal, it is the only bone left. Pictures also show the change from homodont condition of reptile to heterodont condition of mammal (teeth of different kinds).

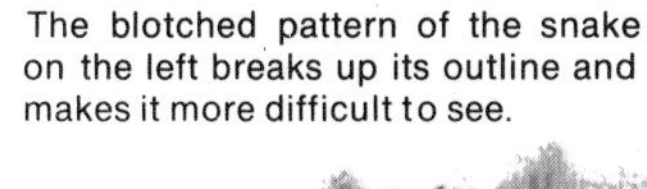

PLATE 29

CRYPTIC COLORATION

The blotched pattern of the snake on the left breaks up its outline and makes it more difficult to see.

lobsters belong. So called because there are five pairs of walking legs. (See *Crustacea*). (2) Group of cephalopod molluscs containing squids and cuttlefish with 10 arms or tentacles. (See *Cephalopoda*).

Dendrites. Fine protoplasmic branches of nerve cells that connect with neighbouring cells. (See *Nerve Cell; Synapse*).

Dental Formula. Reptile teeth are usually numerous and all of the same type. Mammals, however, have a fixed number of teeth (for each species) which are of four basic types. At the front of the jaws there are a number of chisel-shaped *incisors*. Behind these, in the typical mammal there is the eye tooth or *canine*. Then come the cheek teeth – first the *premolars* and then the *molars*. They are normally covered with ridges and serve to grind up the food. Molars and premolars differ mainly in that the adult premolars are preceded by milk teeth and the molars are not. Not all mammals have the same number of teeth, for example, many herbivorous species have no canines. The dental formula is a convenient way of expressing the number and arrangement of the teeth. The numbers of incisors, canines, premolars, and molars on one side of the upper jaw are written – in that order – above the corresponding numbers for the lower jaw. The dental formula for the primitive placental mammals is $\frac{3143}{3143}$, making a total of 44 teeth in all, but only a few mammals retain the full set. An adult human has 32 teeth with the formula $\frac{2123}{2123}$. A rabbit has no canine teeth and its dental formula is $\frac{2033}{1023}$. (See *Tooth*)

Dentary. The lower jaw bone of mammals. In other vertebrates there are several bones in the lower jaw but during the evolution of mammals from reptiles the other bones disappeared, except for the articular which evolved into one of the tiny bones in the mammalian ear. The possession of only one bone in the lower jaw is diagnostic of mammals and it is a valuable clue when dealing with fossil skulls. (See Plate 29).

Denticle (=*Placoid Scale*).

Dentine. Bone-like substance forming the body of teeth. (See *Tooth*).

Dentition. The arrangement of teeth in the jaws. (See *Dental Formula*).

Dermal Bone. Any bone (q.v.) formed directly from the cells in the ectoderm and not by replacement of cartilage.

Dermaptera. Order of insects containing earwigs. Characterised by short, leathery forewings and forcep-like cerci at the hind end. (See *Insecta*) and (Plate 114).

Dermis. Lower layer of *skin* (q.v.).

Dermoptera. Order of mammals containing the flying lemur or colugo. (See Plate 122). The animal glides among the trees by using a web of skin stretched between the front and back legs.

Devonian Period. Geological period beginning about 330 million years ago. (See *Geological Time Scale*).

Diapause. A period of suspended development in the life history of some insects. Hibernation of the larva and pupa are forms of diapause but the larvae of some species go into diapause even in the summer. Without this period of rest they seem unable to complete their growth and development.

Diaphragm. Sheet of muscle separating the thorax from the abdomen in mammals. (See *Respiratory Movement*).

Diaphysis. The shaft of a long bone (See *Bone*).

Diapsida. Sub-class of *Reptilia* (q.v.), containing the extinct dinosaurs and all living reptiles except the turtles and tortoises. (See Page 280).

Dictyoptera. Order of *Insecta* (q.v.), containing cockroaches and mantids. They have biting mouths and show many other primitive insect features. The front wings are leathery and are folded flat over the back. Eggs are laid in horny cases (oothecae) and they hatch into nymphs not unlike the adults. Cockroaches are scavenging insects, feeding on a wide range of materials. This is what makes them such pests in kitchens and warehouses. Mantids are carnivorous and their front legs are specially adapted for catching other insects. Most of the order are tropical or sub-tropical. (See Plate 64) and (Page 268).

Differentiation. Change in the structure of cells and organs during their development.

Digestion. The breakdown of complicated food substances into simpler compounds which can be used by the animal to build up its own body and to provide energy. Digestion is performed by enzymes, mainly in the food canal, and the products are absorbed into the body. In some animals, however, food particles are actually taken into the cells and digestion occurs there (See *Coelenterata*). The actual enzymes concerned vary according to the animal and the type of food it eats. Plant-eating animals rely largely on bacteria to break down the cellulose that forms a large part of their diet. Man is an omnivorous creature, eating all kinds of food. His digestive processes therefore embody all the main features of mammalian digestion.

Digestion begins in the mouth where the food is mixed with saliva. This watery fluid contains ptyalin – an enzyme that acts on starch and converts it to maltose sugar. Food is also broken down mechanically by the teeth. The rhythmic movement (*peristalsis*) of the oesophagus carries the food down to the stomach whose lining cells produce hydrochloric acid. This sterilises the food and also enhances the effect of another enzyme – pepsin – which is produced

DIGESTIVE ENZYMES AND THEIR WORK

Region	*Enzymes*	*Action*
mouth	ptyalin in saliva	starch to malt sugar (maltose)
stomach wall	pepsin	proteins to peptones
	rennin	acts on milk protein
duodenum: juice from pancreas	trypsin	proteins to proteoses, peptones and smaller units.
	amylase	starch to maltose
	lipase	fats to fatty acids, etc.
small intestine	erepsin	proteoses and peptones to amino acids
	lipase	fats to fatty acids and glycerol
	various enzymes acting on carbohydrates	break down carbohydrates into sugars (mainly glucose)

PLATE 30

BEAR

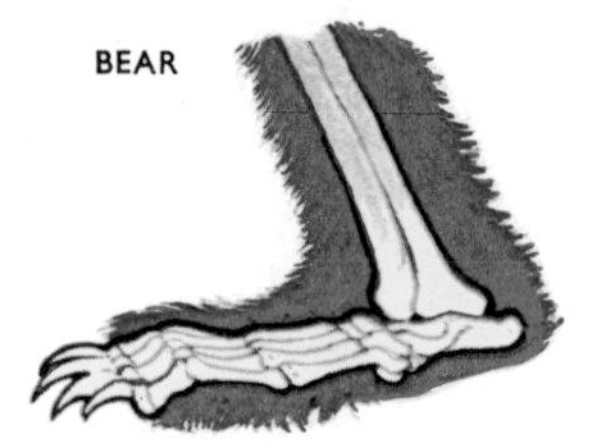

PLANTIGRADE

CAT

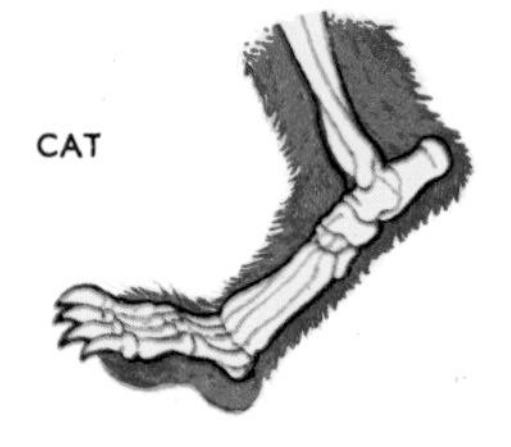

DIGITIGRADE

PIG

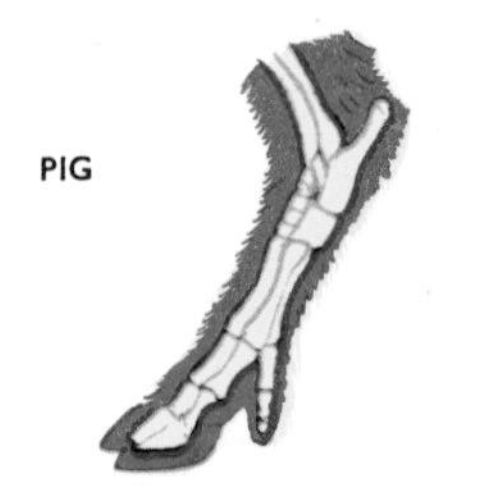

UNGULIGRADE

METHODS OF WALKING

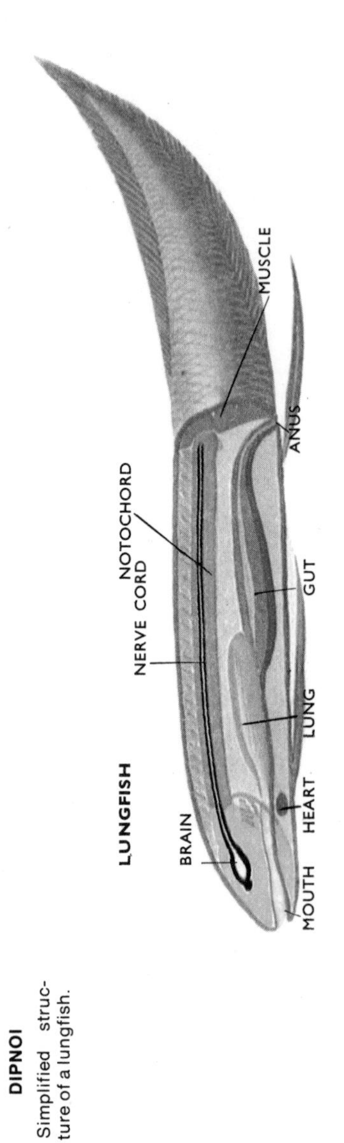

DIPNOI
Simplified structure of a lungfish.

DIMORPHISM

An example of sexual dimorphism where male (left) differs from female in general appearance as well as in sexual structures.

by certain cells in the stomach wall and which begins to break down proteins. Rennin is produced in the stomach too and this enzyme clots milk. The food is thoroughly mixed in the stomach and forms a thick paste called chyme.

A muscular ring regulates the passage of food from the stomach into the small intestine where bile from the liver and pancreatic juice from the pancreas are mixed with the chyme. Salts in the bile split fat droplets into smaller particles so that they can be digested more easily. Pancreatic juice contains amylase which breaks down starch to sugar, and lipase which breaks up fats. It also contains trypsinogen which itself has no effect on the food, but when the pancreatic juice mixes with the intestinal juices, enterokinase from the latter acts on the trypsinogen to form trypsin, a powerful protein-splitting enzyme. The acidic chyme is neutralised in the small intestine and gradually the food becomes more and more liquid. Proteins become broken down into amino-acids and carbohydrates into sugars – all relatively small molecules that can pass through the gut wall and into the blood stream for distribution round the body. Fats are split into glycerol and fatty acids which pass into special ducts (lacteals) in the ridges of the intestinal wall and join the blood stream later. Almost all the absorption occurs in the small intestine. The large intestine is concerned mainly with the reabsorption of water from the undigestible remains which pass out of the gut as faeces. (See **Alimentary Canal**) and (Plates 1 and 2).

Digitigrade. Walking on the whole of the toes as opposed to just the tips (*Unguligrade*) or the sole of the foot (*Plantigrade*). Cats and dogs, among others, are of this type. (See Plate 30).

Dimorphism. The existence of a species in two distinct forms. Sexual dimorphism in which males and females differ occurs in all bi-sexual animals of course but it is particularly marked in birds and many insects. Many butterflies show seasonal dimorphism where spring and summer broods differ in colour and/or size. The occurrence of melanic and non-melanic forms is also an example of dimorphism. (See Plate 31).

Dinosaur. Name given to a large assemblage of extinct reptiles now divided into two distinct orders according to the structure of the pelvic girdle. The order Saurischia had a typical reptilian pelvic girdle but the order Ornithischia had a bird-like pelvic girdle with a pre-pubic bone pointing forwards. Surprisingly, perhaps, this division does not correspond with the division into quadrupedal and bipedal forms: each order contains quadrupedal and bipedal species. Saurischians included huge animals such as *Brontosaurus* and *Diplodocus* which, at 80 feet long, were the largest land animals ever to have lived, but not all dinosaurs were large – some were no bigger than modern lizards. *Brontosaurus* and *Diplodocus* were herbivorous but the order also includes the fierce *Tyrannosaurus*, a carnivore some 50 feet long and with dagger-like teeth more than six inches long. The Ornithischia including such forms as *Iguanodon* and *Triceratops*, were all herbivorous and never reached the huge size of some saurischians. Dinosaurs became extinct, for some as yet unexplained reason more than 70 million years ago. (See *Reptilia*) and (Plate 119).

Diploblastic. Having a body wall of only two layers. (See *Coelenterata; Coelom; Triploblastic*) and (Plate 24).

Diploid. Having a double set of chromosomes in the nucleus. Normal body cells are diploid. Sex cells are formed by a special process in which only one set of chromosomes goes to each cell. Cells with only one set of chromosomes are called *haploid*. When sex cells join together at fertilisation the diploid number is regained in the resulting zygote. (See *Zygote; Chromosome; Meiosis*).

Diplopoda. Millipedes – sub-class of *Myriapoda* (q.v.).

Dipnoi. Order of crossopterygian fishes including the living lung-fishes and related fossil forms. There are three living genera – *Neoceratodus* of Queensland, Australia; *Lepidosiren* of South America; and *Protopterus* of tropical Africa. They live in sluggish rivers and all of them can breathe air. The African and American forms can survive drought by burying themselves in the mud (See *Aestivation*). Compared with the early dipnoans of Devonian times, the living forms show a great reduction of bone: there are no vertebrae and the notochord remains throughout life. *Neoceratodus* has lobed fins typical of the crossopterygians but the paired fins of the other two genera are reduced to thin filaments. (See *Crossopterygii*) and (Plate 30).

TYPES OF DIPTERA

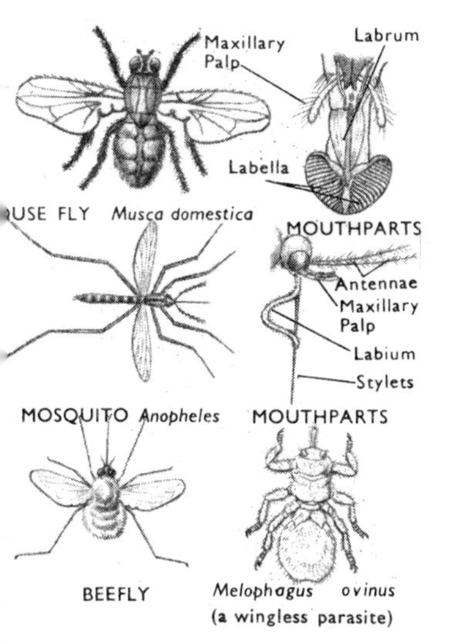

Diptera. Order of insects containing the true flies which have only one pair of wings. The hind pair are modified as balancing organs called *halteres*. These can be well seen in crane-flies (daddy-long-legs) but are less conspicuous in other groups. It is a very large order with such diverse types as the mosquitoes, bluebottles, and the large robber flies. They all have sucking mouths, frequently adapted for piercing and blood-sucking. Metamorphosis is complete and the larvae are always legless. Many larvae live in water. (See *Insecta; Housefly; Mosquito*) and (Plates 55 and 78).

Distal. The far end, away from the body. For example, the hand is at the distal end of the arm. Opposite of *proximal*.

Dogfish. Small cartilage fish of the class *Elasmobranchii* (q.v.), which is often studied in schools as an introduction to vertebrate anatomy. (Plates 35, 36, 37).

Dominant. A gene whose character will be apparent in an animal whether it (the gene) is present on one or both of its particular pair of chromosomes. (See *Heredity; Chromosome*).

Dormant. In a resting condition – e.g. hibernating.

Dorsal. On or near the side of an animal that is normally uppermost. Man's back is his dorsal side, for in most mammals that side is on top. Opposite of *ventral*.

Dorsal Aorta. (See *Aorta*).

Dorsal Root. (See *Spinal Nerve*).

Dragonfly (See *Odonata*).

Duodenum. First part of the small intestine. (See *Alimentary Canal*).

Dura Mater. Tough connective tissue covering the brain and spinal cord of vertebrates.

PLATE 32

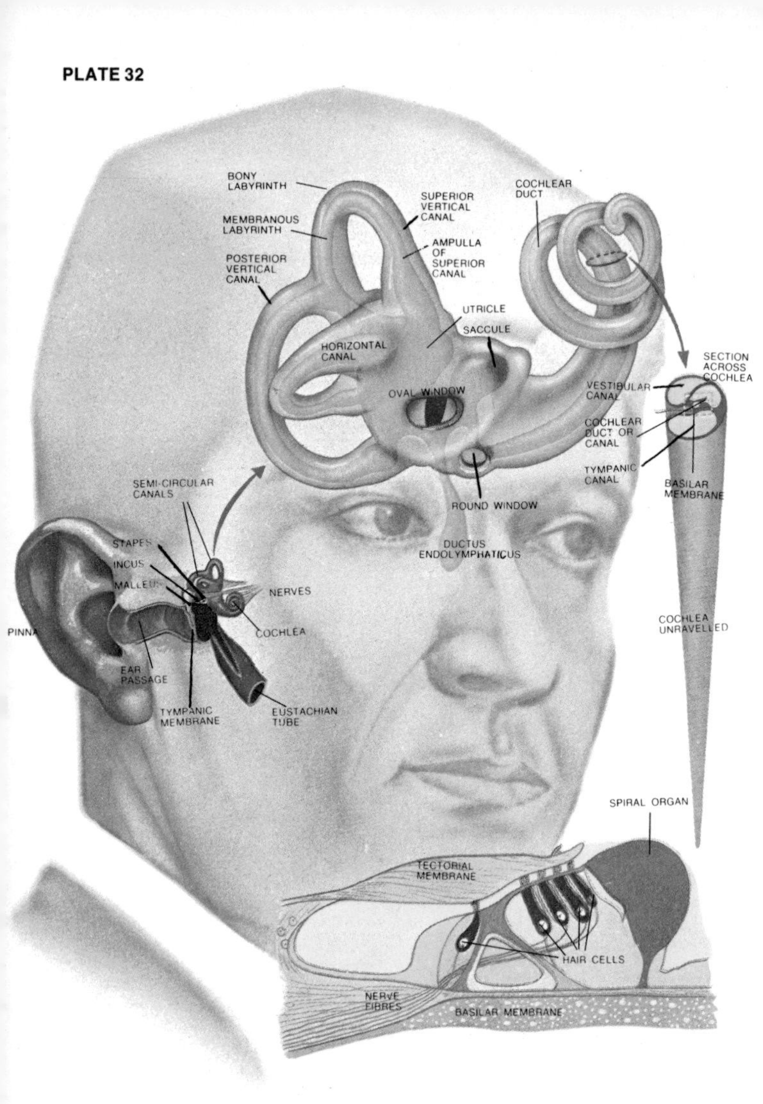

EAR

The right ear partly cut away to show its structure. (Above right) the bony labyrinth showing the position of the membranous labyrinth and a section across the cochlea combined with a view of it unravelled. (Below right) a simplified diagram of a section through the cochlea to show the structure of the basilar membrane and the spiral organ.

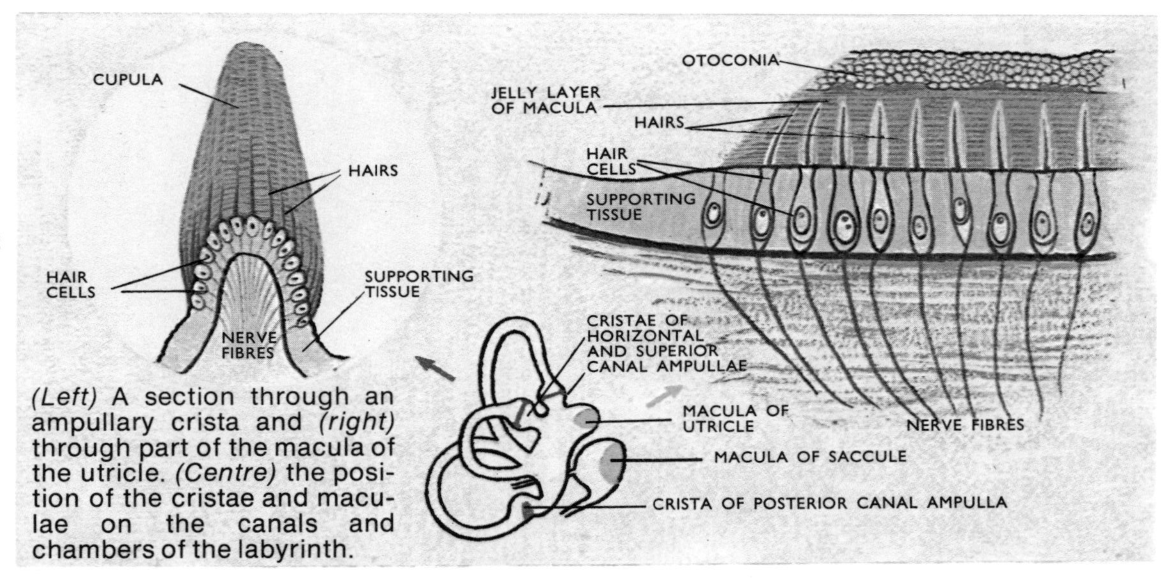

(Left) A section through an ampullary crista and *(right)* through part of the macula of the utricle. *(Centre)* the position of the cristae and maculae on the canals and chambers of the labyrinth.

Ear. Organ which, in vertebrates, is concerned with the detection of sound and also with the sense of balance. 'Ears' also occur in other animals such as insects but these are far less complicated structures and are concerned merely with the detection of sound.

The human ear described here is typical of mammals and differs only in small details from that of most other vertebrates. There are three main regions of the ear: the outer ear consisting of the ear lobe or pinna and the passage leading to the ear-drum (*tympanic membrane*); the middle ear which contains tiny bones transmitting sounds from the drum to the inner ear and which connects with the throat by means of the eustachian tube; and the inner ear itself which, encased in the bone of the skull, contains the actual sense organs of hearing and balance.

Fishes, newts and salamanders, and snakes have neither outer nor middle ear regions and they are unable to detect sound waves in the air. They can, however, detect vibrations in the water or the ground. These vibrations are transmitted through the body to the chambers of the inner ear.

Hearing. Sound waves are collected by the pinna and pass along the tube to the ear-drum which is thus made to vibrate. Attached to the inner side of the ear-drum is a tiny bone called the *malleus* or hammer. This articulates with the *incus* or anvil which in turn connects with the *stapes* or stirrup. This is joined to the *oval window*—a thin membrane separating the middle and inner regions of the ear. The three bones, or *ossicles* as they are called, are all present in mammals but in lower vertebrates there is only one—the *columella auris*—which becomes the stapes in mammals. The mammalian incus evolved from the quadrate bone of the reptile skull and the malleus from the articular bone of the lower jaw.

The ossicles transmit vibrations of the ear-drum to the oval window and thus to the inner ear. This consists of a series of spaces (bony labyrinth) within the bones surrounding the inner ear. Inside the bony labyrinth is the membranous labyrinth, a closed system of communicating sacs and canals. The membranous labyrinth is filled with a fluid called endolymph. It consists of two sacs, the utricle and saccule. Leading off from the saccule is the cochlear canal—a long, coiled tube enclosed within the perilymph of the cochlea.

The cochlear duct lies at one side of the cochlea and is attached to a separating wall, the spiral lamina. This divides the cochlea into two, the vestibular canal and the tympanic canal which communicate with each other through a tiny opening within the tip of the cochlea.

When the oval window is set in motion its movements disturb the perilymph at the bottom of the vestibular canal. The pressure changes in the fluid within the vestibular canal are transmitted down the tympanic canal and each time the oval window bulges inwards another membrane—the *round window*—bulges outwards. The pressure changes in the cochlea affect the basilar membrane—part of the spiral lamina. The membrane is a band of tissue running almost the length of the cochlea—about one and a quarter inches. Arranged across it are a number of fibres, the lengths of which increase as the bore of the cochlear duct gets smaller. On top of these fibres is the spiral organ or organ of Corti. This contains hair cells, the hairs of which project into a gluey flap—the tectorial membrane—which lies above them. Different parts of the basilar membrane are sensitive to sounds of different frequencies. When it vibrates the hairs also vibrate. The hair cells are linked with nerve fibres and movement of the hairs results in impulses being sent along the nerve fibres in the auditory nerve to the brain. This translates the signals it receives as sound. The ear does not hear – it merely receives sound waves which are transmitted as signals to the brain.

Balance.

Three responses are involved – static responses, dynamic responses and the maintenance of tonus (this is the resting tension in muscles; at rest muscles are not limp, they have tonus).

Static responses are concerned with maintaining the centre of gravity of the body on movement (e.g. if a frog is held in the hand and tilted to one side, its head moves in order that the eyes keep the same horizon). Dynamic responses are concerned with the body's movement when it accelerates rapidly in a straight line (as when going up in a lift) or in a curve (as when spinning round and round).

The three semi-circular canals are arranged at right angles to each other. They open into the utricle. At one end of each canal is a swelling or ampulla within which is a ridge of sensory cells together with supporting cells, the crista. The sensory cells have hairs that project into a jelly-like mass, the cupula. Nerve fibres of the auditory nerve are intertwined round the bases of the hair cells. When the head rotates the fluid moving in the canals pushes against the cupula and the hair cells are thus stimiulated. Signals pass via the lower parts of the brain to the eye, back, and limb muscles which act to make amends for the head movements.

The utricle and saccule communicate by a narrow tube branching off which is a blind tube – the *ductus endolymphaticus.* Parts of the utricle and saccule lining contain a patch of hair cells and supporting cells (maculae) like those of the cristae. The hairs of the former are embedded in a jelly-like mass though this is flattened. The jelly contains numerous small bodies consisting of calcium carbonate crystals mixed with protein. These are called otoliths and the weigh down the jelly so that it is in firm contact with the hair cells. The maculae are upright but at right angles to each other so that each position of the head affects the hair cells in a different way. Signals from the sense cells of the maculae are continuous and supply the parts of the brain that control the motor nerves with information so that these can maintain the state of muscle tone. The sense cells of the cristae, however, are stimulated by movements of or pressure changes in the fluid round the cupulae. They are concerned with dynamic responses. Pressure receptors in the feet and the many proprioreceptors in the muscles of the body also provide the brain with information on the posture of the body and are thus concerned with maintaining balance. (See Plates 32, 33, 34 and 35).

Earwig. (See *Dermaptera*).

Earthworm. (See *Oligochaeta*).

Ecdysis. The periodic shedding of the hard cuticle in arthropods to allow for growth. By swallowing air or water the animal stretches the soft new cuticle which then hardens at a somewhat larger size than the old one. (See *Insecta*) and (Plate 34).

Echinodermata. Large phylum of entirely marine animals including the starfishes and sea-urchins. They are radially symmetrical and the outer covering contains numerous chalky plates, sometimes produced into spines, which give the animals a rough appearance. There is no brain nor is there even any structure that can be regarded as a head. The nervous system consists merely of a network with thicker strands around the mouth and along the arms or radii. Sense organs are poorly developed and special excretory systems and respiratory organs are lacking in most of these animals. There is a true coelom, tiny projections from which reach the surface as skin-gills. The skin is very thin and oxygen can diffuse in from the surrounding water. This is especially so in starfishes.

PLATE 34

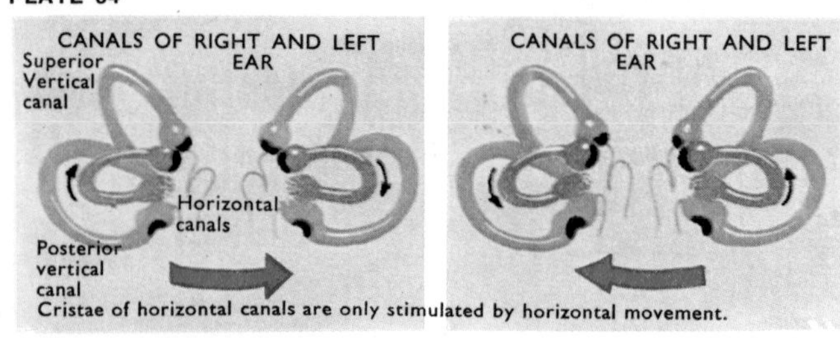

EAR

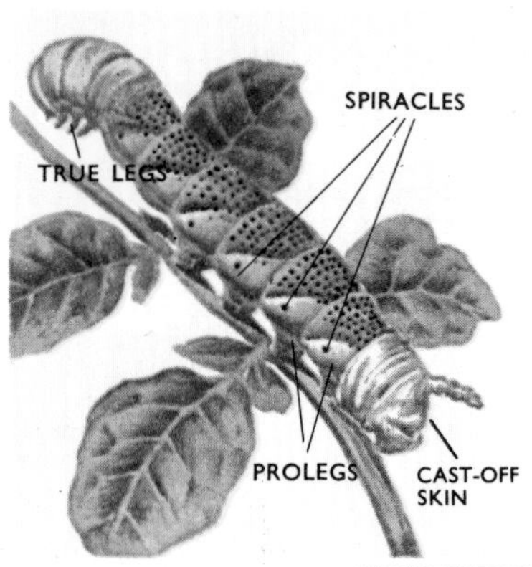

ECDYSIS

The shedding of a skin by a caterpillar.

ECHINODERMATA

Section through a star-fish arm showing how the tube feet fasten on to the rocks and pull the animal along. Also a highly magnified section of the skin.

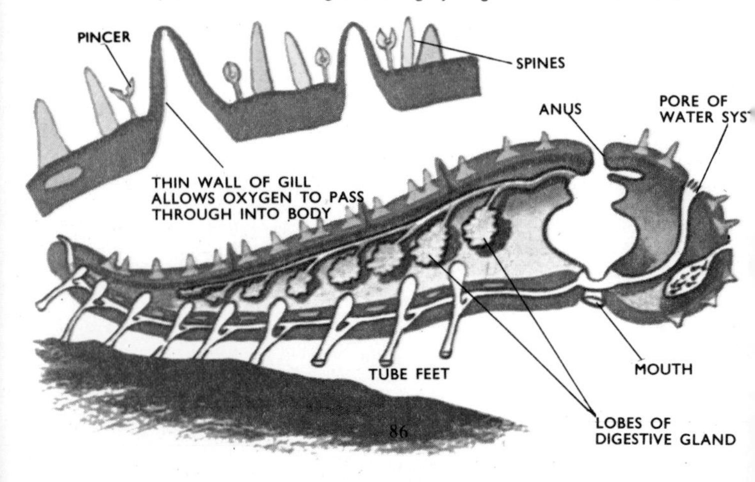

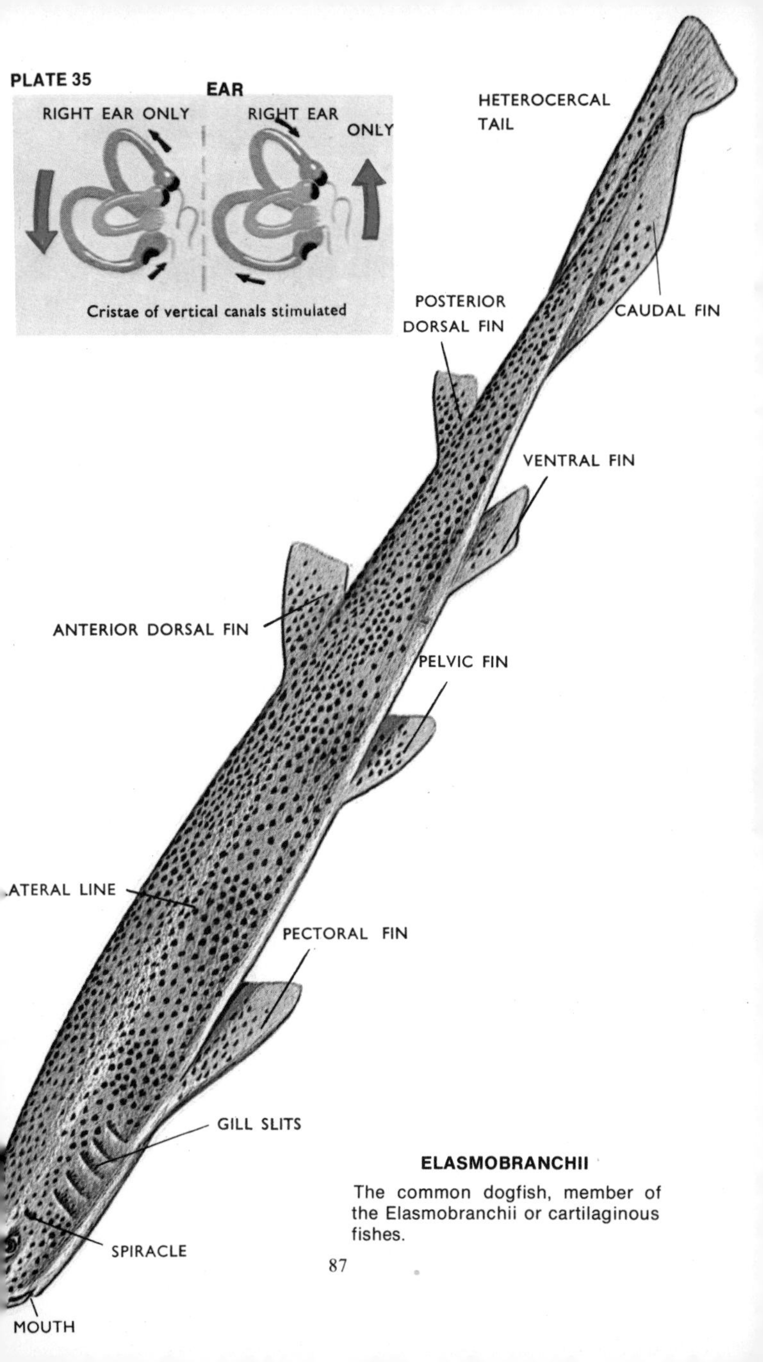

ELASMOBRANCHII

The common dogfish, member of the Elasmobranchii or cartilaginous fishes.

A feature unique to these animals is the water vascular system – a system of water-filled canals which runs in the body. Tiny branches reach the surface and are known as tube feet. They are used for moving about and also aid respiration. In general, the sexes are separate but a few species are hermaphrodite. The sex cells are usually shed freely into the water where fertilisation occurs. The young stages show similarities with certain chordates, rather than with any other invertebrates. The phylum has a long fossil history and there are many extinct groups. Five living classes are recognised, in the two sub-phyla. Sub-phylum *Eleutherozoa*: Class *Asteroidea*. These are the starfishes such as *Asterias*. The arms are broad and each contains a branch of the digestive system. Class *Ophiuroidea*: the brittle stars. Although star-shaped, these differ somewhat from the asteroids in that the central disc is very distinct and the arms do not contain branches of the gut.
Class *Echinoidea* contains the sea-urchins – rounded animals whose skeletal plates join up to form a complete shell or test. The tube feet project through tiny pores in the test. Class *Holothuroidea* contains the sausage-shaped sea-cucumbers with tentacles around the mouth. Sub-phylum *Pelmatozoa* contains only one living class – *Crinoidea*. These are the sea-lilies which are fixed to the sea bed by a stalk for at least part of their lives. Some, such as *Antedon*, break free when mature. Their delicately branched arms give them their name of feather stars. (See Plates 34 and 116).

Echinoidea. Sea-urchins (See *Echinodermata*). (See Page 273).

Ecological Niche. A term used to describe any small habitat or food source that is colonised or made use of by a group of animals. For example, cattle dung is a food and refuge for a number of insects. This is their ecological niche and here they live efficiently and protected from competition. Every animal has its niche and by filling it helps to maintain the balance of nature. The same niches occur in all parts of the world but are filled by different animals – e.g. kangaroos in Australia and antelopes in Africa occupy similar niches as grazing animals.

Ecology. The study of animal (and plant) communities and the ways in which they react with each other and to any changes in the environment.

Ectoderm. Outer layer of embryo and all the tissues derived from that layer – mainly skin and its derivatives, and nerves. (See *Embryology*).

Ectoparasite. Parasite (q.v.) that lives and feeds on the outside of its host, e.g. flea, tick and louse.

Ectoplasm. The outer region of a cell's protoplasm. It is usually in a semi-solid state and it is especially important in the movement of amoeboid cells. (See *Amoeba*).

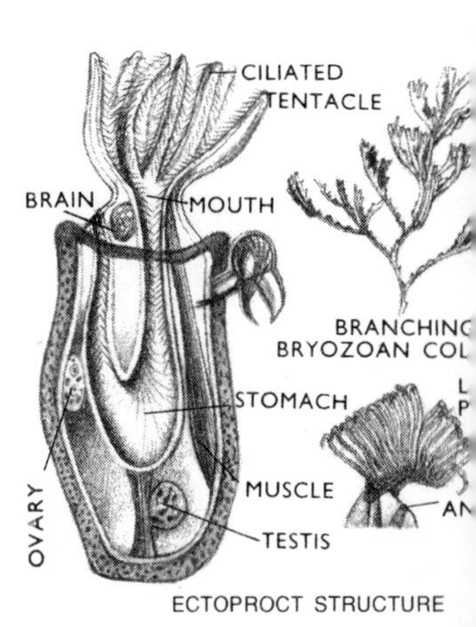

ECTOPROCT STRUCTURE

Ectoprocta. A small phylum of coelomate animals, often joined with *Endoprocta* (q.v.) as the Bryozoa. They live mainly in the sea and are normally colonial – many individuals joining up so that their hard cases make branched fern-like structures, or encrust rocks and sea-weed. When feeding, the body emerges partly from the case and a ring of tentacles around the mouth collects small organisms from the water. (See Plate 110).

Edentata. An order of mammals confined to South America. Many strange mammals evolved in that continent while it was isolated during the Tertiary period. When it was reconnected to North America most of these mammals died out in the face of competition from the invading carnivores but the edentates – the armadilloes, ant-eaters, and sloths – have survived. The teeth are reduced to small pegs in the armadilloes, absent in the ant-eaters, and modified for grinding in the herbivorous sloths, but fossils show that the sloths passed through an insect-eating stage in their evolution. The claws are well-developed for digging, or hanging in the case of sloths. (See Plate 122).

Eelworm. (See *Nematoda*).

Effector. An organ that acts in response to a signal. Muscles and glands are the main effectors. *Receptors* (q.v.), receive stimuli from outside the body and send messages to the brain. The brain then sends the appropriate message to the effectors which act to prepare the body for a coming event or to move the body away from some harmful thing.

Efferent. Leading away from. E.g. efferent branchial arteries leading from gills.

Elasmobranchii. (=*Chondrichthyes*). Sharks, rays, and other fishes whose skeletons are made entirely of cartilage with no trace of true bone. They are almost entirely marine, feeding on other fishes and bottom-living invertebrates. The skin is rough and covered with placoid scales which are modified as teeth on the skin over the jaws. The tail is upturned or heterocercal and tends to drive the head down but this tendency is countered by the flattened head and the large pectoral fins which provide lift in much the same way as an aeroplane wing. There is no swim bladder. The gill slits are not covered by an operculum except in *Chimaera* which represents an early offshoot of the elasmobranchs. The class as a whole has a long fossil history but they became nearly extinct in Permian times. Modern forms have evolved from the few species that survived into the Jurassic.

Internally the sharks are characterised by a short intestine containing a spiral valve which effectively increases its length. The dogfish is normally taken as an example to show the typical elasmobranch structure. (See Plate 117–2, 3 and Plates 35, 36, 37).

Elytron (plural elytra). Hard front wing of beetle. (See *Coleoptera*) and (Plate 25).

Embryo. A young animal or plant living exclusively on food provided by its female parent. It may be a young plant in a seed, a chick inside the egg, or a young mammal in the mother's womb.

Embryology. The study of embryos and the changes that occur in them during their development from fertilisation until the time that they begin an independent life. The stages that the embryo passes through vary according to the species but within a class the stages, especially the early ones, are similar. When the egg-cell is fertilised it begins to divide quite rapidly, forming a ball of tiny cells little bigger than the original egg-cell. This rapid division is called cleavage. The embryo then grows in size and the cells arrange themselves in three regions corresponding to the endoderm, ectoderm, and mesoderm of the animal. When the three formative or germ layers are laid down the main body structures begin to develop and from then on the

PLATE 36

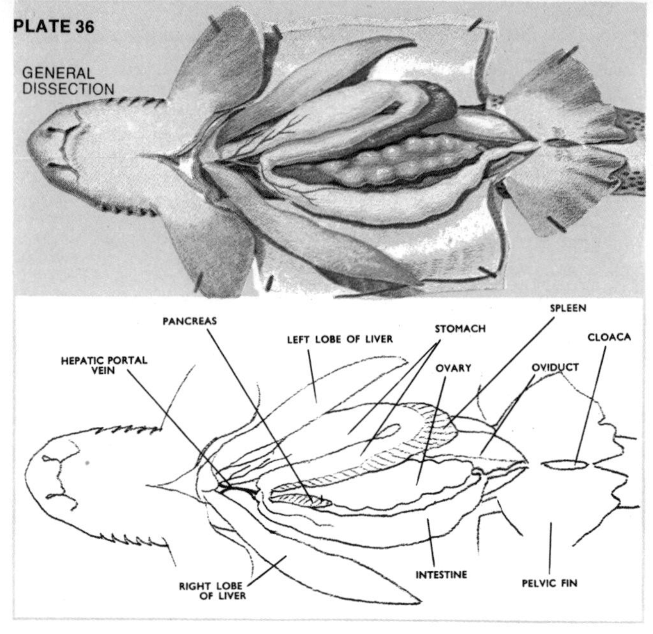

ELASMOBRANCHII

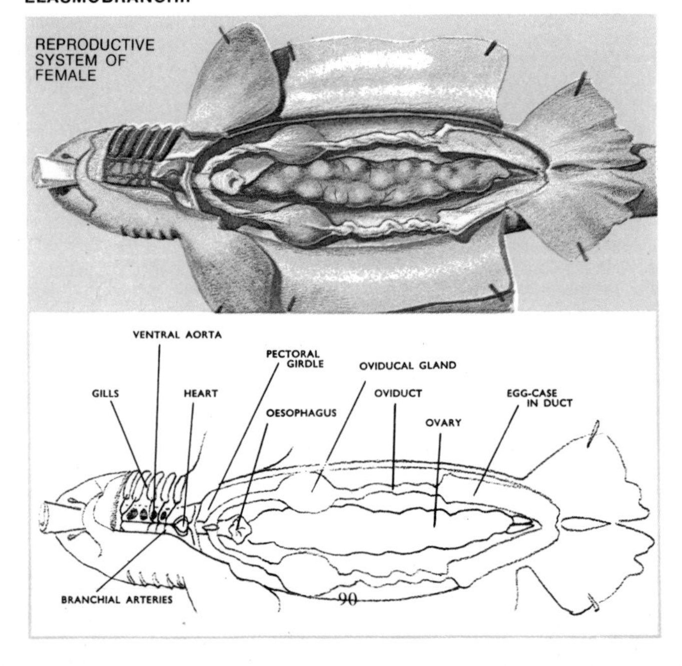

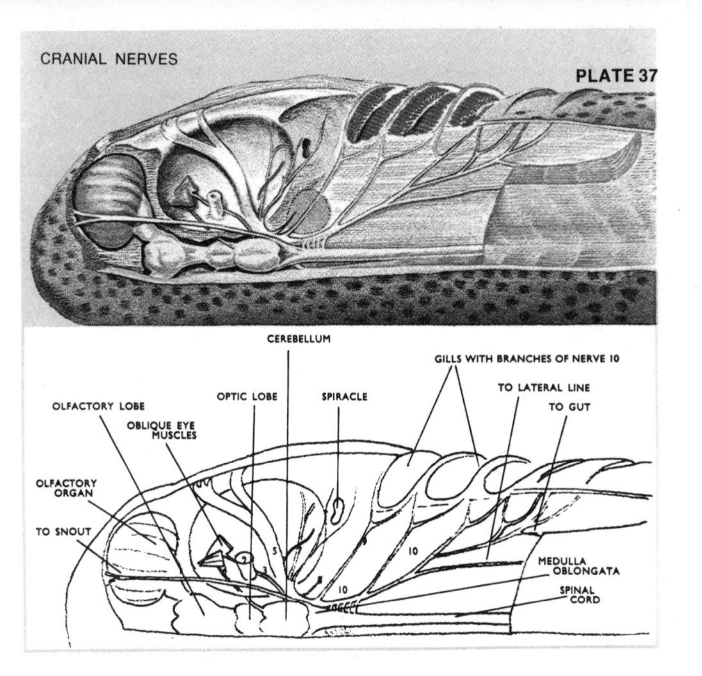

ELASMOBRANCHII

'Mermaid's Purses' – Egg-cases of sharks.

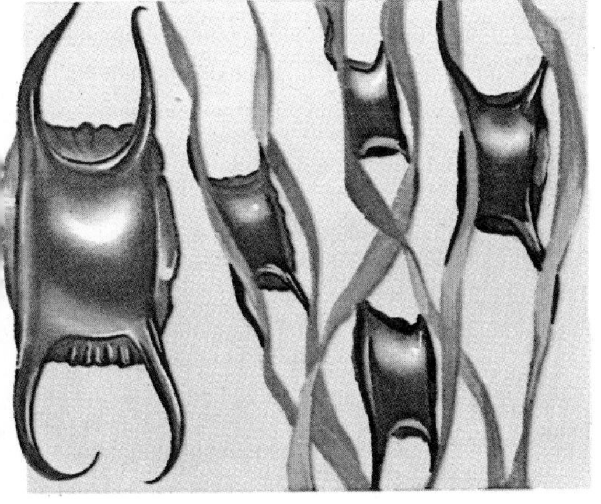

embryos gradually take on the form of their own species. (See Plates 38, 39). When all the main features can be recognised the mammalian embryo is called a foetus.

Enamel. Hard white covering of teeth. (See *Tooth*).

Endocrine (=*ductless*) **Gland.** (See *Gland*).

Endocrinology. The study of endocrine glands and their hormones.

Endoderm. Inner layer of early embryo and the tissues derived from it – mainly the gut and its associated organs. (See *Embryology; Triploblastic*).

Endoparasite. Parasite (q.v.) that lives within the body of its host. E.g. Tapeworm; liver fluke.

Endoplasm. Inner part of a cell's protoplasm. (See *Amoeba; Ectoplasm*).

Endoprocta. Small phylum of acoelomate animals, usually colonial, living in fresh or salt water. *Pedicillina,* often found encrusting seaweeds, is a typical example. Unlike the ectoprocts with which they are often linked, the anus is inside the ring of tentacles. (See *Ectoprocta*) and (Plate 109).

Endopterygota. Insects whose wings develop inside the body and which have a full metamorphosis with a larva quite unlike the adult. (See *Insecta*). (See Page 268).

Endoskeleton. Skeleton (q.v.), which is inside the musculature of the body. Vertebrate skeletons are endoskeletons. (See *Exoskeleton*).

Entomology. The study of insects.

Environment. Surroundings.

Enzyme. A complicated substance – mainly protein – that is produced in the body and that promotes some reaction in the body. An enzyme is, in fact, an organic catalyst, increasing the rate of a reaction without itself being used up. Enzymes normally affect only a single reaction or a group of related reactions: they enter into temporary combinations with substances and the new compounds immediately undergo further alteration, releasing the enzyme unchanged. Without the enzymes, many of the reactions in the body would be so slow as to be unnoticed. All bodily processes – digestion, respiration, etc. rely on enzymes to speed up their rates. Enzymes are very unstable substances except within the range of conditions they normally meet: temperature variations and pH changes effect their activity. They are destroyed by heat.

Eocene Epoch. Division of geological time started some 60 million years ago. (See *Geological Time Scale*).

Ephemeroptera. Mayflies – order of delicate flying insects with three long threads at the hind end. Always found near water for the young stages live in water. The nymphs may live for two years or more but the adults have no functional mouths and live only for a few days at the most. Mayflies are peculiar in that the nymphs develop into a flying sub-imago stage which moults again to give the true adult or imago. Normally a flying insect is full grown and does not moult again. (See *Insecta*) and (Plate 114).

Epidermis. Outer layer of skin (q.v.).

Epigamic Character. A feature, other than the sex organs and their associated structures, that is concerned with sexual reproduction. For example, the splendid tail of a peacock that is believed to attract a mate.

Epiglottis. Flap of cartilaginous tissue that closes the windpipe opening (*glottis*) when food is swallowed. (See Plate 105).

Epiphysis. Head of a long bone. (See *Bone*).

Epipubic Bone. (See *Marsupialia*) and (Plate 41).

Epithelium. A sheet of cells held together by a small amount of cementing substance. The skin, the lining of the gut and other organs, such as the lungs and blood vessels are examples. Below most epithelia there is a thin sheet of connective tissue, the basement membrane. The free surface (the surface which is not attached to other tissue) is often cilated. When the epithelium has several layers of cells it is said to be stratified.

The cells of epithelia may serve very different purposes. Those lining the salivary glands and the glands in the intestine for example, produce digestive enzymes. The ones forming the outer covering of the skin are mainly protective, while the cells of the lung lining produce the wet mucus in which the oxygen dissolves before passing to the blood. The cells may vary in shape and size. Some are thin and flat like crazy-paving stones. They form pavement or squamous epithelium which is found, for example, in the lining of parts of the kidney tubes. When the cells of squamous epithelium have wavy outlines (e.g. cells lining the blood vessels) they are said to be tesselated. Other cells are approximately as wide as they are tall. These form cuboidal or cubical epithelium which is found in many glands (e.g. liver). In columnar epithelium the cells are tall and column-shaped. Such epithelium lines most of the gut.

If columnar cells bear cilia the epithelium is then called ciliated columnar epithelium. Ciliated cells occur in the lining of the windpipe. The cilia beat to help remove dirt partiles.

The outer cells of the skin and the lining of the cheek form stratified squamous epithelium. (See Plate 40).

Erythrocyte. Red blood corpuscle. (See *Blood*).

Erythrism. Excess of red pigment in the body.

Eurypterida. An extinct order of aquatic arachnids some of which reached a length of six feet. They were like scorpions in some ways and the larger ones were probably fierce predators.

Eustachian Tube. Tube running from the middle ear to throat of most tetrapods. Enables pressures on each side of the ear drum to remain equal. (See Plate 32).

Eutherian. A placental mammal. (See *Mammalia; Placenta*).

Evolution. The process whereby living things are believed to have arisen from less advanced forms by gradual change. A great deal of evidence supports the idea of evolution, especially the evidence provided by the fossil record. Darwin and Wallace put forward a theory of how these gradual changes could be passed on to succeeding generations. (See *Darwinism; Natural Selection*) and (Plates 1, 74 and 75).

Excretion. Living organisms burn up fuel to produce energy needed for movement, growth, and the replacement of worn-out tissues. This burning process goes on in the cells and produces waste material just as a fire in the hearth produces ash and smoke. The waste materials must be removed from the body otherwise they would poison it. Carbon dioxide and various nitrogenous compounds are the main waste products. Carbon dioxide diffuses out of the body or may be expelled through the breathing organs. While this is a form of excretion the term is normally restricted to the breakdown and removal of nitrogenous waste.

The main nitrogen-containing waste substance that must be removed from an animal's body is ammonia. This is

PLATE 38

EMBRYO

7-DAY STAGE (IMPLANTATION OCCURS)

TROPHOBLAST

INNER CELL MASS

Cell mass has hollowed out to form outer sphere (trophoblast) and inner cell mass

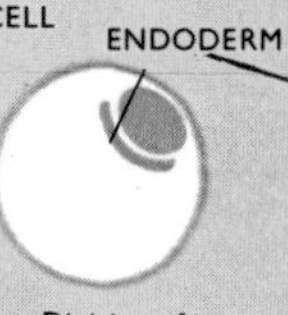

Division of inner cell mass into distinct parts

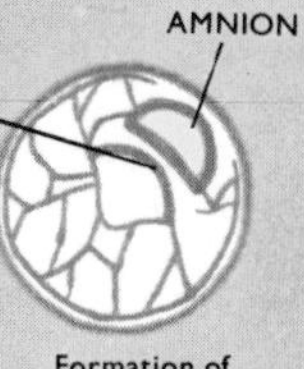

Formation of amnion and beginning of yolk sac

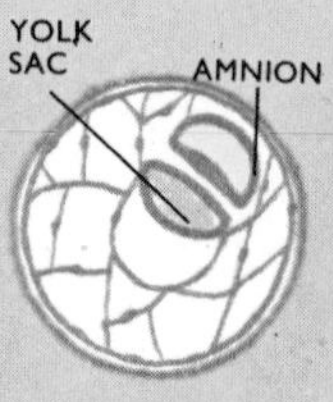

Yolk sac and amniotic cavity are now obvious

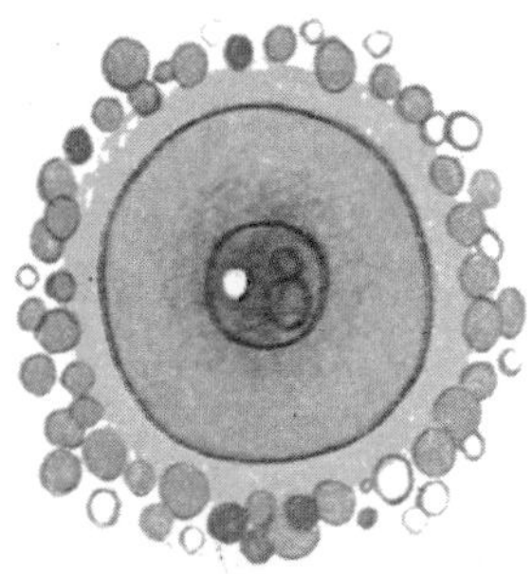

FERTILISED EGG CELL

THREE AND A HALF WEEK OLD EMBRYO

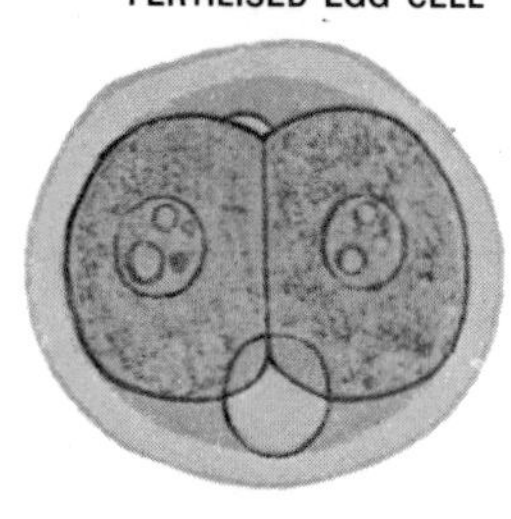

TWO CELL STAGE

ENORMOUS GROWTH OF BRAIN AT THIS TIME

SEVEN WEEKS

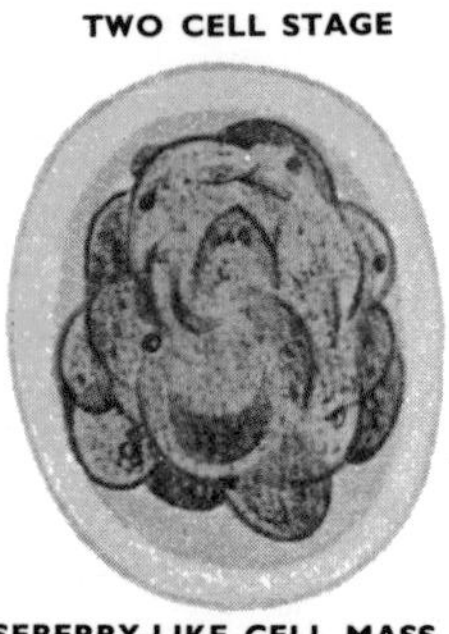

GOOSEBERRY-LIKE CELL MASS

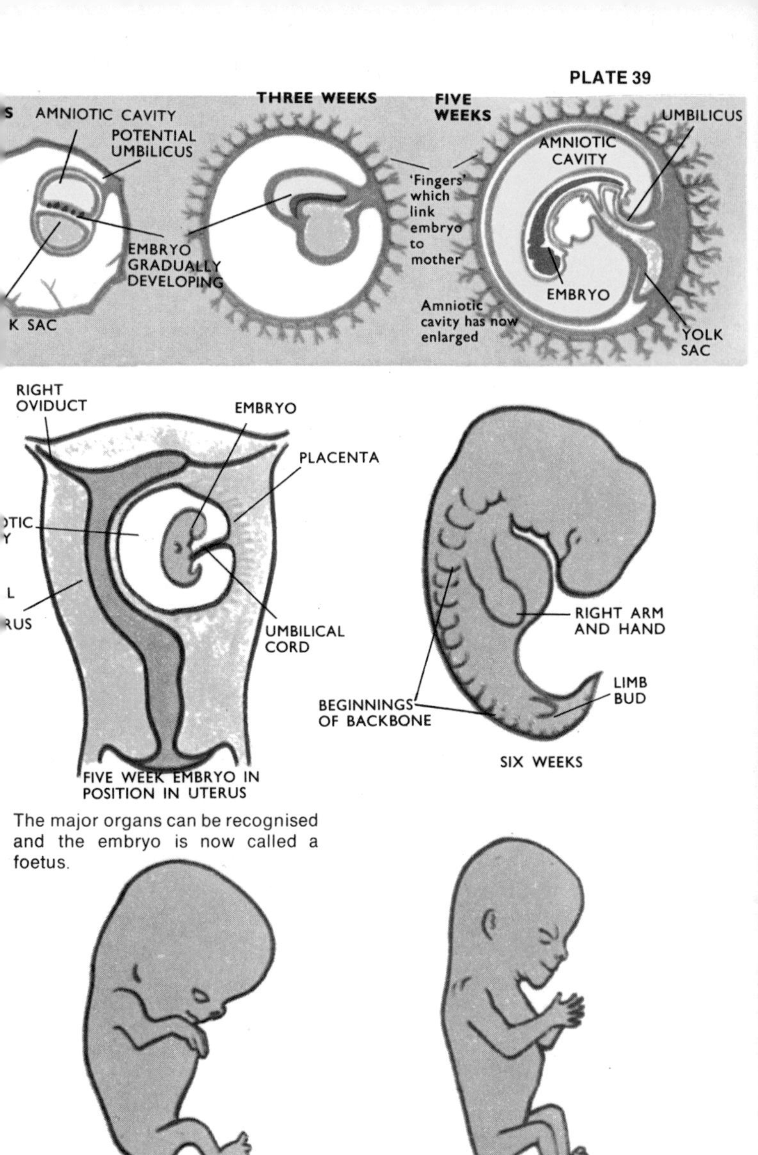

The major organs can be recognised and the embryo is now called a foetus.

EIGHT WEEKS

Stages in the development of a human embryo.

mainly formed when organic food materials containing nitrogen, that are surplus to the body's requirements, are used as fuel. Ammonia is a very poisonous substance and must be removed rapidly or converted into a less harmful substance (e.g. urea) $CO(NH_2)_2$.

In many simple animals that live in water ammonia seeps (diffuses) out of the body in solution (ammonia dissolves readily in water). Its removal in this way is rapid and efficient. Our present knowledge is that most protozoa excrete mainly ammonia compounds. Urea, and, to a lesser extent, urates (salts of uric acid) are also excreted by some. In many protozoa there are one or more water-filled spaces or contractile vacuoles. These swell in size, pumping out water from the surrounding protoplasm, and then burst, releasing their contents to the exterior. It is possible that waste materials may be dissolved in the fluid discharged, and that this may be a means of removing them.

More complicated animals have special excretory organs. The excretory system of most flatworms consists of a pair of canals on either side of the body opening in places to the exterior. The canals branch many times before ending in the excretory organs, tiny structures called flame cells. Within the cavity of each flame cell is a bundle of hairs which flicker like a flame (hence the name 'flame cell') and as a result water, waste materials and other substances pass into the flame-cell cavity. Lower down the tube, useful substances are reabsorbed and the 'urine' passes to the exterior. Primarily, however, the flame cells are concerned with regulating the fluid content of the flatworm.

In ringed worms or annelids (e.g. the earthworm) the excretory organs are called nephridia, of which there is one pair per segment. The nephridia also regulate the content of the body fluids. In the earthworm the intestine is covered with yellow cells that extract nitrogen-containing waste matter (guanin) from the bloodstream. When they are full of waste they break up and float in the coelomic fluid, the finest particles being carried to the exterior through the nephridia. The nephridia have a good blood supply and the middle part of the tube extracts urea and ammonia from the blood, passing them out in the urine. Since the strength of the urine is below that of the blood unwanted water must also be removed. The funnel of each nephridium is not open all the time. Each has a ring muscle that opens at intervals to allow fluid to escape. Waste also passes from the body fluid into the gut, carried in special amoeboid cells.

The main excretory organs of crustaceans are two pairs of glands near the *antennae* and mouthparts. These are rarely present together, often one pair serves as the 'kidneys' in the larva and the other in the adult. For example, in crabs and lobsters the antennal glands are the kidneys of the adult, but in most adult crustaceans the pair associated with the mouthparts is present.

The excretory structures consist basically of an enlarged sac (end sac) and a duct leading to the exterior. Water, salts and waste substances (e.g. ammonia salts) pass into the end sac and the upper parts of the tube. Valuable salts are reabsorbed in the middle part of the tube to produce a very weak urine containing much water. The organ thus serves for excretion and the removal of unwanted water that enters through the gills. The latter function of the excretory glands is most important in freshwater animals and, since the urine is so dilute, highly poisonous substances such as ammonia have no harmful effects while they are within the excretory system.

The formation of a hard outer shell in crustaceans and insects is another means of excretion. The shell contains a large proportion of chitin, a compound with a similar structure to cellulose, but into which ammonia is incorporated. When the shell is cast off during a moult the ammonia is removed.

Most insects also have a well-developed system of excretory tubes – Malpighian tubules – which lead into the junction between the mid gut and hind gut. Uric acid crystals have been found within the Malpighian tubules, showing that they are responsible for removing waste materials from the blood. The tubules also reabsorb water. This may take place in special cells scattered along their length or the cells may form the lower half of each tube. There is also evidence that the urine changes from an alkaline to an acid solution as it passes down the tubules so that they play a part in regulating the pH (alkalinity and acidity) of the blood, as do the tubules of the human kidney.

Other means of excretion in insects include the deposition of uric acid crystals in such structures as wing scales (e.g. white butterflies).

The majority of insects live on land and, being small, have a large surface/volume ratio. The need to conserve water that they can obtain by drinking or in their food is critical, therefore. The waterproof cuticle is of great importance in reducing loss through evaporation.

The kidneys are the main excretory organs of vertebrates. Each kidney consists of a number of tubules made up of a capsule and tube. The capsule contains a knot of blood capillaries from which water and waste, together with some useful materials, pass into the tube. Various parts of the tube reabsorb water and useful salts. Because different animals live under different conditions some need to be more careful about water loss than others and so details of kidney structure vary.

Freshwater fishes face a similar problem to freshwater invertebrates. Their body fluids are more concentrated than the water in which they live. Thus they tend to imbibe water and lose salt. Various special modifications restrict these tendencies. Bony fishes have a covering of waterproof scales, and in many (e.g. eels) the skin produces large quantities of slime. The entry of water into the body is therefore restricted and the kidneys have extra glomeruli for removing large amounts of water. Sea fishes have fewer glomeruli and conserve water. They also swallow sea water and get rid of the extra salt through special salt-secreting cells in the gills. Nitrogenous waste may also be removed in the gills.

Frogs have a moist skin and, when they return to water to breed, large quantities of water must pass in through it. Their kidneys have many glomeruli (the tubules are short) and measurements on the common frog show that they may produce about one third of an ounce of urine per day – a third of their weight. Adult frogs excrete urea and so lose less water than their eggs and tadpoles which excrete ammonia.

Reptiles and birds live in relatively dry surroundings and most of them excrete uric acid. The kidney capsules are small and only small amounts of water are filtered off. Mammals excrete urea but the kidney tubules have a reabsorbing loop and produce a concentrated urine. (See *Flame Cell; Kidney; Oligochaeta*) and (Plates 41, 42, and 43).

Exocrine Gland. (See *Gland*).

Exopterygota. (=*Hemimetabola*) Insects whose wings develop outside the body and become progressively larger at each moult. Metamorphosis is incomplete and the young stages are nymphs resembling the adults in all but size and the small wings. (See *Insecta*) and (Page 268).

Exoskeleton. Skeleton (q.v.) that is outside the body – e.g. of crabs, insects, and snails. Muscles are attached to the inside. (See *Endoskeleton*).

PLATE 40

Pavement or Squamous Epithelium lining parts of the kidney tubes.

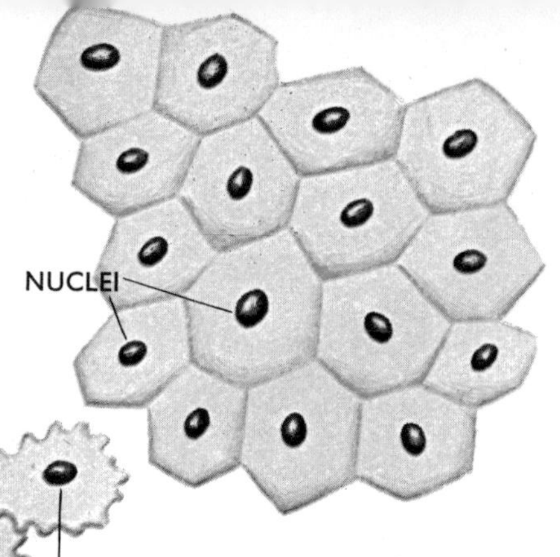

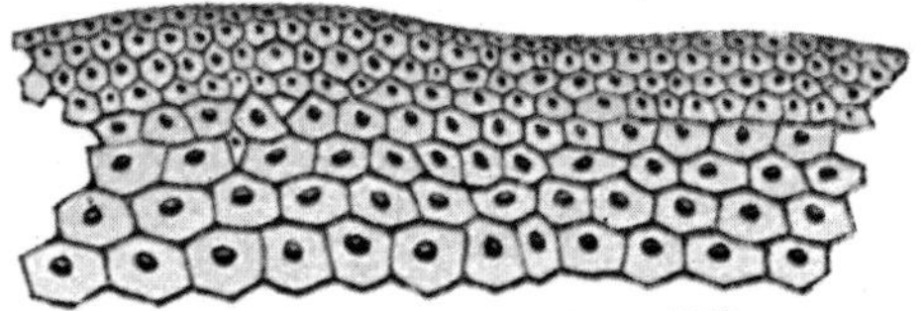

Tesselated epithelium lining the blood vessels.

Stratified Epithelium of the skin.

EPITHELIUM

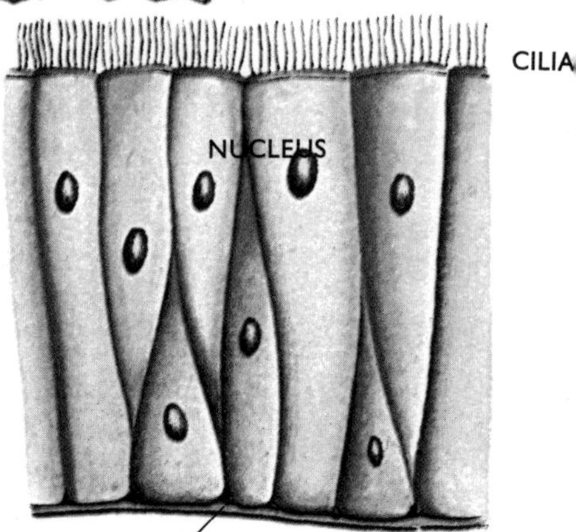

Ciliated Columnar Epithelium lining the windpipe.

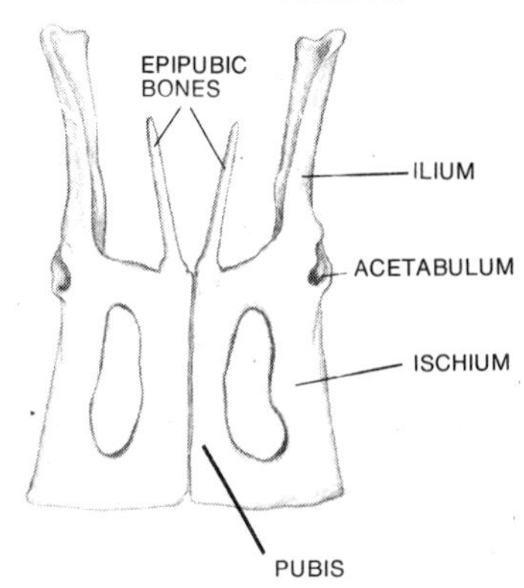

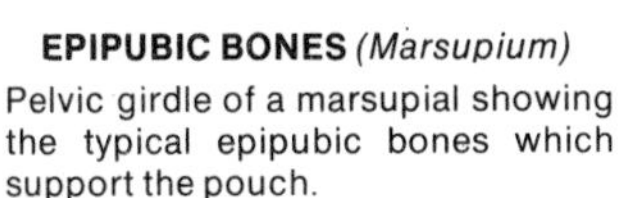

EPIPUBIC BONES *(Marsupium)*

Pelvic girdle of a marsupial showing the typical epipubic bones which support the pouch.

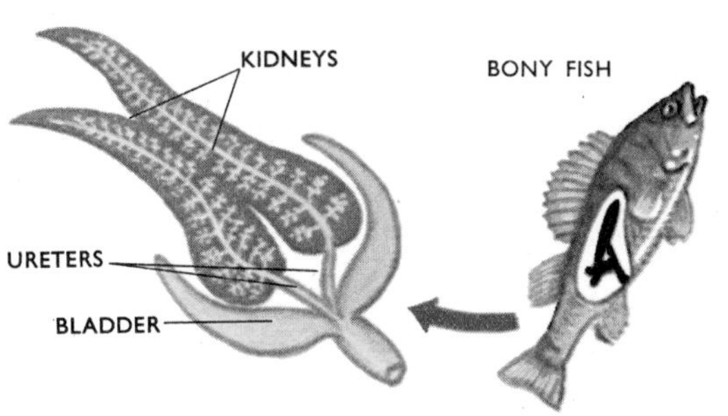

EXCRETION

The kidneys and associated organs in a fish and a frog.

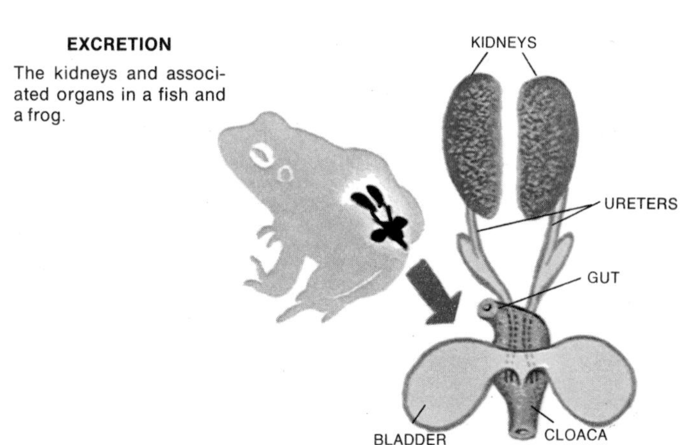

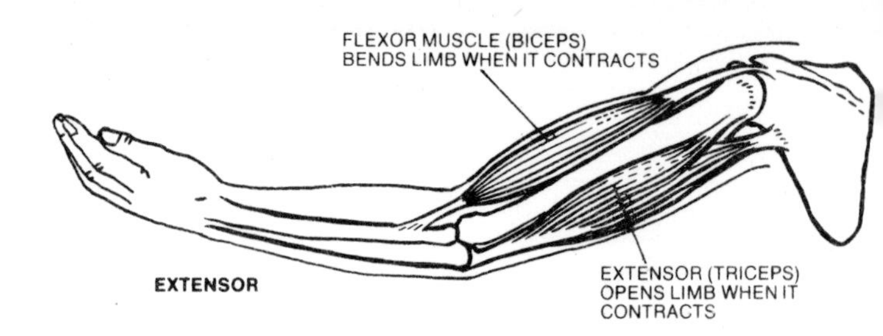

Extensor Muscle. One that stretches a limb – e.g. the triceps. (See *Flexor*).

Extra-. Outside. E.g. extra-cellular digestion – digestion outside the cell.

Eye. Organ of sight. Eyes vary from simple cells capable only of detecting light and dark, to the highly elaborate sense organs of vertebrates. Most insects and other arthropods have compound eyes made up of many separate elements called ommatidia. (See *Eye, Compound*). Cephalopods have elaborate eyes which are remarkably similar in almost every way to vertebrate eyes. The human eye is described here as a typical vertebrate eye.

Each eye is a hollow sphere embedded in its orbit in the skull. The eye wall has three main layers, a tough, fibrous outer coat – the sclera; a layer inside this containing pigment and blood vessels – the choroid; and an inner lining – the retina which contains the light sensitive cells, the nerve fibres leading from the retina to form the optic nerve, and nerve cells that connect the receptors and the nerve fibres.

At the front of the eye the three layers are modified. The sclera, which is visible as the white of the eye, is transparent and forms the cornea, whose outer surface is covered by a thin, transparent protective layer – the conjunctiva. The latter is a continuation of the eyelid lining. The choroid is modified to form the iris – the visible blue or brown pigmented part of the eye – which in its centre has an aperture, the pupil. The swollen outer part of the iris is the ciliary body which contains muscle fibres whose action changes the shape of the lens. This is a transparent crystalline structure which is suspended from the ciliary body by the suspensory ligament. The retina ends just behind the attachment of the suspensory ligament.

The iris divides the part of the eye in front of the lens into anterior and posterior chambers. These are filled with a watery fluid the aqueous humour, and the hind part of the eye,

The tear glands keep the cornea moist, nourish it and also wash away grit and dust. The eye is moved in its orbit by the action of six eye muscles. Those of each eye are coordinated, so normally both eyes are moved in the same direction.

Light enters the hind chamber of the eye after passing through the cornea, the pupil and the lens. The cornea forms an important part of the focusing mechanism, bending the light far more than the lens does. The latter produces a sharp image of the object on the retina.

The iris is equivalent to the diaphragm of a camera. It has two sets of muscle fibres, one arranged radially (in a similar manner to the

EYE

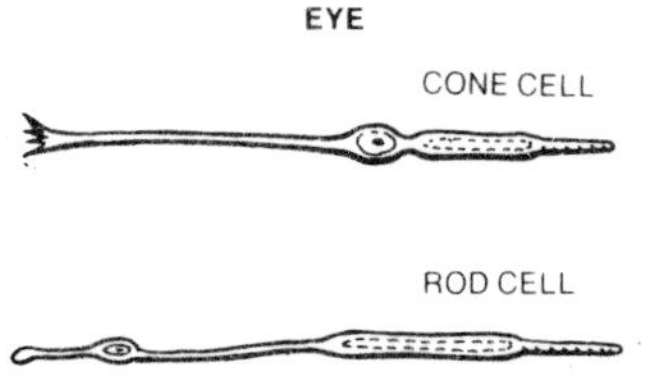

DEFECTS OF THE EYE

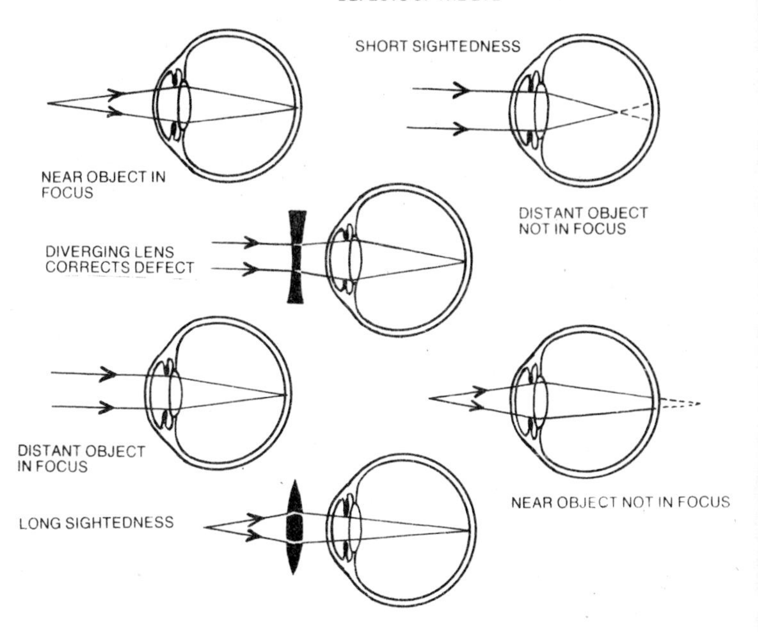

CONVERGING LENS CORRECTS DEFECT

spokes of a bicycle wheel) and the other in a circle in the inner part of the iris. The radial fibres contract in dim light enlarging the pupil and thus allowing as much of the available light as possible to enter the eye. Contraction of the circular fibres reduces the size of the pupil and cuts down the amount of light that enters the eye – as in bright conditions (in daylight the pupil is much smaller than it is at dusk).

The shape of the lens can be changed so that the images of either near or distant objects can be focused sharply on the retina. The lens consists of a 'plastic' arrangement of fibres surrounded by a thin capsule. The fibres of the suspensory ligament are inserted in this. If the tension on the ligament is altered the shape of the lens changes. When the eye is relaxed or looking at a distant object, the elastic force of the sclera pulls on the suspensory ligament and stretches the lens capsule, causing the lens to flatten and become thinner. When the eye is doing close work the ciliary muscles contract; the pull of the sclera is resisted and the tension on the suspensory ligament is relaxed, thus allowing the lens to become fatter.

The structure of the retina is extremely complicated. The light sensitive cells have their tips touching the pigment layer while their bases connect with nerve fibres. The nerve fibres run over the inner surface of the retina and join up to form the optic nerve. Light entering the eye therefore has to pass through the retinal nerve cells before it can stimulate the receptors. The retina is said to be inverted.

This is the main difference between

PLATE 42

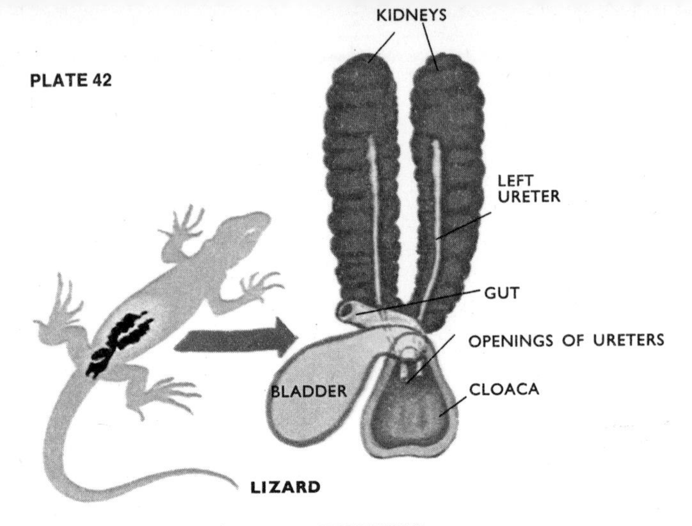

EXCRETION

Kidneys and associated organs of reptile, bird and mammal.

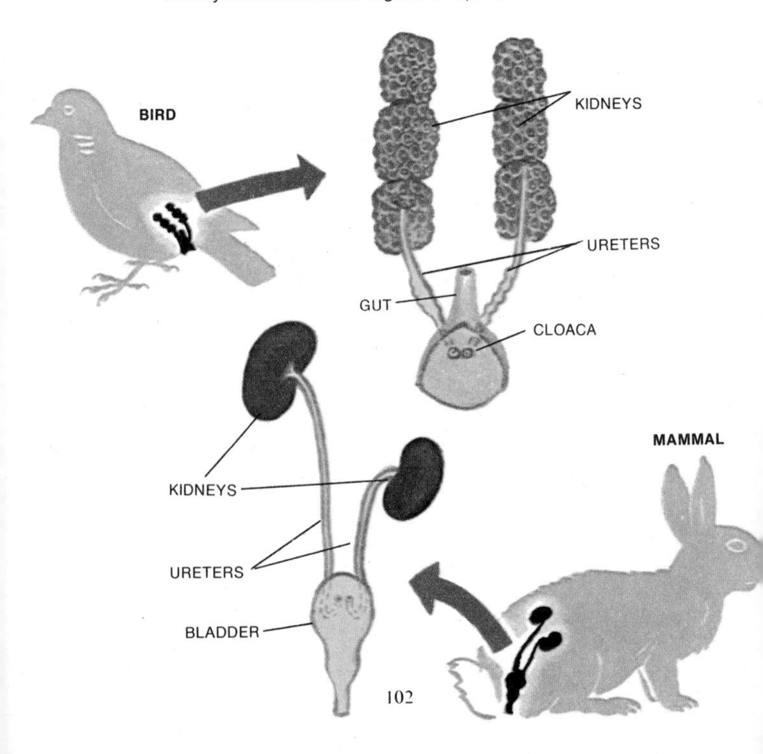

Terrestial animals face the problem of obtaining sufficient water and restricting its loss through the kidneys, and through the skin by evaporation. Frogs have a moist skin and tend to remain in the shade. The excretory systems of birds and reptiles are highly specialised for saving water. The cuticle of insects acts as a waterproof covering and their excretory tubes absorb water.

EXCRETION

the vertebrate eye and that of cephalopods: the cephalopod retina is not inverted.

Where the optic nerve leaves the eye there are no light sensitive cells. Light falling on this region is not perceived. Consequently it is known as the blind spot.

The light sensitive cells are of two kinds, called rods and cones. Most of the cones are concentrated in a small round depression, a short distance to the side of the blind spot. This is called the yellow spot or fovea centralis. The fovea is yellow because the cells of the retina at this point contain a yellow pigment. It is the region where the light is principally focused and only the part of an image which falls upon the fovea is seen sharply. This is because the cones are very small and set close together. They are sensitive to colour. The whole of the rest of the retina contains rods, sensitive to weak light but not showing colour. For this reason we see no colours by moonlight. It is of interest that many nocturnal animals have few cones in their retina and some (e.g. bats) have an all-rod retina.

The sensitivity to light depends upon the pigment visual purple in the ends of the receptor cells. When light falls on the retina visual purple undergoes chemical change. It is thought that its breakdown into other compounds stimulates the rods and so signals pass from them by way of the ganglion cells to fibres of the optic nerve and hence to the brain. The latter interprets these signals as light. In the dark the chemical change is reversed and visual purple is reconstituted. Presumably a similar chemical change stimulates the cones, though no substance has positively been shown to undergo such a change. (See Plates 44, 45 and 46).

Eye, Compound. Compound eyes are the main organs of sight in insects and crustaceans. The outer part of each eye consists of numerous tiny lenses or facets varying in number from ten to thirty thousand in different insects. These are usually hexagonal, forming a honeycomb-like mosaic. Each facet is at the top of a cone-shaped tube (ommatidium) at the bottom of which are the light receptive cells. All the ommatidia together produce a mosaic of spots of light, each spot representing the part of the field of view in line with a particular ommatidium. In effect each picture consists of a series of dots – rather like a printed picture in a newspaper. The picture an insect sees, however, is indistinct. Insects can certainly distinguish shapes and can recognise certain patterns, but their eyes are best suited to pick out moving objects or those moving across their flight path. A dragonfly, for example, is an expert at catching its prey on the wing. In most insects the fields of view of both compound eyes overlap so that they have stereoscopic vision somewhat like our own. (See Plates 46 and 47).

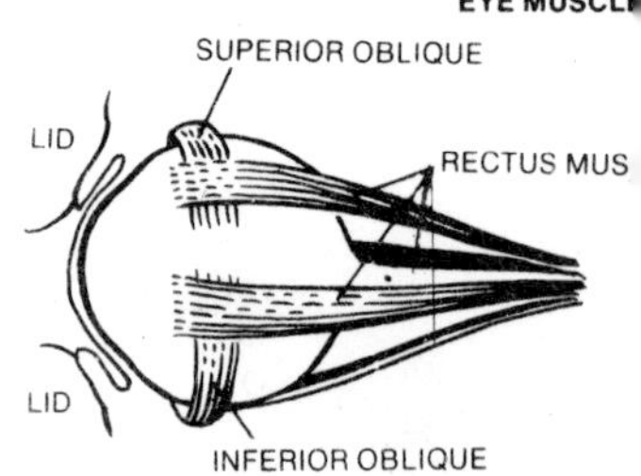

Eye Muscles. The eye-ball is moved in its socket by six small muscles; the superior and inferior *oblique* muscles, and the internal, external, anterior, and posterior *rectus* muscles. These muscles are supplied by the cranial nerves (q.v.).

F_1. Denotes the first filial generation, i.e. the first generation of descendants of a particular pair of organisms. (See Plate 59).

F_2. Second filial generation, i.e. the grandchildren of a particular pair of organisms. (See Plate 59).

Facial Nerve. The seventh cranial nerve of vertebrates. (See *Cranial Nerves*).

Faeces. Undigested material passed out of the food canal at the anus.

Fallopian Tube. Funnel shaped tube in female mammals leading from ovary to uterus. Eggs are normally fertilised on their way down the tube. (See *Urinogential System*) and (Plate 103).

Family. A category used in the classification of organisms. Zoological family names end in -idae. (See *Classification*).

Fauna. The animal life of a certain region or time.

Feather. An outgrowth of the skin that is found only in birds. Feathers probably evolved from reptile scales and, although they are used for flight now, their first function was almost certainly as a protection against cold.

Feathers are made of keratin, a horny substance produced by the upper layers of the skin, and there are four types.

Contour feathers are large and sheathe the body of the bird, as well as covering the tail and wings. The actual quill of the feather is the section of the stem which remains embedded in the skin. It is usually hollow with two small openings, one at its base and one where the quill perforates the skin surface.

The rest of the contour feather above the skin's surface is called the vane; it consists of a central, solid shaft continuous with the quill and a very large number of small branches (barbs) coming off from either side. The barbs are so closely packed together that they appear to form a continuous surface. In actual fact they are separate units, though each one is attached to its neighbours by a series of hooked and notched barbules.

Down feathers are much smaller and simpler. The quill is very small and at the surface, instead of continuing as a main stem, it divides to form a spray of slender branches. The fluffy coats of young chicks are made up entirely of down feathers.

Pin-feathers are even simpler. They consist of just the quill and a short stem which divides at the top into a bunch of small barbs. Powder-down feathers are possessed by only a few birds, e.g. bitterns and herons. They break down into a powder useful for removing slime and dirt from the rest of the plumage.

Contour feathers, fitted to the wings and tails of birds, provide a large surface area to push against the air during flight. The sheath of smaller contour feathers formed over the whole body gives the bird a stream-lined shape essential for movement through the air. The smooth, flat surfaces of the contour feathers are formed by the tightly linked barbs. If the barbs become disarranged by unhooking of the barbules, the birds' preening action soon repairs them. Smooth, stream-lined feathers are not necessary for flightless birds: ostriches have plume-like contour feathers.

Down feathers are concerned with insulation of the body from the cold. They help trap a layer of air against the skin. In adult birds they are not usually conspicuous as they are covered by the contour feathers.

Feathers can be moved by the action of muscles just as the hairs that cover mammals can be moved. Ruffling of feathers occurs during cold weather (the additional trapped air gives extra warmth) and the position of contour feathers on the wings and on the tail can be controlled in flight.

Again like hairs, feathers are supplied with nerve fibres and can be used as organs of touch. Birds that fly at night have very sensitive hair-like feathers on their faces, rather like the whiskers of cats. (See Plates 48 and 49).

PLATE 44

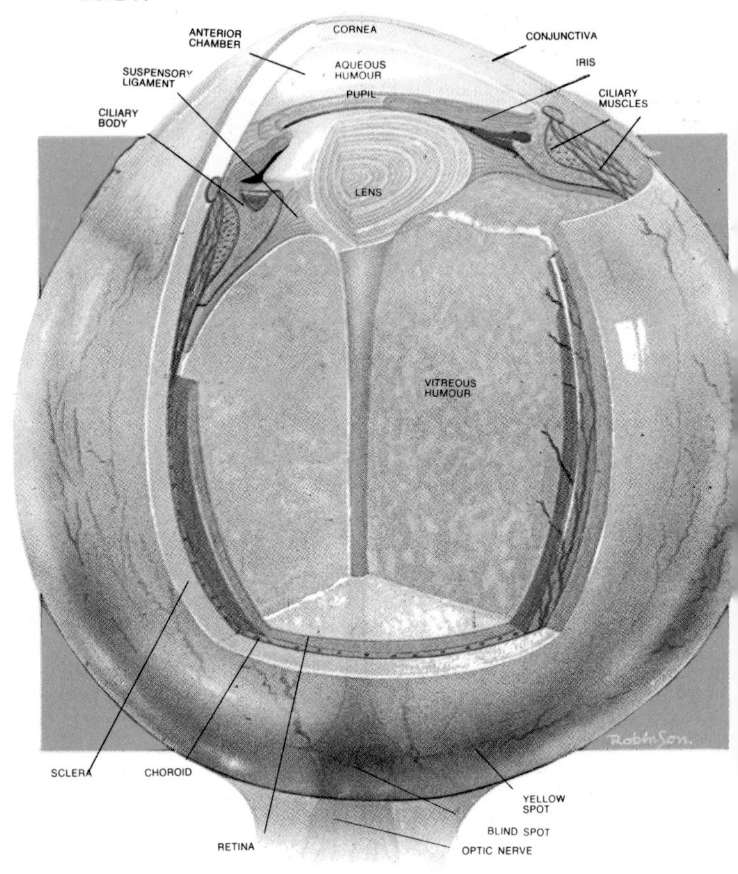

EYE

The human eye, partly cut away to show its structure.

PLATE 45

EYE

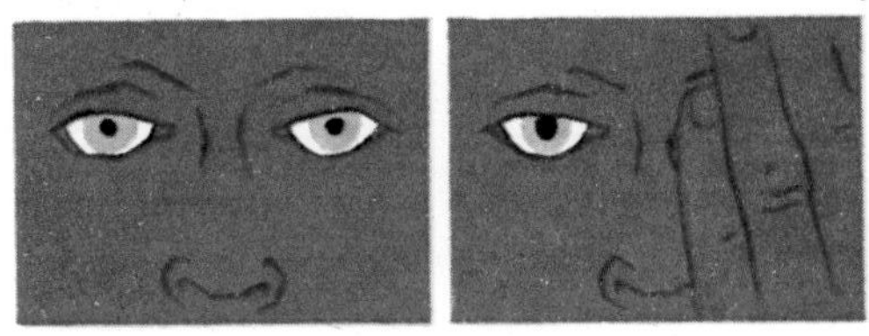

If one eye is covered, the pupil of the other opens up as a result of a reflex linking the two eyes.

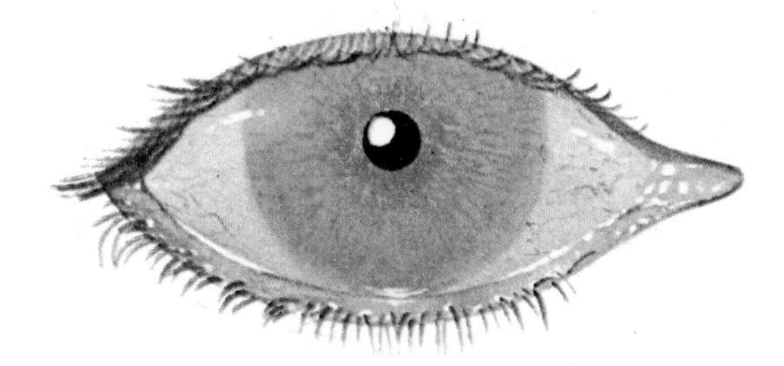

In bright light the pupil is small.

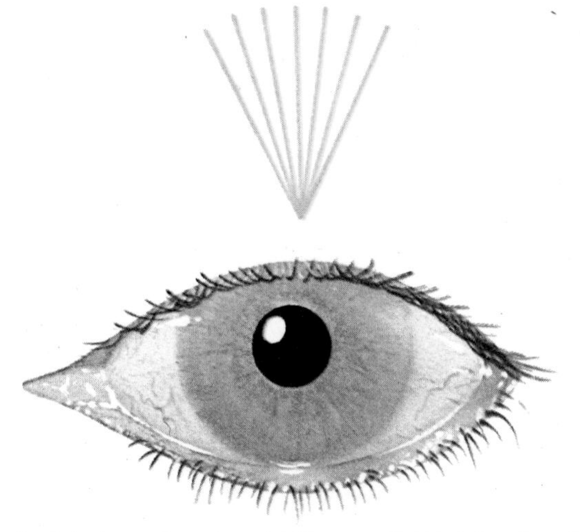

In dim light the pupil opens up to allow more light to fall on the retina.

Femur. Thigh bone. (See Page 217).

Fertilisation. The joinging together of two sex-cells (*gametes*) to form a *zygote*—the first cell of a new generation.

Fibrinogen. A soluble protein in vertebrate blood which is converted into insoluble fibres of fibrin when blood vessels are damaged. The fibres trap corpuscles and form a clot or scab which prevents further blood loss and allows healing to begin. (See *Blood*).

Fibula. Smaller of the two bones in lower part of the hind leg. (See Page 217).

Fishes (See *Teleostei; Elasmobranchii; Dipnoi*).

Flagellata (=Mastigophora). Class of protozoans in which the main stage has one or more flagella. Sex cells are formed by some species but reproduction is normally affected by simple division. There are both plant-like and animal-like flagellates and some, such as *Euglena*, that appear to be midway between the two. Many flagellates are parasitic, e.g. *Trypanosoma*, the organism causing sleeping sickness. (See Plate 106).

Flagellum. Fine whip-like thread projecting from certain cells. There are rarely more than a few per cell. They move the cell about (in the case of protozoans or motile sex cells) or they may create a current of water in an animal (in the food cavity of *Hydra* and in sponges). (See *Flagellata*).

Flame Cell (=Solenocyte). Excretory organ of flatworms. Nitrogen-containing excretory products diffuse in solution through the body tissue into a series of branching tubules—the water vessels. There are two main tubules, one on either side of the body opening by excretory pores on the upper surface of the body. Branches of the tubules terminate in flame cells—hollowed-out structures containing a number of hair-like flagella. The flickering movement of the flagella (which gives the cell its name) keeps the fluid in the tubules continually circulating. No doubt this speeds up the loss of excretory products and also helps to eliminate excess water passing into the animal's body by osmosis. (See *Platyhelminthes; Excretion*) and (Plates 50 and 101).

Flatworm (See *Platyhelminthes*).

Flea (See *Siphonaptera*).

Flexor Muscle. One that bends a limb, e.g. biceps bending arm. (See *Extensor*).

Fluke. A flatworm of class *Trematoda* (q.v.). (See also *Platyhelminthes*).

Foetus. Mammalian embryo when all main features are recognisable. (See *Embryology*) and (Plates 38, 39 and 88).

Food Chain. Aphid eats plant; spider eats aphid, bird eats spider; bird of prey eats smaller bird. This is a typical food chain. Material passes from the plant, through several animals before it reaches the last link in the chain. The cycle is completed with the death and decay of the last animal in the chain. The simple substances formed by decay will be used again by a plant and a new cycle will start. We can make the food chain complicated by including all the other animals that eat aphids or by including all the parasites found on the birds. Every living organism belongs to one or more food chains and, if parasites are excluded, the higher up the chain one goes, the fewer individuals will be found. This must be so, for if in the example above there were more birds than spiders, the latter would soon disappear. All the food chains in a habitat link up to form the *food cycle*.

Foramen. Literally a hole but normally restricted to holes in the skull through which nerves run. E.g. Foramen magnum, the large opening at the back through which the spinal cord emerges.

Foraminifera. A group of protozoans, usually with a chambered shell and fine, thread-like pseudopodia. They are mainly marine and the shells sometimes accumulate in vast quantities on the sea bed to form oozes, e.g. *Globigerina* ooze, made up of the chalky shells of *Globigerina*. (See Plate 106).

Fossil. The remains of an organism preserved in the rocks. Normally only those animals with hard skeletons have been preserved and they are most commonly found in rocks that were laid down under water. The dead organism fell to the bottom and became covered with sediment. Soft parts generally decayed but the hard shells and skeletons remained while the sediments became compressed into rocks. The actual material of the skeleton has in most cases been wholly or partly replaced by minerals, leaving what is known as a cast, but this still shows the original overall structure. In some cases the whole skeleton has been washed away by percolating water, leaving only a hollow mould but this is still a valuable clue to the structure of the dead organism. Fossils are very important for geologists and also provide strong evidence to support the theory of evolution. (See *Geological Time Scale*) and (Plate 50).

Fovea. Highly sensitive part of retina. (See *Eye*).

Frog. (See *Amphibia; Anura*).

Gall. Abnormal plant growth caused by a parasite – often an insect or mite. E.g. oak apple; robin's pincushion. (See Plate 51).

Gall Bladder. Thin-walled sac in liver which collects bile. When food enters the intestine the gall bladder contracts and bile passes to the intestine. (See *Digestion*).

Gamete. Sex-cell, i.e. sperm or ovum (egg-cell).

Ganglion. Swelling in a nerve which contains the actual cell bodies and nuclei of the nerve cells as opposed to their conducting axons. (See *Nerve Cell; Nervous System*).

Ganoid Scale. Primitive fish scale with a thick bony layer overlain by a thick layer of enamel-like ganoine. (See *Cosmoid Scale*).

Gasteropoda. Class of *Mollusca* (q.v.), with a distinct head, eyes, tentacles, and a flat, muscular 'foot'. The internal organs are contained within the visceral hump which is often coiled and covered by a single shell. These animals are the slugs and snails and there are marine, fresh-water, and land-living forms. They feed on plant and/or animal material which they rasp off by means of a mass of horny teeth called a radula.

The ancestral molluscs almost certainly had their mantle cavity containing the gills at the hind end of the body but the gasteropod body has undergone a curious twisting process (torsion) so that the mantle cavity opens at the front in the typical gasteropods. The order Prosobranchiata contains mainly marine forms, including all the common sea-shore gasteropods such as limpets, whelks, and periwinkles. There is almost always a shell and an operculum – the horny plate closing the shell when the animal retreats into it. In most gasteropods the shell is coiled in such a way that when viewed from the front, the opening is on the right of the coil (dextral condition). A few species have the opening on the left (sinistral). There may be one or two gills (ctenidia) in the mantle cavity, although in land-living forms they are modified for air-breathing. The sexes are separate. The order Opisthobranchiata contains hermaphrodite animals which have undergone a detwisting process so that the mantle cavity (if present) opens towards the

EYE

IN MAN,
MUSCLES IN THE
SURROUNDING IRIS
CONTRACT TO CLOSE
THE CIRCULAR PUPIL.
THE MUSCLES INCREASINGLY
INTERFERE WITH EACH OTHER
AND AT THE LIMIT OF
CLOSURE, THE PUPIL
IS STILL AN EIGHTH
OF AN INCH ACROSS

THE SLIT
PUPIL OF
CATS, ALLIGATORS
AND OTHER ANIMALS
CONSISTS OF A
PAIR OF CURTAINS.
THEY CAN BE DRAWN
EVEN CLOSER THAN
ILLUSTRATED SO THAT
JUST A PIN HOLE, TOP AND
BOTTOM, IS LEFT OPEN

EYE, COMPOUND

The compound eye of an insect cut away to show the arrangement of the ommatidia.

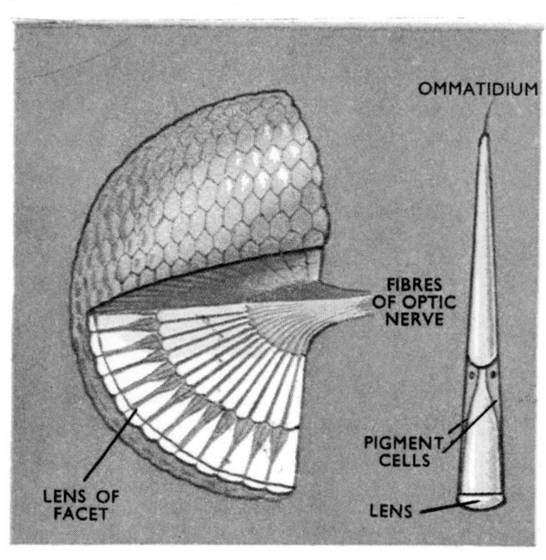

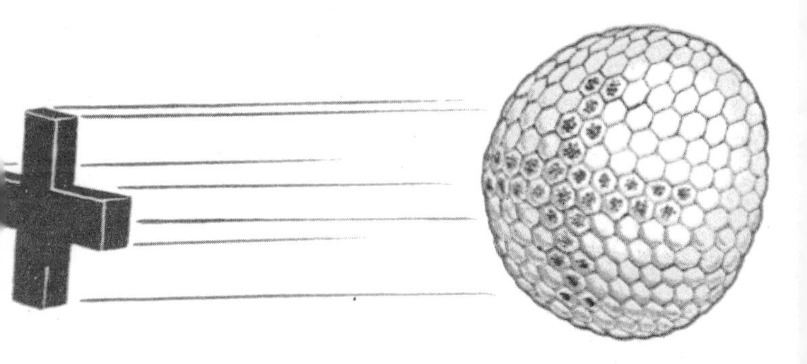

EYE, COMPOUND

ompound eye with many facets (ommatidia) is far more sensitive to shape
d movement than one with few facets. The lower eye receives a picture
de up of only 10 points of light, whereas the upper one, with more facets,
eives a picture made up of many more points of light. A slight movement
shape change will alter the number or position of the points.

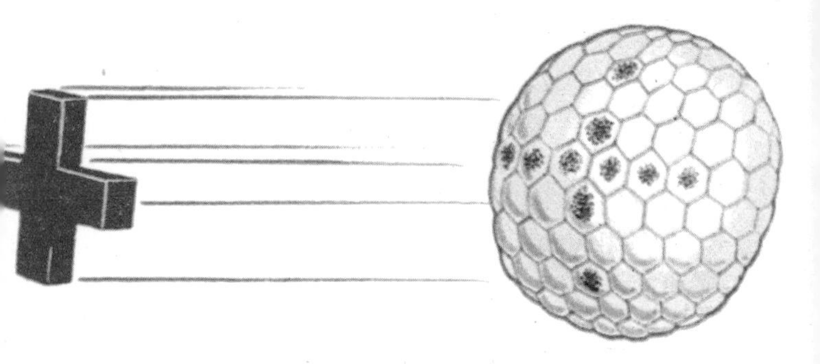

hind end as in the primitive molluscs. The shell, mantle cavity and gills are reduced and sometimes absent altogether. These animals are the sea-slugs and sea-hares.

The order Pulmonata contains mainly terrestrial and fresh water dwellers – the slugs and snails of our gardens and ponds, although there are a few pulmonates on the sea-shore. The gills have disappeared and the mantle cavity is modified as a lung for air-breathing (pond-snails come to the surface to breathe). There is never an operculum. The eyes are often at the tips of retractable tentacles. Slugs are merely pulmonates that have lost their shells; their basic structure is similar to that of the shelled snails. (See *Torsion*) and (Plates 51, 52 and 115).

Gastric. Concerning the stomach.

Gene. An hereditary factor passed on from cell to cell and from generation to generation, which has a particular effect on the cell or organism containing it. Genes are carried on the *chromosomes* (q.v.), in the cell nuclei and each gene has a particular place on a certain chromosome. Because each body cell has two sets of chromosomes, it has two genes concerned with each feature. But the two genes are not necessarily identical: every now and then the molecular structure of a gene may become altered so that, although it still affects the same feature of the organism, it has a different effect. The gene is said to have mutated. A pair of different genes which occur at the same place on the chromosomes but have different effects on the development of the organism are said to be alleles or allelomorphic genes. As a rule, one allele over-rules the effect of the other and is said to be dominant. The other allele is the recessive and its presence is made apparent in the organism only if it is present in both sets of chromosomes. If the two chromosomes carry identical genes, the organism is said to be homozygous for that character. If two different alleles are carried, the organism is heterozygous.

Genes are believed to be composed of nucleic acids which control the development of the cells by controlling the types of protein formed. The vast number of instructions carried by the genes of an organism is made possible by the enormous variation in the arrangement of the molecules making up the nucleic acids. When a cell divides (except when forming sex-cells) the chromosomes and genes duplicate themselves exactly so that the same instructions go to each new cell. But even then the new cells may not be exactly like the parent for their position in the body also influences their development. When sex-cells are formed the chromosomes do not duplicate themselves but one member of each pair goes to each sex cell. When sex cells join at fertilisation, there are again two sets of chromosomes but the genes that they carry are not identical with those of either parent and, as the effect of a gene is modified by the action of those genes around it, the new generation will not be identical with either parent. (See *Heredity* and *Natural Selection*). (Plates 58 and 59).

Genetics. The study of genes and the way in which characteristics are passed on to offspring. (See *Heredity*)

Genotype. The actual genetic constitution of an organism, which may not be apparent from the outward appearance. (See *Phenotype*).

Genus. A category used in classification, consisting of a number of closely related species, all of which share the generic name. (See *Classification*).

Geological Time Scale. During the Earth's long history there have been many changes: land has been submerged and uplifted many times; animal groups have appeared, flourished, and become extinct. Geological time has been divided into a number of periods separated by episodes of mountain building or abrupt faunal changes. The time scale is of great importance to zoologists dealing with evolution and with fossil groups. (See Plate 52).

Germ Cell. A gamete or sex-cell.

Gestation Period. Period from fertilisation to birth in mammals. It varies from about three weeks in house mice, to about 40 weeks in man and nearly two years in elephants.

Gill. Respiratory organ of various aquatic animals. Consists of thin plates of tissue, well supplied with blood. Gills may be inside or outside the body but they are open to the water from which they extract oxygen for *respiration* (q.v.). (See Plates 70 and 81).

Gill Book. Respiratory organ of certain aquatic arachnids, consisting of plates of tissue arranged somewhat like the leaves of a book.

Gill Slit. An opening from the pharynx to the outside of the body. Gill slits are diagnostic characteristics of chordate animals, although they are found only in the embryos and young stages of tetrapods. In *Amphioxus* and the sea-squirts there are many gill slits and they are concerned with filtering food particles from the water. In fishes there are fewer slits and they are modified for respiration. (See Plate 90).

Gizzard. Muscular region of the alimentary canal of certain animals where food is ground up prior to main digestive processes. (See *Alimentary Canal*) and (Plate 2).

Gland. An organ that manufactures certain substances and passes them out into the body where they fulfil particular functions. Digestive juices are produced in glands such as the liver and pancreas. These have ducts to carry away the secretions and are called *exocrine* glands. There are, however, several ductless or *endocrine* glands, such as the thyroid and adrenals. These produce hormones which are carried to their sites of action by the blood. (See *Hormone*) and (Plate 54).

Glenoid Cavity. Cup-shaped depression in shoulder girdle into which head of humerus fits.

Glomerulus. Knot of blood capillaries in Bowman's capsule of *kidney* (q.v.).

Glossopharyngeal Nerve. Ninth *cranial nerve* (q.v.), supplying throat region.

Glottis. Opening of the windpipe (trachea) into the pharynx.

Gluteal Muscles. Muscles of the buttocks, concerned with erect posture and therefore small in quadrupeds.

Glycogen. 'Animal starch'–a polysaccharide that is stored by various animals in their bodies and which can be converted into glucose when required for respiration.

Gnathostomata. Term sometimes used in classification to refer to all the jawed vertebrates. (See *Agnatha*).

Golgi Apparatus. (See *Cell*).

Gonad. Organ where sex cells are formed–i.e. testis or ovary.

Graafian Follicle. Structure in mammalian ovary in which an actual egg-cell develops and which bursts to release egg-cell at ovulation. (See *Ovary*) and (Plate 86).

Graptolite. Extinct animal whose relationship to other groups is not clear. Graptolite fossils are abundant in palaeozoic rocks and they are of great importance to geologists for correlating outcrops in different parts of the world. The fossils are normally found as white markings on slaty

PLATE 48

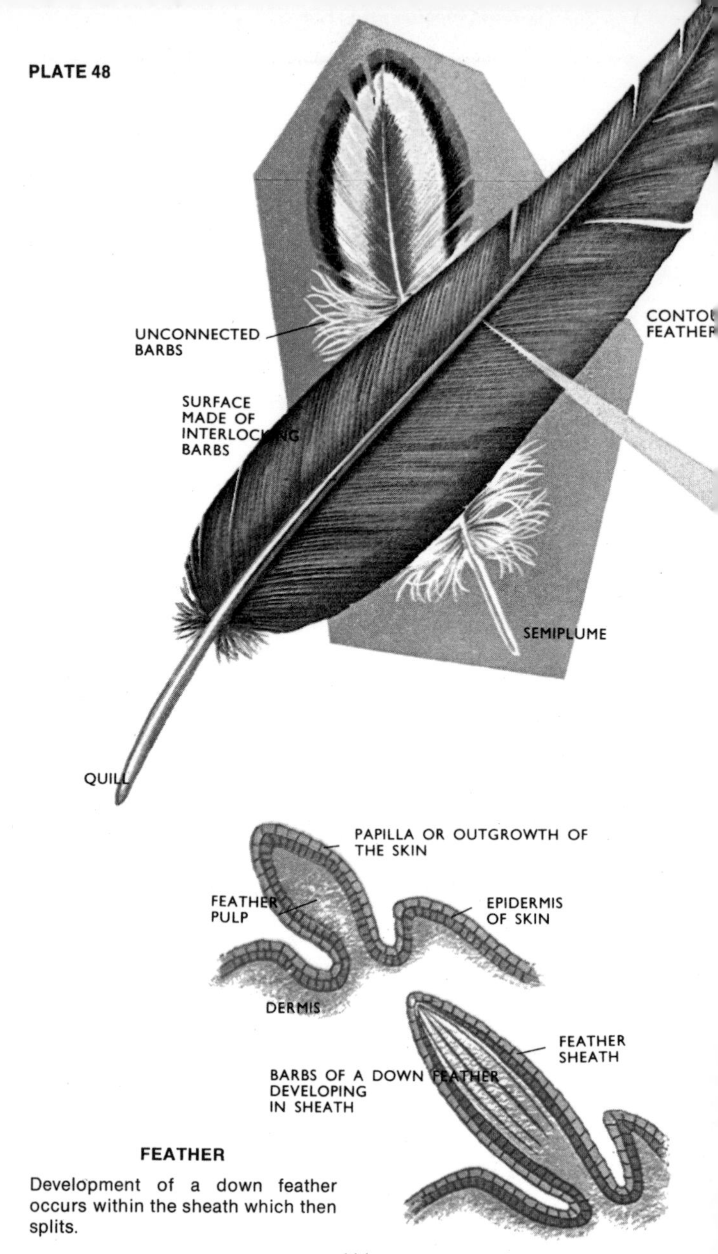

FEATHER

Development of a down feather occurs within the sheath which then splits.

PLATE 49

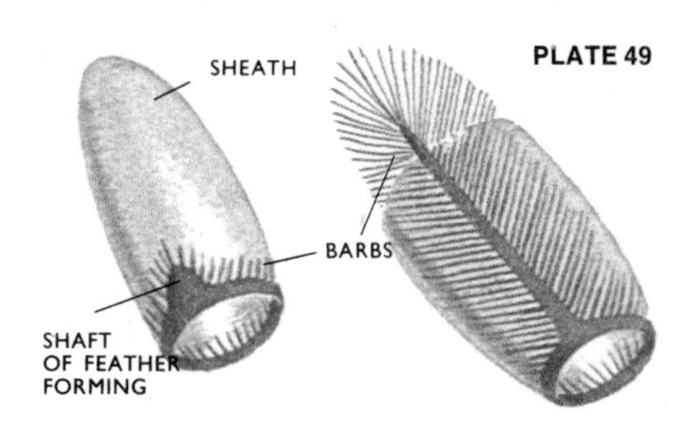

The barbs of contour feathers develop at the base of the shaft which grows up through the sheath.

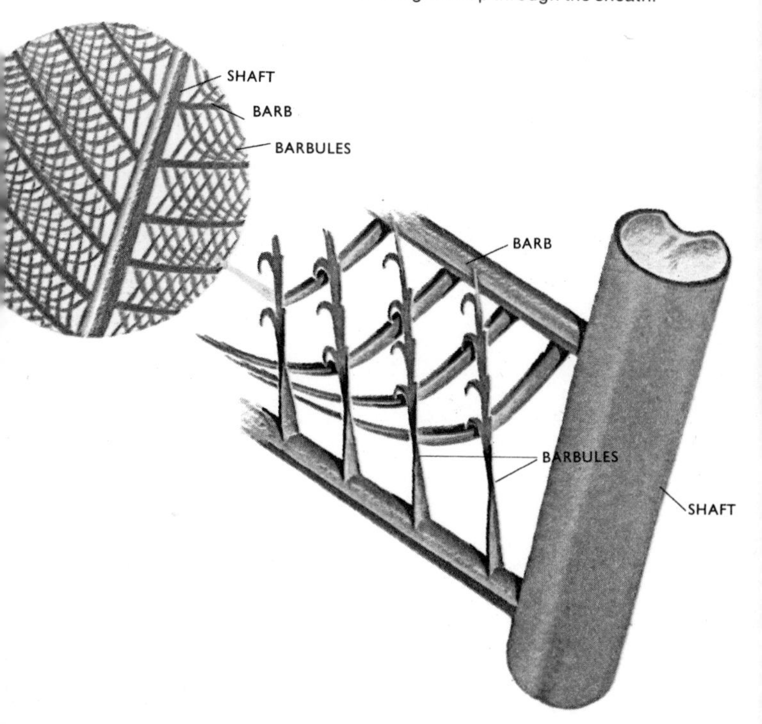

Contour feathers consist of numerous interlocking barbs and barbules. The barbs of semi-plumes are unconnected.

rocks. There are many species but all appear to have been colonial – the individual animals living in tiny cups on branched or unbranched stalks. (See Plate 54).

Green Gland. Excretory organ of crustaceans. (See *Excretion*).

Grey Matter. That part of the vertebrate central nervous system that contains most of the actual nerve cell bodies. It makes up the central part of the spinal cord and also the cerebral cortex of the brain. There are vast numbers of nerve connections (synapses) in the grey matter and it is the seat of co-ordination.

GYNANDROMORPH COMMON BLUE BUTTERFLY

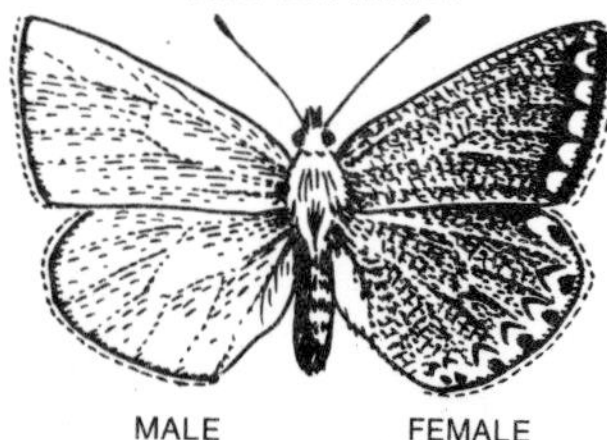

Gynandromorph. An animal in which, through disturbance of the sex-controlling mechanism during embryonic development, part of the body is genetically male and part genetically female. The phenomenon is quite common in insects and may result in one side of the insect having male features and the other side female features. (See *Hermaphrodite; Intersex*) and (Plate 55).

Habitat. A particular type of environment, such as woodland or marsh.

Habituation. Suppression of an instinctive action through learning. The stimulus is still the same but there is no reaction. Wild animals flee from man as a rule through an instinctive fear but they can be tamed and when they learn that man will not hurt them the instinct is suppressed. (See *Instinct; Association*).

Haemocoel. A type of body cavity which, although it may form large spaces around the internal organs, is actually part of the blood system. The haemocoel is well-developed in arthropods and molluscs where the true body cavity or coelom is reduced. The body cavity of vertebrates is a coelom and the haemocoel is represented only by the blood vessels and heart. Unlike a coelom (q.v.) a haemocoel never contains sex organs and never opens to the outside of the body. (See Plate 55).

Haemoglobin. Iron-containing *respiratory pigment* (q.v.), of vertebrates and certain other animals.

Haemocyanin. Copper-containing *respiratory pigment* (q.v.) of certain arthropods and molluscs.

Hair. Skin outgrowth characteristic of mammals.

Although hairs appear to come from the dermis they start in the epidermis. The epidermis grows down into the dermis to form tiny pits. They are found all over the body except the soles and palms. The pits, called follicles, have a bulge at the bottom rather like that at the bottom of a wine glass. Under the bulge is the hair papilla which feeds the hair. Cells at the base of the follicle divide repeatedly and the new cells are pushed outwards. They soon die but do not break off: the chain of dead cells forms the hair. The hair colour is determined by pigments. Its greasiness is caused by the secretion of the sebaceous gland.

Hair traps a layer of air between itself and the body and helps to maintain an even temperature. A tiny muscle attached to each hair can alter its position, although these muscles are very weak in Man. Hairs have tiny nerves around the base and are sensitive to touch. Some hairs have extra nerves and are extra-sensitive. The cat's whiskers are very sensitive to touch. (See *Skin*) and (Plate 92).

Hallux. The first, often backward pointing, toe of birds. (See *Aves*).

Haltere. Modified hind wing of true flies (Diptera) used as balancing organs in flight. (See Plate 55).

Haploid. Having only a single set of chromosomes in the nucleus. (See *Diploid; Chromosome*).

Haversian Canal. (See *Bone*).

Hearing. (See *Ear*).

Heart. The 'engine-room' or pump of the blood system, consisting of one or more muscular chambers which contract rhythmically and force blood round the body. The insect heart is a long tube on the dorsal side. It has openings at intervals allowing blood to enter from the surrounding haemocoel. The earthworm has two main blood vessels, one dorsal and one ventral. Near the front there are five pairs of pseudo-hearts which pump blood from the dorsal vessel and send it back along the ventral vessel. The vertebrate heart shows an interesting evolutionary series connected with the change from aquatic to terrestrial life and the increasing complexity of the body.

The primitive vertebrate heart – typical of shark-like fishes – consists of four chambers. From back to front these are the sinus venosus, the atrium or auricle, the ventricle, and the conus arteriosus. The four chambers of the bird and mammalian heart do not correspond to these, for the sinus and conus have been lost, and the auricle and ventricle have each been divided in two, so that the heart is a double pump and not a single one.

The growth of the heart is not uniform in all parts – some parts grow faster than others. This produces a kinking which becomes so exaggerated that even in a fish the auricle lies in front of and above the ventricle. Valves develop between each chamber and the pacemaker where the heartbeat starts develops near the border between the sinus and the auricle.

The sinus serves as a reservoir in which venous blood collects upon returning from the body. The auricle is thin-walled and contracts weakly. The ventricle is a powerful pump whose contraction is mainly responsible for moving the blood. The conus is muscular and provided with valves. Blood returning sluggishly in the large sinuses causes the thin-walled sinus to swell. As it contracts, blood is forced into the auricle, since the valves at the hind end of the sinus close. The auricle swells and contracts, forcing blood into the ventricle and swelling it. This contracts to drive the blood forward through the gills. The pressure of blood flowing to the gills is thus gradually built up in the heart.

In both bony and shark-like fishes the blood passes through all the chambers of the heart on its way to the lungs to be oxygenated. These fish are said to have a single circulation. The pressure of the blood is lowered by its passage through both the gill capillaries and the capillaries in the head and body.

In land vertebrates we can follow the probable lines which the evolution of double circulation has followed. With the development of lungs in place of gills, both oxygenated blood from the former and deoxygenated blood from the body are passing into the heart together. This is an undesirable situation, for much of the oxygenation is wasted and blood passes to the body containing only a moderate amount of oxygen instead of being rich in oxygen. Obviously, then, a state of affairs is preferable where oxygenated and deoxygenated blood are kept apart. In lung-fishes, relatives of which were the ancestors of land vertebrates, both the auricle and ventricle are partly divided into two and the ventral aorta is short and twisted. Its valves are arranged so that most of the blood from the left side of the auricle passes into the first two aortic arches and that from the right side passes into the hind two arches. Thus some degree of

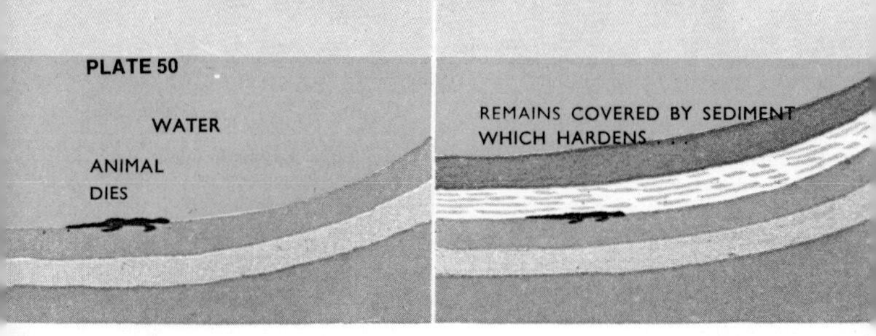

FOSSIL

Diagrams showing the stages by which an animal may be fossilised and later discovered.

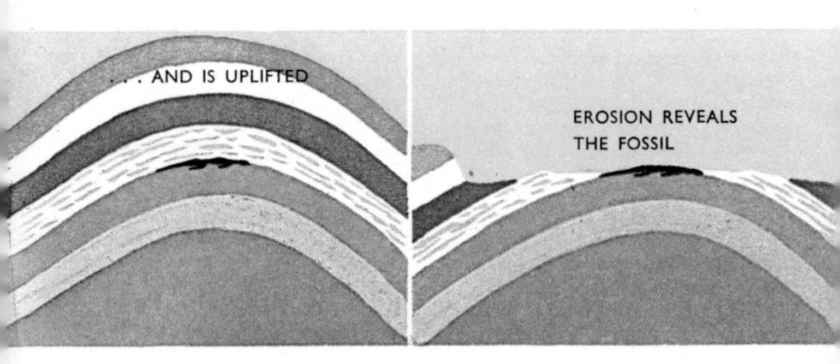

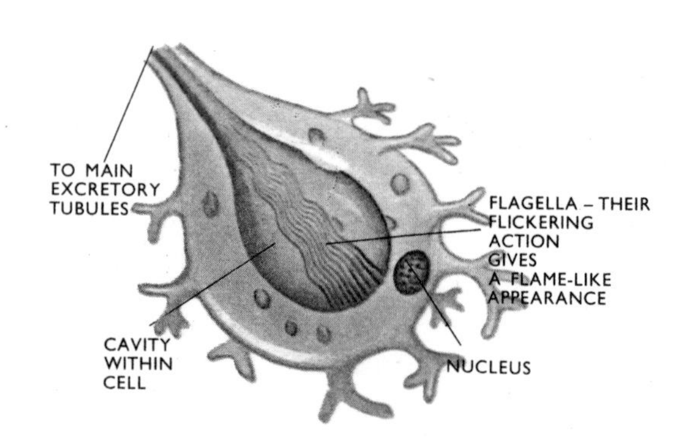

FLAME-CELL

The excretory organs of flatworms and some other worm-like animals.

PLATE 51

A DEXTRAL SHELL

OPENING ON RIGHT

ROBINS' PINCUSHION ON ROSE PLANT PRODUCED IN RESPONSE TO ATTACK BY A GALL-WASP

GALL

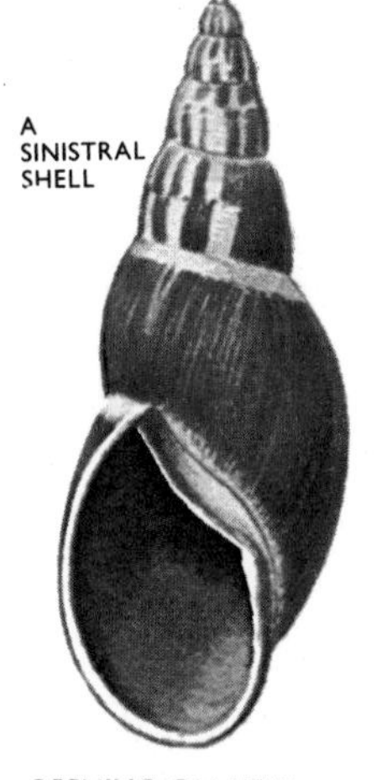

A SINISTRAL SHELL

OPENING ON LEFT

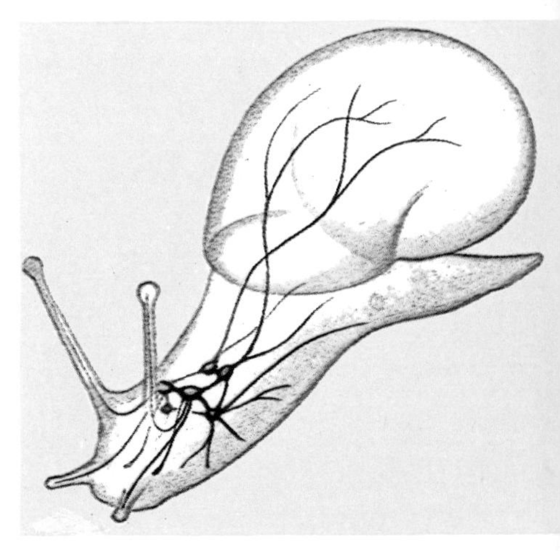

GASTEROPODA

The twisted nervous system of the snail shows the torsion characteristic of the group.

separation is obtained.

In amphibians the auricles are completely divided into two. Blood poor in oxygen that is returning from the body enters the right auricle and blood from the lungs enters the left auricle. The ventricle is not divided, but flaps of spongy tissue probably prevent complete mixing of the blood in the ventricle.

In most reptiles the ventricle is almost completely divided into two. There is a slight gap in the dividing wall where the arteries to the body and lungs leave the heart so that a little mixing can take place. It is only in birds and mammals that we see a complete division of the ventricle into two and consequently complete separation of oxygenated and deoxygenated blood. (See *Aortic Arches*).

Heart muscle is striped in appearance but, unlike striated (voluntary) muscle fibres, its fibres are branched. The branching and interlacing of neighbouring fibres is ideally suited to that of an elastic bag-shaped organ which is repeatedly contracting and expanding. (See *Muscle*) and (Plates 7, 16, 17, 56 and 57).

Hemichordata. Sub-phylum of *Chordata* containing the worm-like, burrowing acorn worms (e.g. *Balanoglossus*) and a few other small animals. They look very unlike other chordates but they show the diagnostic features – gill slits, notochord, and hollow dorsal nerve cord, although the latter two are confined to a small anterior region of the body. All are marine and the larvae show striking similarities with those of echinoderms. Some zoologists place the graptolites (q.v.) with the hemichordates. (See *Cephalochordata; Urochordata*) and (Plate 116).

Hemimetabola. (=*Exopterygota*). (See Page 268).

Hemiptera. A large order of exopterygote insects all with sucking mouths which are used to feed on the juices of plants or other animals. These insects are the true bugs. The majority are winged. There are two groups, sometimes regarded as separate orders. The Heteroptera are characterised by a hardening of the fore-wings although the tip remains membranous. At rest these hardened wings cover the membranous fore-wings and overlap each other. Some Homoptera show hardening of the fore-wings but if so, the tips are hardened too, and the wings are folded roofwise over the body when at rest. Homopterans are always land-living and plant feeders (e.g. aphids, cicadas, and frog-hoppers) whereas heteropterans include the water bugs and many blood-suckers. (See *Insecta*) and (Plates 58 and 114).

HOMOPTERA FOREWING (ABOVE) AND HINDWING (BELOW)

Homoptera. Forewings of uniform structure, may be harder than hindwings, but both pairs are membranous, and held in a sloping position over body.

HETEROPTERA FOREWING (ABOVE) AND HINDWING (BELOW)

Heteroptera. Fore-wings are not membranous and form horny regions near the body.

Hepatic. Concerning the liver. E.g. Hepatic Portal Vein carrying blood to the liver.

Herbivore. Any plant-eating animal.

Heredity. The study of the way in which characteristics are passed on from one generation to the next or inherited. Gregor Mendel, a monk living in the middle part of the 19th century, was the first person to study this subject systematically and the term 'mendelism' is sometimes used for heredity.

Mendel experimented with garden peas which he grew in the garden of his monastery. He noticed that not all the plants were alike: some were tall, others short; some seeds were round while others were wrinkled. These characters were clear-cut and obvious and Mendel decided to study them individually. The fact that the flowers are normally self-pollinated was a great help to Mendel, for his flowers were not contaminated by unknown pollen. Mendel selected plants with opposed characters (e.g. tall and short) and bred them individually until he was satisfied that he had true-breeding lines, i.e. the tall plants produced only more tall ones. He then transferred pollen from tall plants to flowers of short ones and vice-versa. In both cases the next generation of plants (the first filial or F_1 generation) were all tall – the shortness characteristic of one parent had been suppressed, and Mendel stated that tallness is produced by some 'factor' in the cells which is dominant to a factor for shortness; the factor for shortness is said to be recessive. When the plants of the F_1 generation were allowed to set seed naturally (i.e. by self-fertilisation), Mendel found that in every case he got about three times as many tall as short plants. Obviously the shortness factor was present in the F_1 plants and was passed on in the pollen or ovule to some of their offspring – the second filial or F_2 generation.

The constant appearance of the 3 : 1 ratio in the F_2 generation activated Mendel's mathematical mind and led him to what is now called Mendel's First Law. He suggested that the tallness and shortness factors carried in the F_1 generation separate during the formation of sex-cells so that half of the gametes carry the tallness factor and half carry the shortness factor.

Mendel's First Law, often called the law of segregation, states that only one of two opposed characters can be carried as a factor in a single sex-cell, i.e. in a pollen grain or an ovule.

If we accept this we can show how the 3 : 1 ratio is produced. Let the tallness factor be called T and the shortness factor, t. As Mendel started with true-breeding lines the original tall plants would produce gametes with only T, and the short ones only t. When these combine in the F_1 generation we have Tt. Because T is dominant all the plants are tall. According to Mendel's First Law, when these plants produce pollen and ovules there will be equal numbers of T and t gametes. Any pollen grain may fuse with any ovule when the pollen is released, and there are therefore four possible combinations in the F_2 generation – TT,Tt, tT, and tt. Three of these combinations contain T and these plants are therefore tall while the remaining quarter are short. Two-thirds of the tall plants contain the shortness factor and, when self-pollinated, produce the monohybrid 3 : 1, tall : short ratio. The other tall F_2 plants, however, are pure-breeding as are all the short ones – they have only one type of factor and are called homozygotes. The impure plants (i.e. those with two different factors) are heterozygotes.

Similar results are obtained with any pair of opposed characters. Mendel then went on experimenting with peas which differed in two characters. He chose two types of plant – one with round, yellow seeds (RY), the other with wrinkled, green seeds (wg), and cross pollinated them. The resulting F_1 generation plants all had round, yellow seeds, so we can see that the factor for round seeds is dominant to that for wrinkled and that yellow dominates green. When the F_2 generation plants grew up and produced seed they showed all four characters in every possible combination. The proportions were very

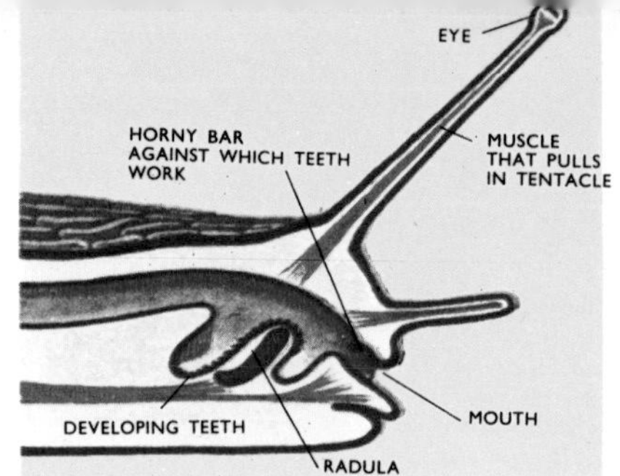

PLATE 52

GASTEROPODA

Section through the head region of a snail showing the two antennae and the radula of horny teeth.

THE GEOLOGICAL TIME SCALE PERIODS AND SYSTEMS AND DERIVATION OF NAMES				DATES IN Y (BEFORE P
PHANEROZOIC EON (*PHANEROS* = EVIDENT, AND *ZOON* = LIFE)	CENOZOIC ERA (*KAINOS* = RECENT)	**QUATERNARY PERIOD** THIS IS A CONVENIENT EXTENSION OF THE TERTIARY PERIOD AND MAY BE INCLUDED IN THE LATTER	RECENT OR HOLOCENE EPOCH (*HOLOS* = COMPLETE)	ABOUT 25,000
			PLEISTOCENE EPOCH (*PLEISTON* = MOST)	ABOUT 1,000,0
		TERTIARY PERIOD THE NAME RESULTS FROM AN OLD DIVISION OF STRATA INTO PRIMITIVE SECONDARY AND TERTIARY. THE NAMES OF THE SUB-DIVISIONS OF THE TERTIARY AND QUATERNARY PERIODS REFERS TO THE PROPORTION OF MODERN MARINE SHELLS OCCURRING AS FOSSILS IN THE ROCKS OF THAT AGE	PLIOCENE EPOCH (*PLEION* = MORE)	12,000,0
			MIOCENE EPOCH (*MEION* = LESS)	25,000,0
			OLIGOCENE EPOCH (*OLIGOS* = FEW)	40,000,0
			EOCENE EPOCH (*EOS* = DAWN)	60,000,0
			PALAEOCENE EPOCH (*PALAIOS* = ANCIENT)	70,000,00
	MESOZOIC ERA (*MESOS* = MIDDLE)	**CRETACEOUS PERIOD**	FROM *CRETA* = CHALK	135,000,0
		JURASSIC PERIOD	FROM THE *JURA* MOUNTAINS ON THE FRANCO-SWISS BORDER	170,000,0
		TRIASSIC PERIOD	FROM THE *THREEFOLD* DIVISION IN GERMANY	200,000,0
	PALAEOZOIC ERA (*PALAIOS* = ANCIENT) UPPER	**PERMIAN PERIOD**	FROM THE *PERM* AREA OF RUSSIA, WEST OF THE URALS	230,000,0
		CARBONIFEROUS PERIOD *CARBON-BEARING* (COAL) — DIVISIONS RECOGNISED IN NORTH AMERICA	**PENNSYLVANIAN PERIOD**	255,000,0
			MISSISSIPPIAN PERIOD	280,000,0
		DEVONIAN PERIOD	FROM *DEVON* (MARINE SEDIMENTS)	325,000,0
	PALAEOZOIC ERA LOWER	**SILURIAN PERIOD**	FROM THE *SILURES*, AN ANCIENT TRIBE OF THE WELSH BORDER	360,000,0
		ORDOVICIAN PERIOD	FROM THE *ORDOVICES*, AN ANCIENT TRIBE OF NORTH WALES	425,000,0
		CAMBRIAN PERIOD	FROM *CAMBRIA*, THE ROMAN NAME FOR WALES	500,000,0
CRYPTOZOIC EON	**PROTEROZOIC ERA** (*PROTEROS* = EARLIER) **ARCHAEOZOIC ERA** (*ARCHAEOS* = PRIMEVAL) **EOZOIC ERA** (*EOS* = DAWN) (THE ABOVE ARE FORMAL ERAS)			THE CRYPTO EON EMBRA ABOUT 80% GEOLOGICAL TIME

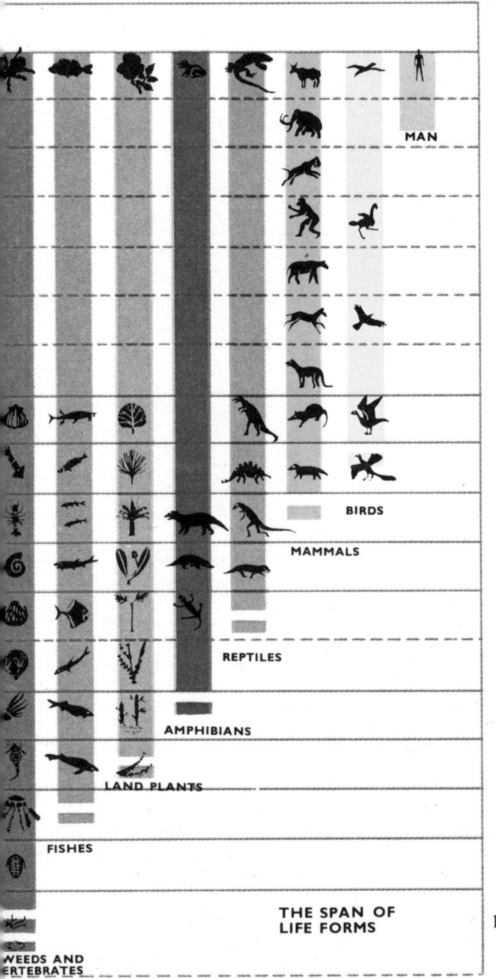

Chart showing the main divisions of Geological Time and the periods at which the main forms of life appeared.

close to 9 round, yellow: 3 round, green: 3 wrinkled, yellow: 1 wrinkled, green. Mendel then stated his second law known as the law of independent assortment: the factor for each one of a pair of opposed characters may combine with any one of another pair when the sex-cells are formed. He reasoned that the impure F_1 plants would be RYwg and that they would produce the gametes RY, Rg, wY and wg. Rw and Yg cannot be produced because according to the first law a gamete can carry only one of a pair of opposed factors. Any pollen grain can again combine with any ovule and from the table (Plate 58) we can see how Mendel explained the 9 : 3 : 3 : 1 dihybrid ratio on this basis. Whenever R and Y occur together there will be round yellow seeds, for these two factors are dominant.

When R is absent they will be wrinkled, and when Y is absent they will be green.

When Mendel published his results in 1865 scientists paid little attention to his work, and it was not until after 1900 that the truth of his statements was realised. By then the chromosomes had been discovered and it was realised that these were the 'vehicles on which Mendel's 'factors' could be carried. The factors are the genes that we now know to be carried on the chromosomes.

The behaviour of the chromosomes when sex-cells are formed is exactly as Mendel had suggested in his laws governing the behaviour of his 'factors'. When sex-cells are formed the chromosome pairs separate, one of each pair going to each sex-cell. Therefore, even if the parent cells contain two opposed factors, the sex-cell can have only one or the other, as Mendel stated in his first law. Again, when sex-cells are formed, any one of a pair of chromosomes can go to a sex-cell with either one of any other pair and so Mendel's second law is obeyed as far as the chromosomes are concerned. But it does not always hold true for the genes.

Because of the enormous number of genes necessary to control all the features of an animal it is obvious that each chromosome must carry a large number of genes. Because they are linked in this way the genes on each chromosome do not normally separate when sex-cells are formed.

Wing length and body-colour are linked in *Drosophila*. When a long-winged, grey-bodied insect is crossed with a short-winged, black-bodied one, the first generation will all be long-winged and grey, because these factors are dominant. In the second generation, without linkage, according to Mendel's Second Law, one would expect long-winged black flies and short-winged grey ones to appear. However, because the genes are linked, only long-winged grey and short-winged black appear – in the ratio 3 : 1. The linked genes therefore act as one gene and produce the monohybrid ratio associated with a single pair of characters.

Mendel was very lucky in his choice of characters for his experiments with peas. Had he selected any that were linked he may not have arrived at his second law.

Mendel's laws can be used to predict the characteristics of the offspring of particular animals as long as the genetic make-up of the parents is known. This has enormous practical importance in the breeding of new and improved strains of plants and farm animals.

The examples so far have been concerned with complete dominance of one gene over another. There are, however, instances of incomplete dominance. When the opposed genes occur together in an impure individual they act together to produce an intermediate form. Some genes in the Andalusian fowl act in this way. This chicken has a fine blue sheen and is in demand by breeders. It occurs when black and splashed white forms are crossed. The genes controlling coloration act together to produce the blue. When the blue ones are crossed among themselves the results are one quarter black, one quarter white and one half blue. This is the monohybrid 3 : 1 ratio modified because there is incomplete dominance.

Many animals and the majority of plants are *hermaphrodite* – i.e. they have both male and female features. In those where the sexes are separate a genetic mechanism normally decides whether an individual may be male or female. Although it is usually stated that man has 23 pairs of chromosomes, there are, in the male, only 22 pairs, plus two odd ones called the sex-chromosomes or the X and Y chromosomes. The female has two X chromosomes, making 23 true pairs. When the sex-cells are formed the pairs separate so that each female cell (egg) has an X chromosome. Half the male cells will contain a Y chromosome and the other half an X. If a male cell containing an X chromosome fuses with an egg-cell a female will develop, whereas a male cell containing Y will produce a male embryo. Because the X and Y are present in equal numbers boys and girls will be produced in nearly equal numbers too. The female is not the XX sex in all animals. In birds the hen is XY while the male is XX. (See Plates 59 and 60).

Hermaphrodite. Having both testes and ovaries in one individual. Many animal groups, notably earthworms and snails, are hermaphrodite and special features have been evolved which prevent self-fertilisation. (See *Intersex; Gynandromorph*).

Heterocercal Tail. Upturned or asymmetrical tail typical of sharks. (See Plate 35).

Heterodont. Having teeth of various types (i.e. mammals) as opposed to the homodont condition of reptiles whose teeth differ only in size. (See Plate 29).

Heterotrophic. Needing complex organic food. All animals are heterotrophic and obtain their food from plants or other animals. Plants, however, can manufacture their food requirements from simple inorganic substances and are said to be *autotrophic*.

Heterozygous. (See *Gene*).

Hexapoda (=*Insecta*).

Hibernation. In cold and temperate regions, many animals disappear at the beginning of winter. They may disappear because they cannot withstand the cold, or because they are unable to obtain food during the cold season. Many birds migrate to warmer lands but among other animals, hibernation is common. This is a state of inactivity or deep sleep during which the body processes slow down almost to a stop. The body temperature, even in mammals, falls to within a degree or two of that of their immediate surroundings.

Aquatic animals do not normally hibernate although many become lethargic during cold weather. Most soil-dwelling animals merely burrow deeper to avoid the cold, but many free-living invertebrates hide away for the winter. Probably the majority of insects pass the winter as eggs which are very resistant to drought and cold, but many overwinter as larvae, pupae, or adults.

Among vertebrates, amphibians and reptiles are well-known hibernators. Frogs, tortoises, snakes and lizards all bury themselves away from the effect of frost. They often huddle together and this habit undoubtedly helps to keep their temperature a degree or two above that of the surroundings. Some of these animals seem able to expel water from their tissues. This makes the remaining fluids more concentrated and lowers their freezing point. The animals can then endure temperatures below 0°C without becoming frozen solid.

True hibernation is not known among birds although the poor-will, an American nightjar, has recently been found to pass the winter in a

PLATE 54

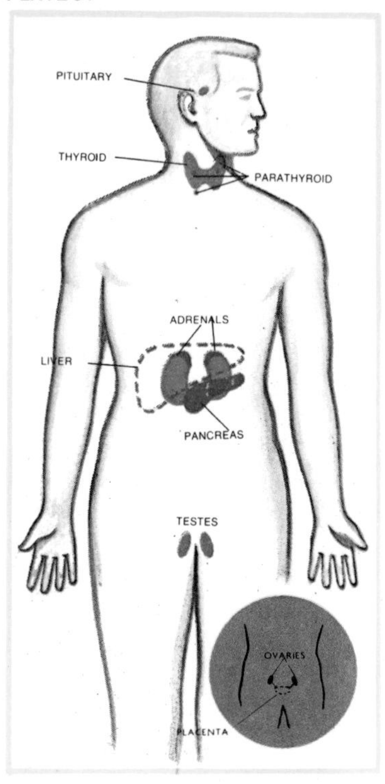

GLAND

Diagram showing the main endocrine glands of the human body.

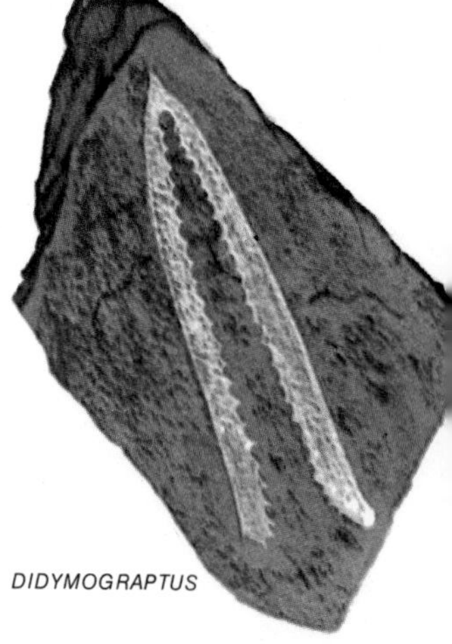

GRAPTOLITE

Two Ordovician graptolite fossils.

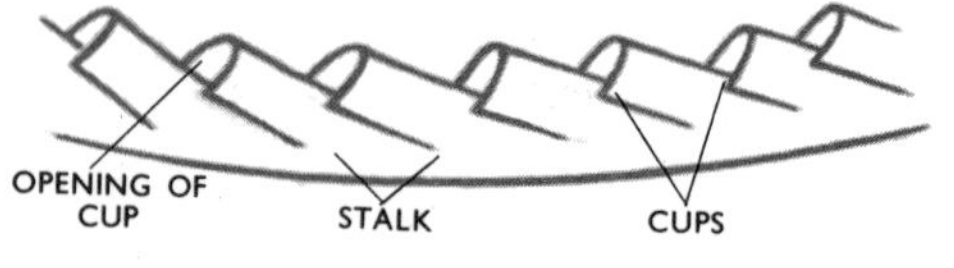

GRAPTOLITE

Highly magnified diagram of a graptolite fossil.

GYNANDROMORPH

Common blue butterfly in which one half is male (blue), the other female.

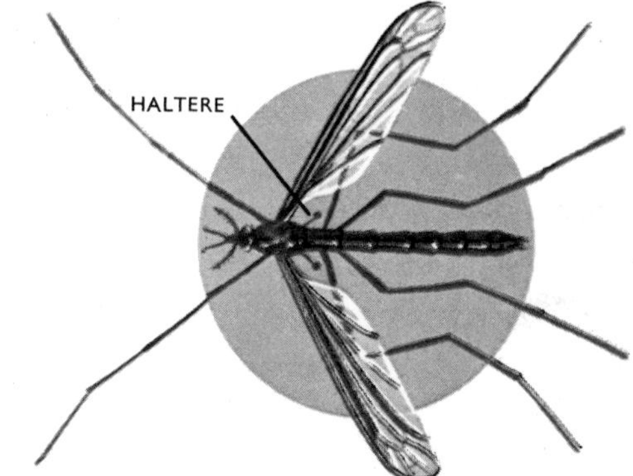

HALTERE

Halteres are modified wings and are concerned with balance in flight.

CIRCULATION OF BLOOD

HEART

DORSAL DIAPHRAGM

VENTRAL DIAPHRAGM

HAEMOCOEL

HAEMOCOEL

Diagrammatic insect section showing the haemocoel—the body cavity which is really part of the blood system.

state of semi-hibernation. The temperature of these sleeping birds is about 65°F instead of the normal 100° of the active bird. Many mammals, too, hide away and remain drowsy during the winter months. Bears, badgers, tree squirrels and others go to sleep for varying periods of time, but they wake periodically and their temperature does not drop more than a few degrees below normal. True hibernation, where the body temperature falls almost to that of the surroundings, is found in only a few groups of mammals. The egg-laying monotremes and some of the opossums are known to hibernate in cold winters. Bats of temperate and cold climates hibernate because they cannot catch insects in winter. Bats are peculiar, however, in that their temperature drops considerably every time they sleep, even in the summertime. In this torpid condition they use less energy and they can be more active when they are awake.

Some insect-eating mammals – notably the hedgehog – and many rodents (e.g. dormice, ground-squirrels and hamsters) also go into a deep winter sleep. Even so, these hibernators often wake up and may feed on stored food. It seems that periodic waking is essential for getting rid of accumulated waste.

Before they go into hibernation, animals often put on weight, in the form of fatty deposits. This extra material is drawn upon during the winter sleep. Others store food on which to draw when they wake at intervals. It is not known what stimulus causes these preparations, nor are the physiological processes of hibernation fully understood. Temperature and lack of food probably contribute to the onset of hibernation and the length of the day may possibly be concerned. There must also be some internal control because close relatives of hibernating animals often remain active in the cold season.

At the start of hibernation the temperature-regulating mechanism is disturbed and the body temperature falls. The regulating mechanism may fail in response to prolonged cold. A short cold spell will not necessarily lead to hibernation. As the body temperature falls, the other activities slow down. Less oxygen is used, less food material is used, breathing slows down and the heartbeat rate also slows down. Its metabolic rate is less than a thirtieth (even as low as one hundredth) of that of the active animal. These changes are probably the result of hormone action. All the while, however, the nervous system is in control. If the outside temperature drops too much, the heart-beat quickens and the body temperature increases to maintain life.

The end of hibernation is brought about by some stimulus such as the temperature rise in the surroundings, and is probably controlled by the nervous system. The body processes increase their rate and shivering often occurs – producing more heat. In the hamster, an hour or two is all that is necessary for the animal to wake and regain its normal temperature. Bats possibly need an even shorter time. During the waking process a great deal of energy is used and so, although a hibernating animal does wake periodically, too frequent disturbances can be fatal. An animal will quickly use up its supplies of fat and, unless it has a store of food on which to draw, it will soon perish. (See *Aestivation*).

Hinge Joint. A joint so arranged that movement can occur in one plane only. The knee and elbow joints are of this type. (See *Ball-and-Socket Joint*) and (Plate 9).

Hirudinea. Class of *Annelida* (q.v.), with marine, fresh-water, and terrestrial leeches. The body is relatively short and composed of a fixed number of segments, but the visible rings do not correspond with the segments as in earthworms, and except for one genus, there are no chaetae. Both ends of the leech bear a sucker – the front one surrounding the mouth. The coelom is reduced to narrow tubes, the rest being filled in with tissue. The mouth is equipped with teeth which tear off the

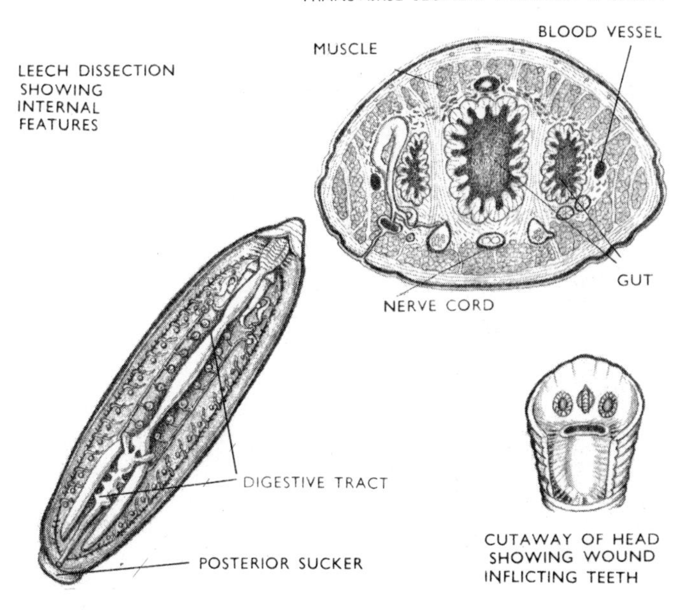

leech's food or, in blood sucking forms, make the initial wounds. Blood-sucking leeches have a number of pouches in the gut in which blood is stored, sometimes for a long time. Like the earthworms, leeches are hermaphrodite. (See Page 266).

Histology. The study of the structure and development of tissues.

Holometabola (=*Endopterygota*). (See Page 268).

Holostei. Order of ray-finned fishes that first appeared in Permian times but now almost completely replaced by modern teleosts. Two genera survive –*Lepidosteus,* the gar-pike, and *Amia,* the bowfin–both of which live in the Great Lakes of America. The swim bladder is used as a breathing organ to some extent. (See Plate 117).

Holothuroidea. Sea cucumbers. (See *Echinodermata)* and (Page 273).

Holozoic. Feeding on solid organic material.

Homeostasis. The maintainance of constant conditions within the body, e.g. constant temperature and constant composition of the blood.

Homodont. (See *Heterodont*).

Homoiothermy. Maintenance of a constant body temperature regardless of the surrounding temperature, a condition found only in birds and mammals. The so-called 'cold-blooded' animals whose temperatures vary with that of the surroundings are *poikilothermic*.

Homologous Chromosomes. Each body cell has two sets of chromosomes (q.v.), which can be arranged in pairs. The members of each pair are said to be homologous and each carries genes affecting the same features.

PLATE 56

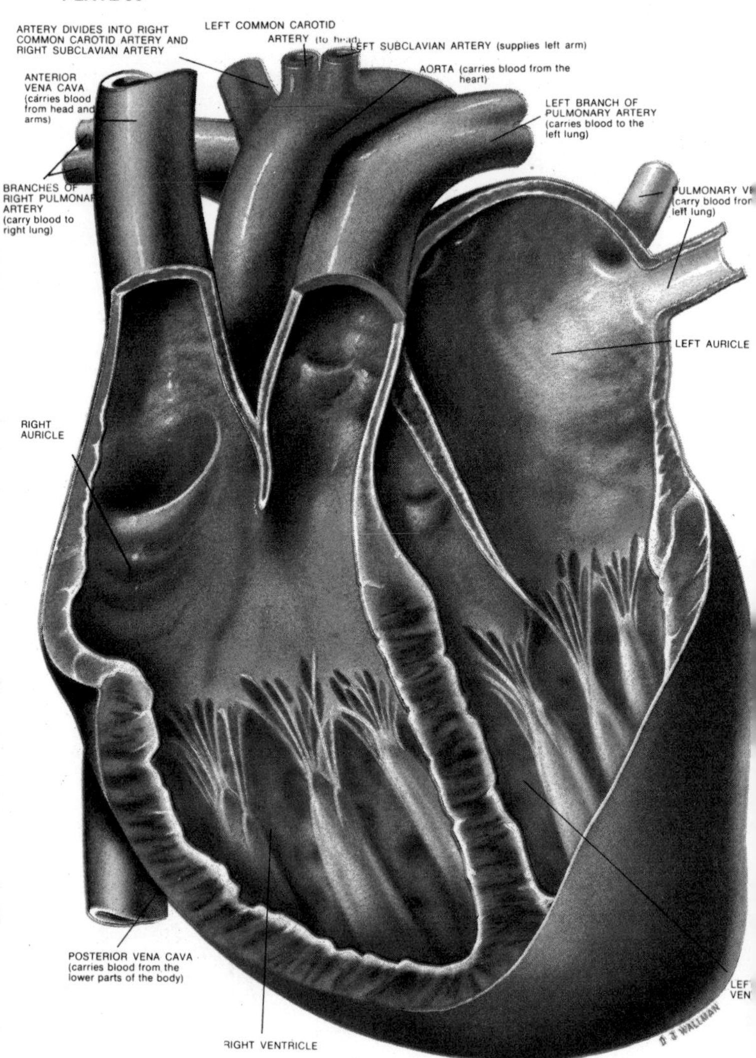

HEART

A section through the human heart.

he Heart Cycle

PLATE 57

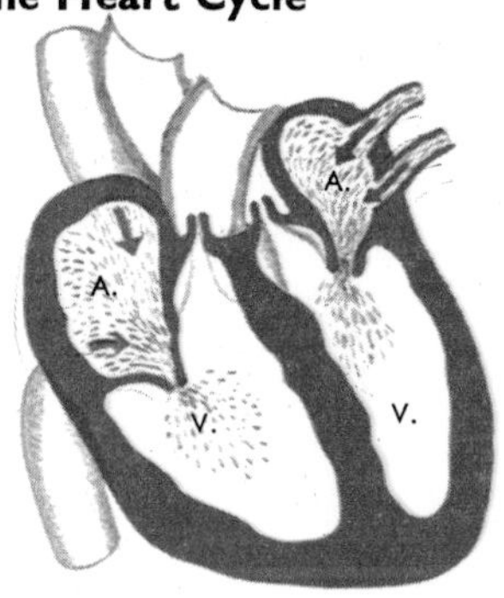

Between heartbeats (i.e. when the heart is relaxed) both auricles (A) are filled with blood. A little enters the ventricles (V).

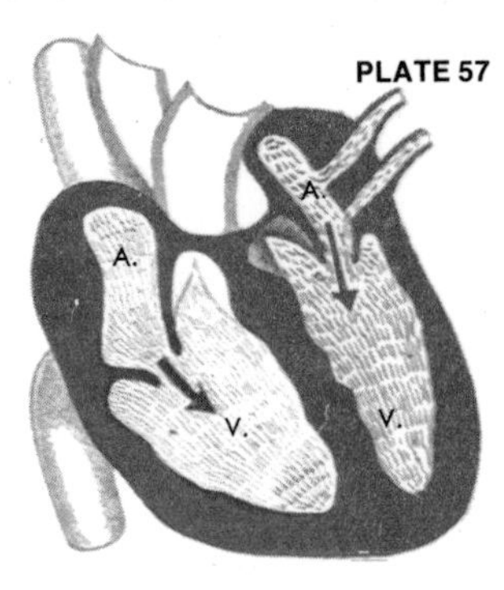

The valve between each auricle and ventricle opens as the auricles contract and the ventricles are filled with blood.

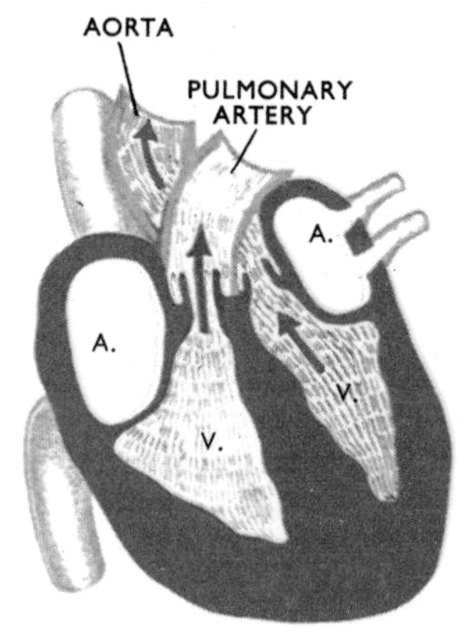

The ventricles contract, forcing blood out of the heart through the valves in the aorta and pulmonary artery.

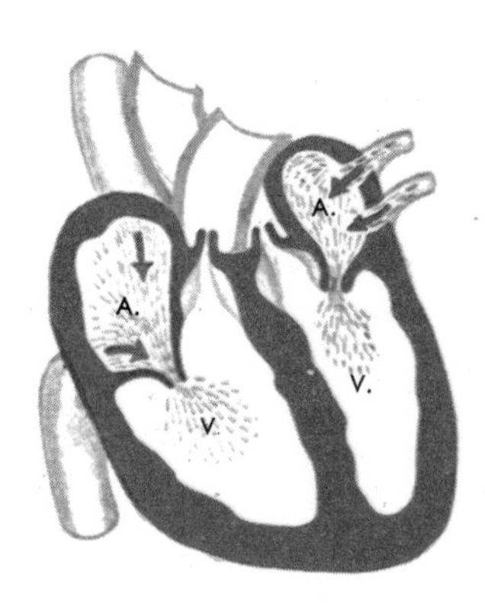

The heart relaxes once more. The auricles fill with blood and the cycle is ready to start again.

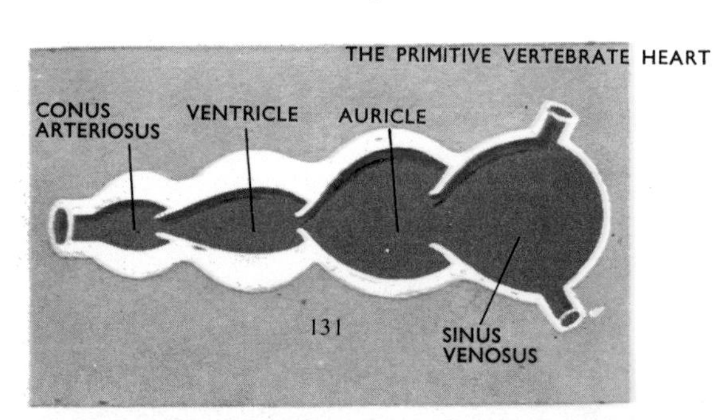

THE PRIMITIVE VERTEBRATE HEART

Homologous Organs. Organs of different animals which have the same fundamental structure and/or develop from corresponding parts of the embryos. The arm of a man is clearly homologous with the wing of a bird or the flipper of a whale, or even the fin of a lung-fish. The bone structure is basically similar and so is their embryological development. But homologous organs are not always similar in structure or in function: the tiny bones that transmit sound in the mammalian middle ear are homologous with certain bones that are concerned with the articulation of the jaw in lower vertebrates. They arise in the same way in the embryo but follow different paths of development. If organs are homologous it implies that the animals concerned have a common ancestor and that a feature of that ancestor has evolved along two or more different lines to produce the homologous organs. (See *Analogous Organs*) and (Plates 27 and 61).

Homozygous. (See *Gene*).

Honeybee. (See *Bee*).

Hormone. A complicated substance produced by certain cells (normally collected into glands) that is released into the bloodstream continuously or periodically. Many hormones are known – e.g. adrenaline, insulin, thyroxine – each with a specific composition and activity. Hormones are extremely important in the regulation of the internal activity of the body. (See *Adrenal Gland, Thyroid Gland; Pituitary Gland; Pancreas; Parathyroid Gland; Thymus*).

Host. Organism that is being attacked by a parasite. A dog is host to the fleas in its hair and a man suffering from malaria is host to the malarial parasites in his blood.

Humerus. Bone of the upper fore-limb. (See Page 217).

Hybrid. An organism resulting from the mating of two different species. Only closely related species can mate and produce offspring and even then the offspring itself is normally unable to reproduce because its two sets of chromosomes do not match and cannot therefore produce sex-cells. The mule, offspring of a horse and an ass, is one of the best known animal hybrids.

Hydra. Small, freshwater coelenterate of class *Hydrozoa* (q.v.). (See Plate 61).

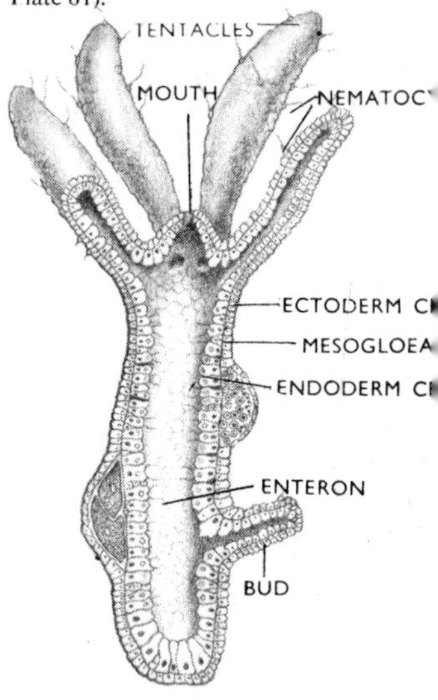

VERTICAL SECTION THROUGH HYDRA

Hydrozoa. Class of *Coelenterata* (q.v.). Usually colonial and showing a well-marked alternation of generations, although *Hydra* itself is an exception to both of these rules. *Obelia* is typical of the class. The Portuguese-man-of-war (*Physalia*) also belongs to this class and each 'individual' is, in fact, a floating colony composed of numerous polyps. (See Plate 107).

Hymenoptera. A large order of insects including the bees, wasps, ants, sawflies, and ichneumon flies. There

phyta, one of the two major divi-
s of the Hymenoptera. This group
udes the primitive members. None
social insects. The best known forms
probably the wood wasps which have
r ovipositors for wood boring.

Pamphilus sp.

Sirex gigas

crita. This division of the Hymenop-
includes all the higher forms. They
characterised by the 'wasp-waist'
ch is lacking in the Symphyta.

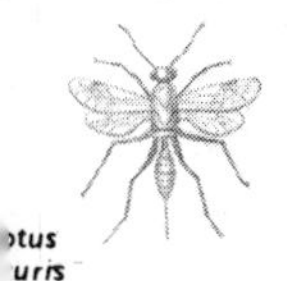

otus
uris

Parasitic chalcid

micoidea (Ants). All the members of
sub-group of the Apocrita are social
ns. The number of different forms of
viduals is remarkable, over 20 being
wn.

Acanthomyops

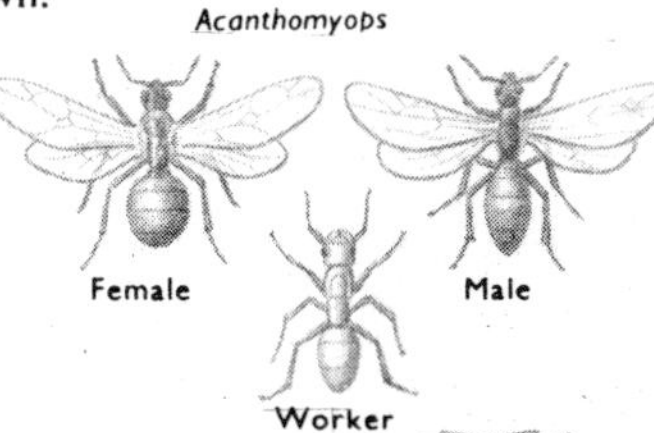

poidea (Wasps).
true wasps,
be solitary or
al forms.

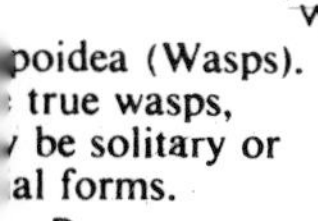

Wasp

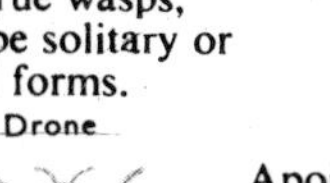

Drone

Apoidea (Bees). This group includes both solitary and social forms.

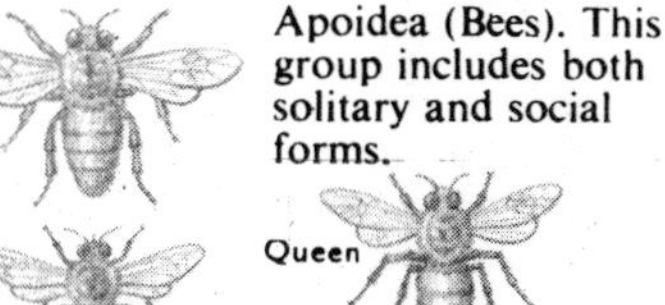

are two pairs of membranous wings with reduced venation. The larvae are generally legless and metamorphosis is complete. The biting mandibles are retained in all members of the group but other parts of the head are often modified for sucking up nectar, etc. There is always an ovipositor, modified for boring or cutting into plants, and sometimes modified as a sting.

There are two sub-orders: Symphyta, which contains more primitive forms such as sawflies and wood wasps which do not have the 'wasp-waist' characteristic of the other sub-order – Apocrita – which contains the parasitic ichneumon flies as well as the bees, wasps, and ants, many of which are social insects. (See *Insecta, Bee*) and (Plate 87) and (Page 268).

Hyoid Arch. *Visceral arch* (q.v.), behind the jaws of fishes. It has an interesting evolutionary history.

Hyperparasite. Parasite that lives in or on another parasite.

Hypoglossal Nerve. Twelfth *cranial nerve* (q.v.), of vertebrates. Found only in amniotes, it serves the tongue. In fishes, the corresponding nerve arises from the spinal cord and serves the muscles under the pharynx.

Hypopharynx. A structure in the mouths of certain insects. It forms an important part of the sucking appartus of the *mosquito* (q.v.).

Hyracoidea. An order of small mammals – conies or hyraxes – that show in their teeth and some other features a perhaps unexpected relationship to elephants. They are herbivorous and are found over large parts of Africa and the Middle East. (See Plate 123–12).

Ichneumon Fly. Parasitic insect of order *Hymenoptera* (q.v.). Lays eggs in larvae of other insects.

Ichthyosauria. An order of extinct, fish-like reptiles abundant in mesozoic times. (See *Reptilia*) and (Plate 119–4).

PLATE 58

HEMIPTERA

This insect order (the bugs) is characterised by the piercing sucking mouthparts used for feeding on plant and animal juices.

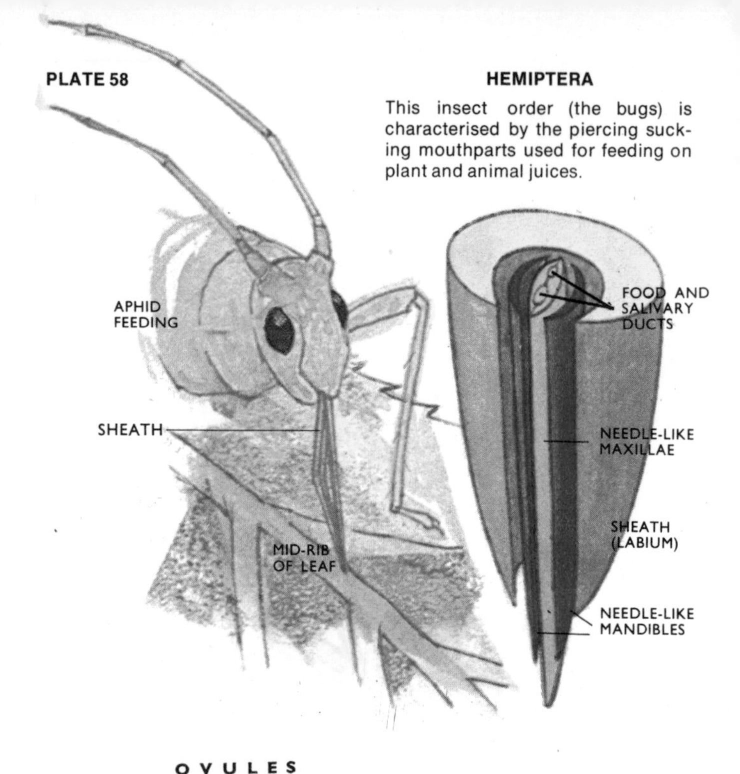

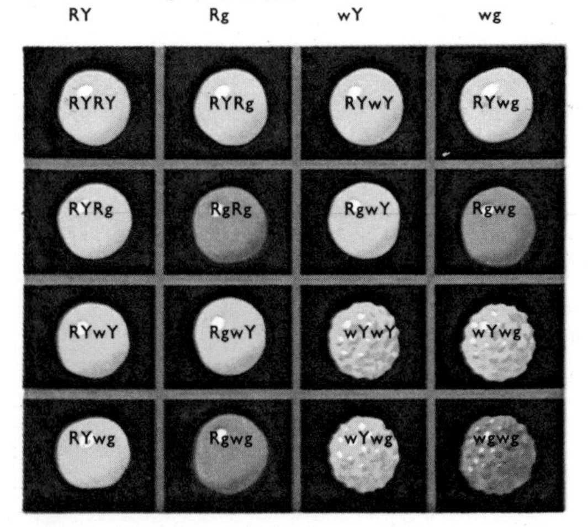

HEREDITY

When round, yellow and wrinkled, green seeded pea plants are crossed the F generation produces 4 types of gamete which combine in every possible way to give the 9:3:3:1 dihybrid ratio.

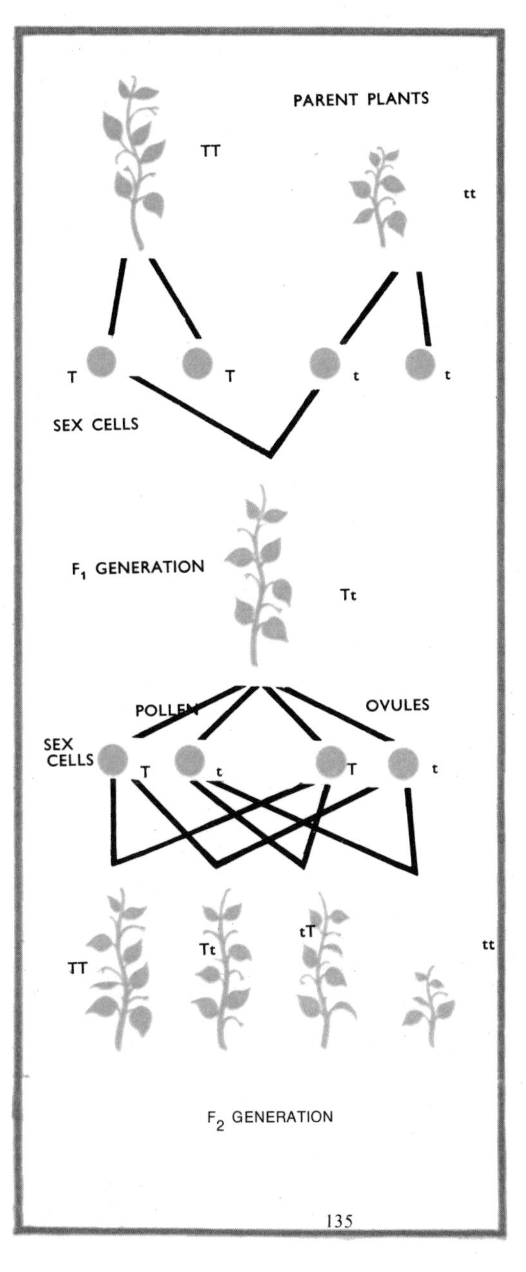

PLATE 59

HEREDITY

Mendel's original experiments with peas. Crossing pure tall with pure short plants he obtained all tall plants. The gene for tallness is dominant to that for shortness. When hybrids are crossed, tall and short plants are produced in the ratio 3:1 – the monohybrid ratio. Of the tall plants one third are pure, the rest impure, i.e. containing both 'tall' and 'short' genes.

Ileum. Last part of the vertebrate small intestine. (See *Alimentary Canal*).

Ilium. That part of the pelvic girdle (q.v.), that is attached to the backbone.

Imago. Final stage of insects life-history – a mature adult. (See Plate 63).

Immunity. Ability to resist attack by or the effect of a parasite.

Implantation. The attachment of the mammalian embryo to the uterine wall.

Impulse. A signal passed along a nerve fibre. It consists basically of an electrical disturbance set up initially by the stimulation of a sense organ or by a reaction within the brain.

Incisor. One of the chisel-shaped cutting teeth at the front of the mammalian jaw. In primitive mammals there are 12 incisors but most mammals have less than this: man has eight while elephants have only two – these are in the upper jaw and are modified as tusks. (See *Dental Formula*).

Incus. One of the mammalian ear-ossicles (See *Ear*), derived from the quadrate bone of lower vertebrates.

Indigenous. Native to a particular area.

Innominate Bone. (See *Pelvic Girdle*).

Inquiline. An animal that shares another's home without interfering in any way with the life of the other animal. There is, for example, a tiny white woodlouse that lives in the nests of certain ants. The ants seem to ignore the woodlouse and, apart from perhaps eating scraps, the woodlouse seems to have no beneficial effect. (See *Symbiosis; Commensalism*).

Insecta. This class of arthropods is the largest of all animal groups with something like a million known species and many more certainly yet to be discovered. Yet even this vast number

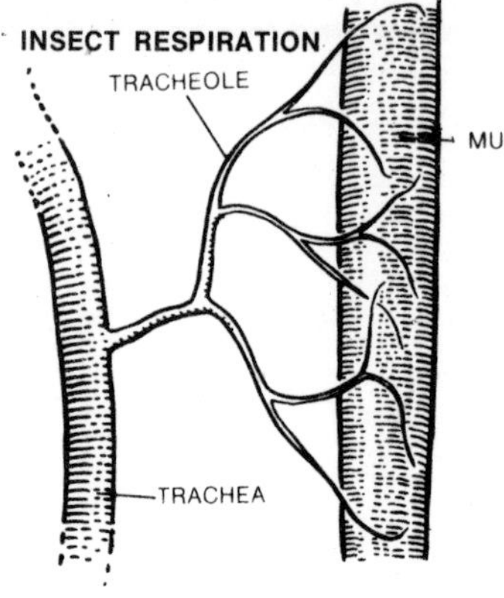

can be reduced to a fundamental pattern.

The body has three regions: head, thorax and abdomen. The head bears one pair of antennae, a pair of compound eyes and a number of mouth-parts which assist in feeding. Behind the head, the thorax bears three pairs of legs and usually two pairs of wings. The abdomen has no limbs. All adult insects breathe air and have numerous fine tubes (tracheae) branching throughout the body. The tracheae carry air to the tissues from the spiracles along the sides of the body. Insects are limited in size by the tracheal system as air cannot diffuse efficiently for more than a short distance along these tubes. Insect bodies are therefore never very thick. The African Goliath beetle is one of the largest insects, with a body about four inches long and two inches thick. Butterflies and moths with large wing spans have relatively narrow bodies.

Most insects lay eggs but a few, however, give birth to active young. Because of its hard cuticle, an insect cannot grow steadily as a vertebrate does. Periodically the insect gets rid of the old 'skin' and replaces it with a new larger one. The new cuticle is formed under the old and then by swallowing air or water, the insect bursts the old one. The new cuticle soon hardens on contact with the air and then, by getting rid of the excess

INSECT CLASSIFICATION (after Imms)

Sub Class		*Order*	*Examples*
Aptery-gota		Thysanura	Silver fish
		Diplura	Small soil-living insects
		Protura	Small soil-living insects
		Collembola	Springtails
Ptery-gota	Hemi-metabola	Ephemeroptera	May-flies
		Odonata	Dragonflies
		Plecoptera	Stone-flies
		Grylloblattodea	Wingless soil insects
		Phasmida	Stick and leaf insects
		Orthoptera	Grasshoppers, crickets and locusts
		Dermaptera	Earwigs
		Embioptera	Web-spinners of tropical countries
		Dictyoptera	Cockroaches and praying mantids
		Isoptera	Termites
		Zoraptera	Little-known soil and bark insects
		Psocoptera	Aphid-like insects living on trees
		Mallophaga	Biting lice of birds
		Siphunculata	Sucking lice of mammals
		Hemiptera	Bed bugs, aphids, water boatmen
		Thysanoptera	Thrips, small insects often on flowers
	Holo-metabola	Neuroptera	Lacewing flies, ant lions
		Mecoptera	Scorpion flies
		Lepidoptera	Butterflies and moths
		Trichoptera	Caddis flies
		Diptera	Mosquitoes, house-flies
		Siphonaptera	Fleas
		Hymenoptera	Ants, bees, wasps
		Coleoptera	Beetles
		Strepsiptera	Stylops – parasites of bees

air or water, the insect leaves enough room for the new growth period. The process of changing the skin (moulting) is called ecdysis. It normally occurs between three and eight times during the insect's life. Mayflies with a long growing stage may moult up to twenty times. When once the adult stage is reached, no further growth occurs. Frequently the young insect is very different from the adult. (Compare a caterpillar and an adult butterfly.) The young insect is, in this case, called a larva. Before it can assume the adult form it must go through a period of rest during which the necessary changes can occur. This period is the pupal period. The change from larval to adult form is called metamorphosis.

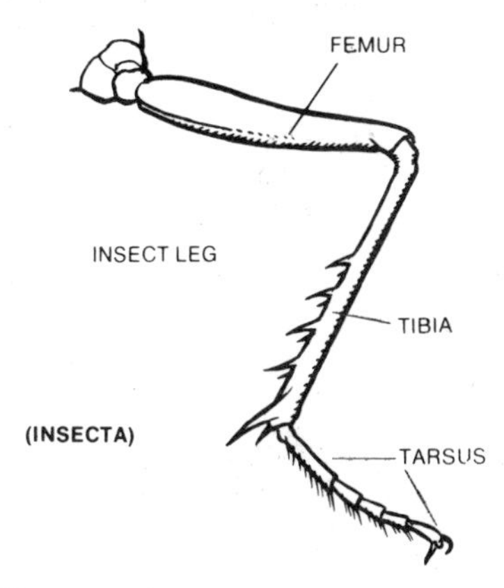

K

PLATE 60

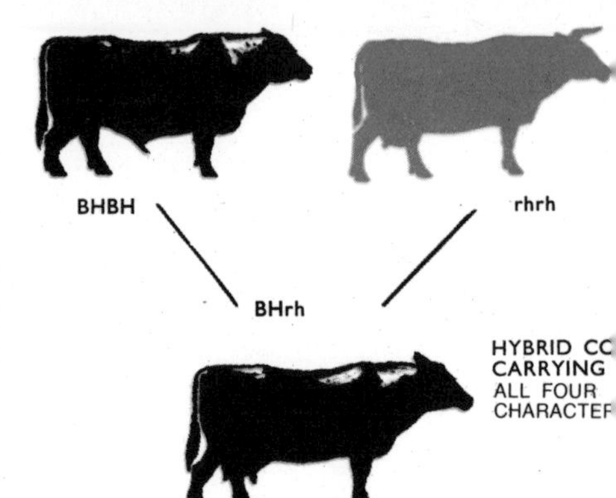

HEREDITY

Black and hornless (BH) characteristics dominate red and horned (rh) so that the hybrid is black and hornless.

SEX-CELLS

	BH	Bh	rH	rh
BH	BHBH	BHBh	BHrH	BHrh
Bh	BhBH	BhBh	BhrH	Bhrh
rH	rHBH	rHBh	rHrH	rHrh
rh	rhBH	rhBh	rhrH	rhrh

HEREDITY

When 2 BHrh cat are mated, four typ of sex-cells a formed and can jc in any combinatic This results in t four types shown the dihybrid ra 9:3:3:1.

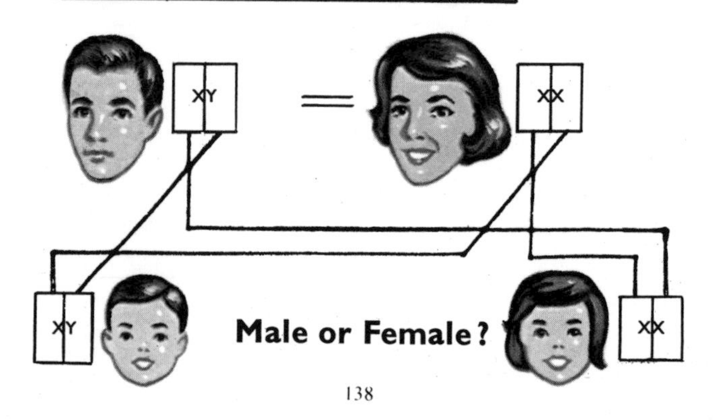

PLATE 61

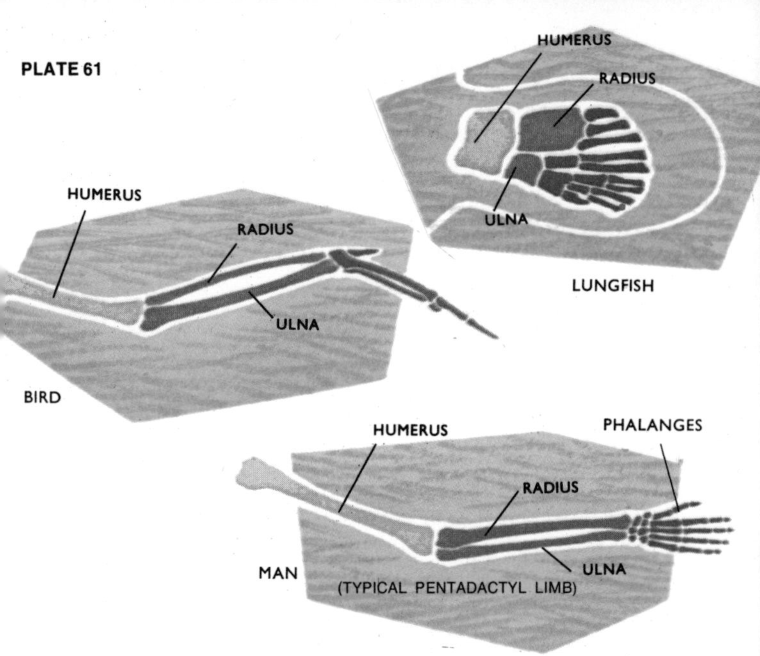

HOMOLOGOUS ORGANS

The fore-limbs of a lungfish, bird and man, although superficially different, develop from the same part of the embryo, and consist of basically similar bones. They are homologous.

HYDRA

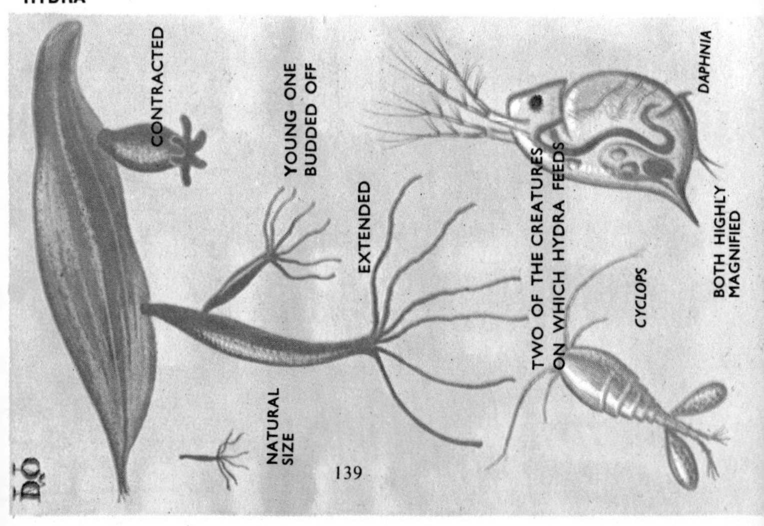

When the young insect is just a small version of the adult (e.g. a grasshopper) it develops gradually into an adult. This young form is called a nymph and its metamorphosis is called partial or incomplete, as opposed to the complete metamorphosis of a butterfly. The life-cycle from egg to adult may be very short – a housefly can, in warm conditions, develop from egg to adult in little more than a week. On the other hand, mayfly nymphs live for two years or more before the adult emerges for its brief life in the air. Some wood-boring moth larvae also live for several years before reaching maturity. Insects are not normally active in the colder months of the year. They may over-winter in any of the life stages.

Insects are very successful animals, having colonized land, water and air. Only the sea, with very few insect inhabitants, has proved a serious barrier to their spread. The main factor in their success on land has been the waterproof cuticle that allows them to inhabit dry places. Their small size enables them to exploit numerous habitats which are unsuitable for larger animals. A given area can support large numbers of insects because the individuals are small. These advantages, combined with the power of flight, have helped to establish insects firmly all over the Earth. The first insects appeared as long ago as the Devonian period. By Miocene times all the present day groups were in existence. (See *Geological Time Scale*).

Imms divided the insects into 29 orders arranged in two sub-classes. The first of these – the Apterygota – contains small, wingless insects. Most of them live in the soil or decaying vegetation although the household silverfish are included in the sub-class. The sub-class Pterygota has two divisions: the Hemimetabola (insects with incomplete metamorphosis) and the Holometabola (insects with complete metamorphosis). (See Plates 10, 11, 62–64, 113 and 114).

Insectivora. Order of mammals including hedgehog, moles, and shrews. They show many features of the primitive placental mammals – such as the full *dental formula* (q.v.), in most cases. They do not feed exclusively on insects – worms, slugs, and even vegetable matter do not come amiss to the hedgehog. (See Plate 122–6).

Instar. Any stage in an insect life-history between two moults.

Instinct. An inborn pattern of activity found in some form or other in almost all animals. Instincts account for much of animal behaviour – courtship displays, protective care of the young, migratory drives and reaction to dangers. The pattern of behaviour begins usually after a stimulus to one or more of the sense organs. Such a stimulus is called a releaser. A loud noise – and instinctively, animals take evasive action, fleeing or crouching motionless to the ground. Instincts like nest-building and web and cocoon spinning are perfect from the start. Caterpillars of different species of moth spin their own types of cocoon once only in their lives – but they do it perfectly. Young birds reared in isolation away from parents nevertheless build exactly similar nests even down to the material used. Other instincts, like Man's instinct to walk, take time and practice to become perfect. All members of a species will usually behave in much the same way to a stimulus. Instincts are just as much a part of an animal as the structures which identify its body.

Some instincts are always present in an animal – defensive attitudes and defensive colour changes for instance. Other instincts appear only at certain times. Such periodic occurrences of instinct are often due to the action of hormones. Marked changes in animal behaviour can often be brought about by upsetting the hormone balance.

The activity of the hormone does not itself directly cause a piece of behaviour. It makes possible one or a whole series of instinctive actions when certain outside signals are received from the outside world. At breeding periods for instance, a male bird may display to a female of the same species whereas the appearance of another male causes aggressive behaviour.

Sometimes instinctive drives may be so powerful that they produce behaviour without the usual outside stimulus. In the absence of a mate, captive birds and animals may display to their keepers instead.

Instincts are obviously of great value to animals. They provide a method of survival and a method of successfully breeding and rearing offspring. They have been built up over the ages by the process of natural selection. The individuals performing certain types of behaviour will survive to transmit them to their young. (See *Association; Habituation*) and (Plate 65).

Insulin. Hormone produced by the Islets of Langerhans in the pancreas (q.v.). It controls the metabolism of glucose sugar in the body and a deficiency of insulin leads to diabetes mellitus (sugar diabetes). Glucose is the body's fuel: it is burnt in the tissues to provide energy. Excess glucose absorbed from the food is normally stored in the liver and muscles as glycogen (q.v.). Insulin encourages this storage. As glucose is used up by the tissues, the level in the blood is maintained by the breakdown of glycogen but a deficiency of insulin results in the over-production of glucose by the liver and the consequent increase in the blood sugar level. The metabolism of fat and protein are also greatly disturbed and abnormally high quantities are broken down into glucose thus enhancing the effects due to the breakdown of glycogen. Insulin lack causes the over-production of glucose, but it also seems probable that the cells are unable to use carbohydrate in its absence or when reduced amounts of it are present. When insulin is deficient, protein and fat are broken down in place of carbohydrate as an alternative means of supplying energy. In a way not yet understood, insulin acts on the cells enabling them to use glucose for providing energy. (See Plate 86).

Inter- (=Between). An intercellular space is one between the cells.

Intersex. An individual animal whose features are neither male nor female, but part-way between the two, as a result of genetical disturbance or a disturbance of the body's hormones. Unlike the *gynandromorph* (q.v.), all the cells of the intersex are the same. (See *Hermaphrodite*).

Intestine. That part of *alimentary canal* (q.v.) which is concerned with digestion and absorption of food and with the reabsorption of water from the faeces.

Intra- (=Inside). Intracellular means inside the cells.

Invertebrata. Collective name for all those animals without backbones. The majority of animals are invertebrates, the backboned, or vertebrate animals being fishes, amphibians, reptiles, birds and mammals.

In Vitro. Biological experiments, such as the testing of digestive juices, that are not carried out in a living animal, are said to be performed *in vitro*. *In vivo* experiments are those performed with a living organism.

In Vivo. (See *In Vitro*).

Iris. Pigmented part of the eye that controls the amount of light falling on the retina. (See *Eye*).

Irritability. A property of all living things – the ability to react to a change or changes in the environment.

Ischium. Part of pelvic girdle (q.v.).

Islets of Langerhans. Insulin-secreting cells of the pancreas. (See *Pancreas; Insulin*) and (Plate 86).

PLATE 62

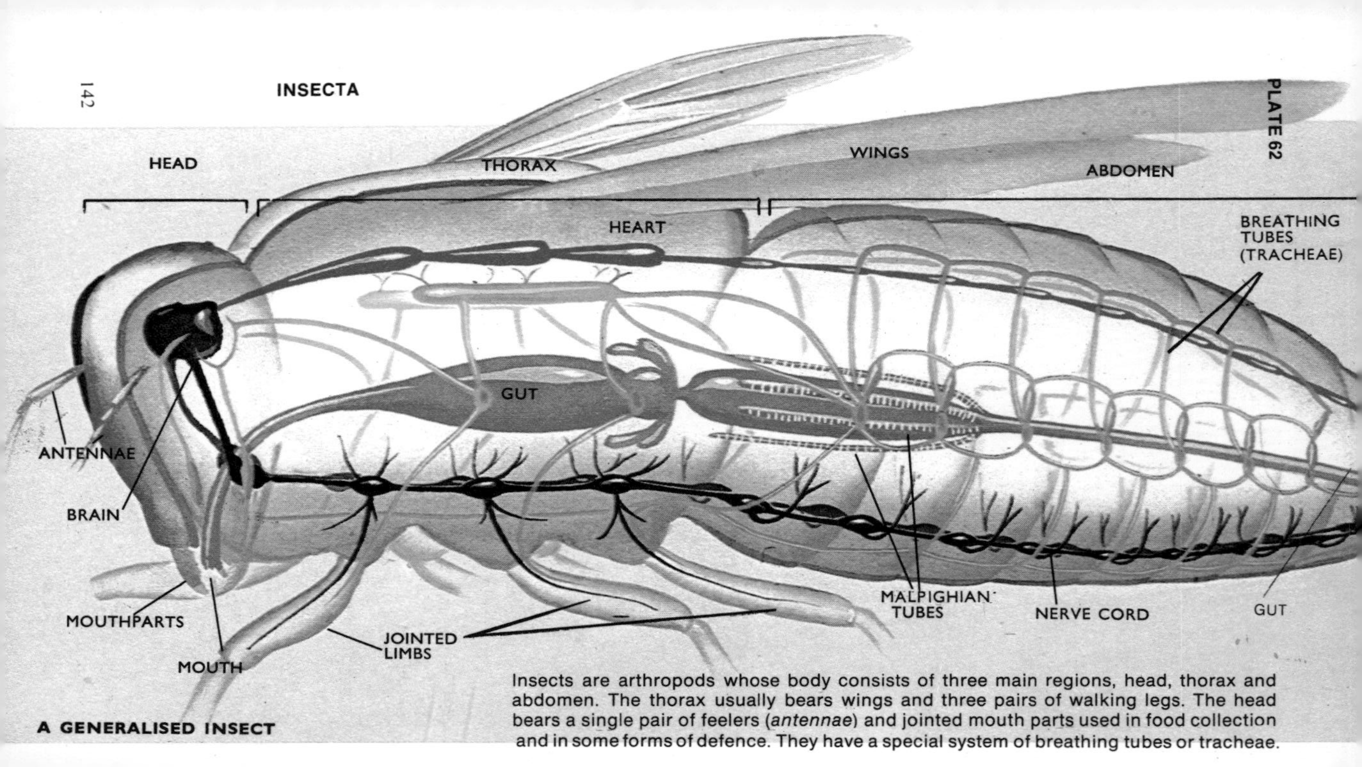

A GENERALISED INSECT

Insects are arthropods whose body consists of three main regions, head, thorax and abdomen. The thorax usually bears wings and three pairs of walking legs. The head bears a single pair of feelers (*antennae*) and jointed mouth parts used in food collection and in some forms of defence. They have a special system of breathing tubes or tracheae.

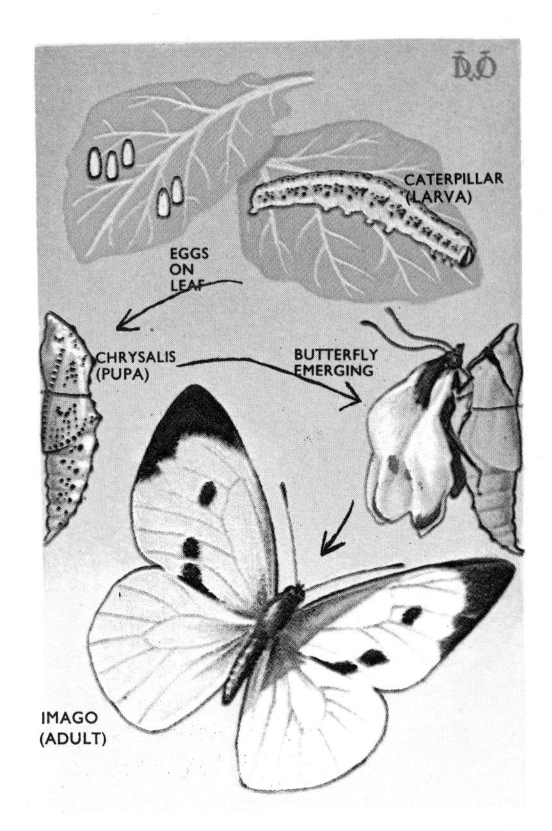

COMPLETE METAMORPHOSIS

The young is very unlike the adult and is called a larva. (A caterpillar is a special type of larva). Metamorphosis is complete.

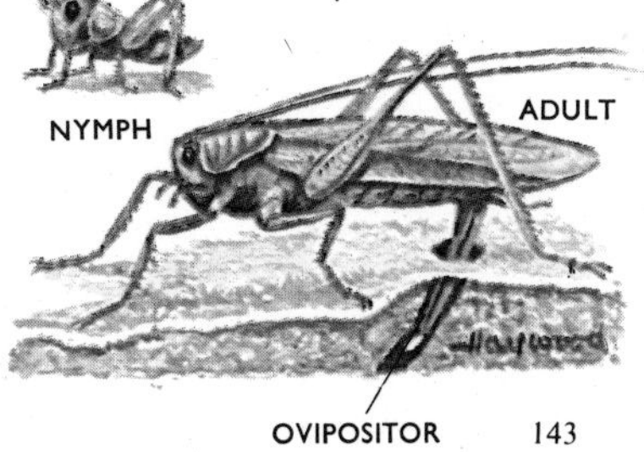

INCOMPLETE METAMORPHOSIS

The young is similar to the adult, except that it is smaller and lacks wings. It is called a nymph. Metamorphosis is incomplete.

Isopoda. Order of *Crustacea* (q.v.), containing the woodlice – the only truly terrestrial crustaceans.

Isoptera. Termites. This order of insects, although primitive and far-removed from the bees, wasps, and ants (See *Hymenoptera*), contains only social insects that live in highly organized communities. They are common in the tropics and two species extend to Europe. Termites feed mainly upon cellulose and are serious pests of timber. They make nests in trees or underground – sometimes making huge mounds on the surface. The soil particles are mixed with saliva and harden into concrete-like structures. The termites are unlike the other social insects in that the males and females are equally important. The mated pair, after their 'wedding flight' form a colony together. They live together in a special 'royal chamber' and are fed by the workers. The queen becomes little more than an egg-laying machine. Unlike the other social insects, mating occurs several times during the life of the queen. There are other reproductive forms in the colony and these can produce more workers but cannot produce kings and queens. The workers and soldiers are of both sexes and carry out the construction and defence of the nest and the food gathering work. Tunnels from the nest often lead for long distances to food gathering grounds. It is remarkable how closely termites resemble ants in their way of life when one considers how unrelated they are. The name 'white-ants' reflects this similarity. (See Plate 67) and (Page 268).

Jugal Bone. Bone of *skull* (q.v.), forming front part of 'cheek bone'.

Jugular Vein. Main vessel returning blood from the vertebrate head.

Jurassic Period. Geological period beginning some 170 million years ago. Famed for dinosaurs and ammonites. (See *Geological Time Scale*).

Keel. Downward projection of breast-bone of birds to which the large flight muscles are attached. Very reduced in flightless birds. (See Plate 66).

Keratin. Tough protein formed in the outer layer of the skin and which also forms hair, feathers, nails, claws, hooves and horns.

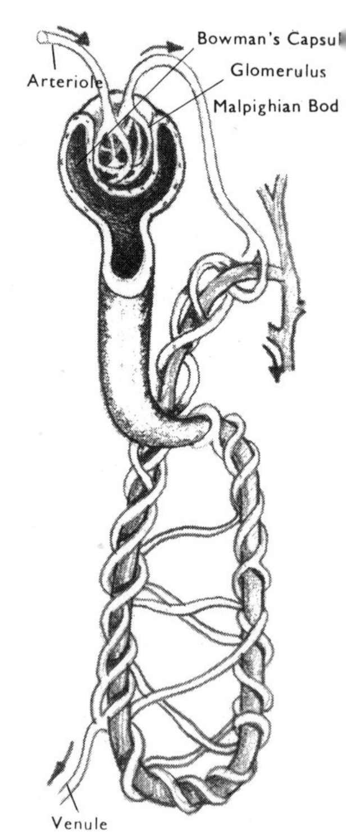

ONE KIDNEY TUBULE

Kidney. Excretory organ of vertebrates. They are concerned with the removal of waste, conservation of water, and the maintainance of the pH and composition of the body fluids. The detailed structure varies from species to species according to the conditions in which it lives (See *Excretion*) but the basic structure is similar to that given here for the human kidney.

A lengthwise section through a kidney shows two main zones: an outer cortex and an inner medulla. The whole is encased in a protective, fatty capsule.

Within the cortex and medulla are masses of tubules. They make up the bulk of the kidney tissue and join up with larger collecting tubes that eventually join the ureter which channels urine from the kidney to the bladder. Each kidney tubule has a rich blood supply: the renal artery and renal vein (together with the ureter) are prominent vessels entering or leaving the kidney.

The blind end of each kidney tubule lies in the cortex and may be likened to a champagne glass, the walls and stem of which are hollow and one cell thick. The 'bowl' of the tubule is called Bowman's capsule and it surrounds an elaborate knot of blood capillaries called the glomerulus. Each Bowman's capsule and glomerulus together form the Malpighian body – there are at least a million such structures in a single human kidney!

The hollow stem of the champagne glass is the upper part of the kidney tubule. This descends into the medulla where it narrows before turning back into the cortex – increasing in diameter again. The thin portion of the tubule is known as the loop of Henle and is primarily concerned with the absorption of water. The ascending limb of the tubule joins a collecting duct which joins with others before eventually discharging its urine into the ureter.

In effect each Bowman's capsule is a tiny filter. Blood containing waste substances, proteins, sugars, etc., passes into the kidneys and, under pressure a solution is driven out of the capillaries of the glomerulus through the walls of the capsule into its hollow interior. The solution in the capsule is blood plasma minus the large molecules that are too big to pass through the capillary wall.

From the capsule the fluid passes along the tubule. Many of the substances in it are reabsorbed through the tubule wall into the blood capillaries surrounding it. Organic molecules such as some amino-acids and glucose, some salts and water are absorbed in the descending or proximal limb of the tubule, whilst more water and salts are absorbed in the ascending or distal limb. Certain poisonous substances that have been rendered harmless (detoxicated) are released into the urine by the tubules, together with potassium and hydrogen. Measurements of the amounts of various substances present in the blood and in the urine show striking differences. The concentration of urea – the principal waste substance in the urine – is normally seventy times as great as it is in the blood, yet, surprisingly enough, some urea is reabsorbed, since a certain blood concentration is needed. Ninety times more sulphate, nine times more potassium and 25 times more uric acid occur in the urine than in the blood. On the other hand no glucose, fatty substances, proteins or bicarbonate ions normally occur in the urine, whereas considerable quantities occur in the blood.

The normal daily output of urine is between two and a half to three pints, yet it is calculated that a total of nearly 300 pints of fluid is filtered by the kidneys during that time. They not only reabsorb a vast volume each day; they also regulate its content so that the correct levels of essential substances are maintained in the body fluids.

The function of the various parts of the tubule has been analysed by inserting tiny pipettes into them and withdrawing small quantities of the fluid. Differences in the concentrations of substances in the fluid in different parts are strong evidence as to the function of a particular part. The content of the urine varies considerably with the type of diet that a person eats, however. For example, the nitrogen content of the urine is much higher in someone taking a protein-rich diet than

PLATE 64

INSECTA

The mouthparts of the cockroach are of the primitive biting type. The mouth-parts of other insects can be derived from this primitive type.

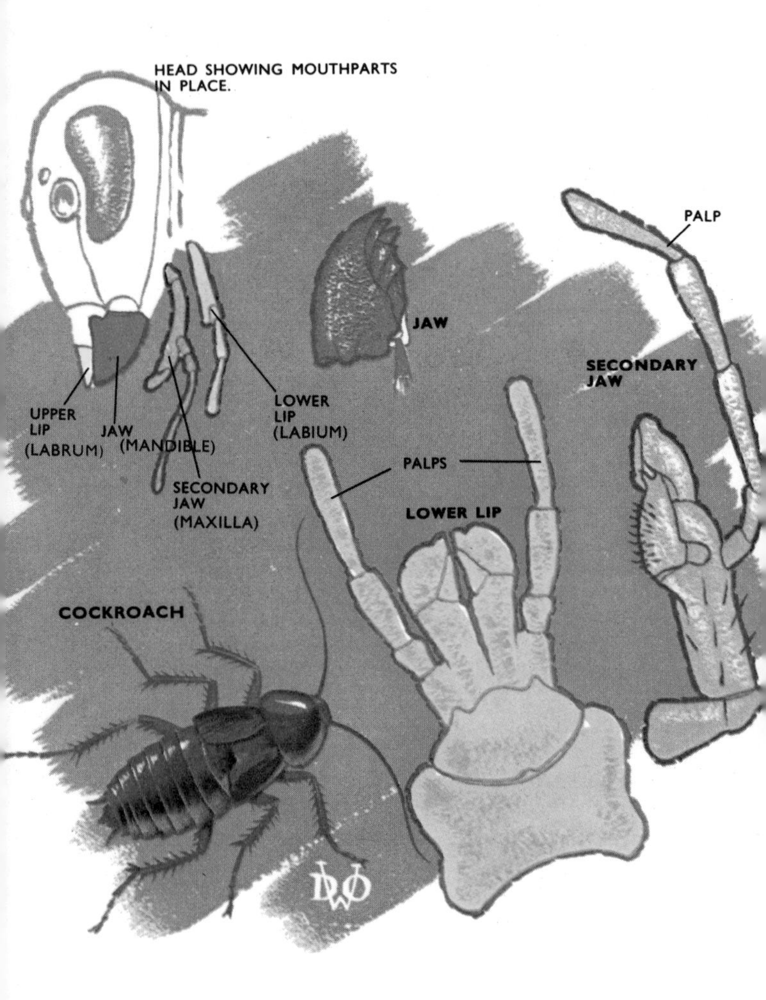

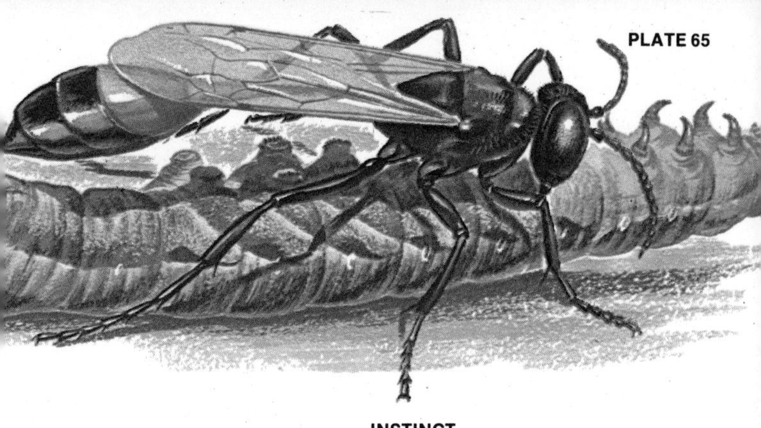

INSTINCT

Ammophila, a hunting wasp, buries a caterpillar and lays eggs in it. The whole process is one of instinct. The insect is never taught what to do.

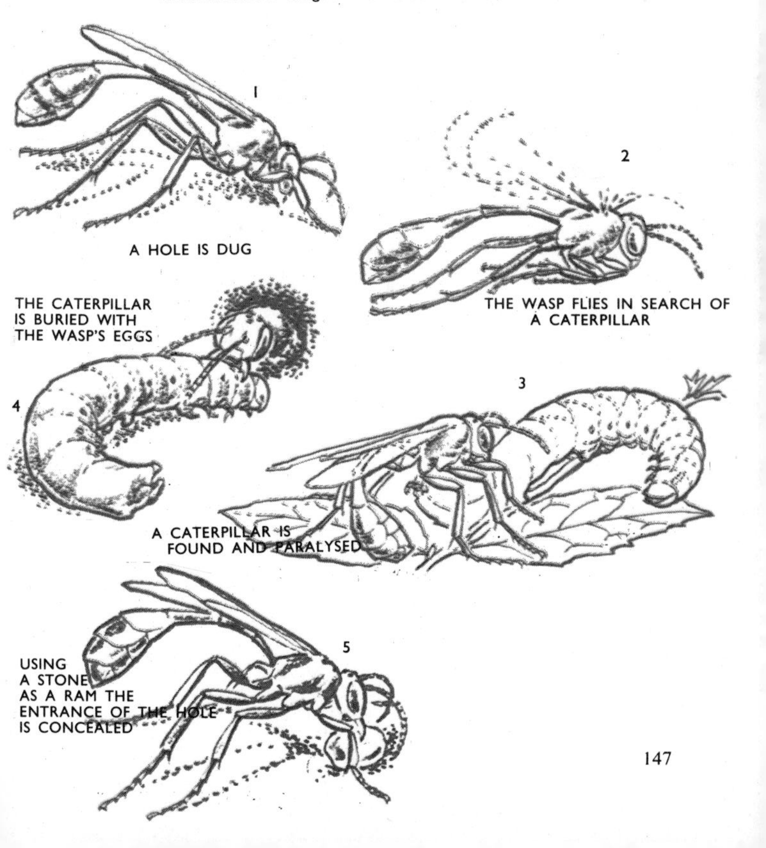

in another who is eating starch-rich food, mainly due to the increased production of urea. (See Plates 40, 42 and 66).

Labium. The 'lower lip' of insects, actually composed of a pair of appendages fused together. This origin is fairly obvious in primitive biting insects such as the cockroach but the labium is sometimes extremely modified, as in the bugs where it forms the sheath of the 'beak'. (See Plate 64).

Lacertilia. Lizards – sub-order of *Squamata* (q.v.). (See also *Reptilia*).

Lacewing. (See *Neuroptera*).

Lachrymal Gland. Tear gland of the eye.

Labrum. The 'upper lip' of insects, formed not from paired appendages but from a part of the head above the mouth. Like the labium, it is sometimes radically modified. (See Plate 64).

Lacteal. Lymph vessel draining each villus in vertebrate intestine and collecting fat. (See *Digestion; Alimentary Canal*).

Lagomorpha. Order of mammals containing rabbits and hares. Although superficially similar to rodents, they differ in many ways, notably in having a small extra pair of incisor teeth in the upper jaws. (See Plate 123–6).

Lamarckism. An evolutionary theory (now disproved) put forward by the French scientist Lamarck (1744–1829). According to this theory, if a man trained hard for athletics and built up powerful muscles, his offspring would also have powerful muscles. In other words, Lamarck suggested that characters acquired during a lifetime could be inherited. It is certainly true that constant use of muscles develops them and that unused muscles deteriorate, but there is no evidence that these features can be inherited. Weissman cut the tails of generation after generation of mice but never obtained one tailless offspring and this was a crushing blow to Lamarckism. (See *Evolution; Darwinism; Natural Selection*).

Lamella. Any thin layer of tissue.

Lamellibranchiata. Class of *Mollusca* (q.v.), in which the gills have evolved into large plates of tissue used for feeding as well as for breathing. The mantle cavity which houses the gills has become elongated, running down either side of the animal, often for almost the entire length. Lamellibranchs are therefore usually long and compressed from side to side, and the shell, which is secreted by the mantle, is in two parts or valves (hence the alternative name of bivalve). But the valves are connected at the top (dorsal) surface. Here a ligament – an elastic strip made of organic material – is secreted, either on the inside or the outside of the hinge. Two adductor muscles run between the valves. When the muscles contract the valves close together but when the muscles relax the elastic ligament at the hinge causes the shell to gape.

Bivalves do not really have a distinct head like snails. The mouth is at the front end of the animal surrounded by two long, bilobed palps (labial palps) but no sense organs are concentrated here and there is no rasping radula.

In more primitive molluscs the gills are simple, consisting of a stalk giving off plume-like filaments – rather like feathers. But in the bivalves the filaments become joined up forming a solid or plate-like structure (lamellibranchiata in fact means, plate-gilled).

In a very few simple bivalves (Protobranchs) the gills remain confined to a cavity at the rear of the body and the filaments are short. In more advanced forms each filament becomes elongated and turns upwards. The gills are also extended so that they run practically the length of the body. Water is drawn into the shell at the rear end where the mantle is often extended backwards to form two siphons. The lower siphon takes the water in. The water provides not only oxygen. Particles of food in the water are swept forward and downward, moved along the bottom of the gill filaments by the rapid beating of tracts of cilia. During the passage forward the particles become entangled in mucus.

From the gills, food particles are swept onto the labial palps about the mouth. The labial palps are also ciliated. Material may be swept into the mouth or rejected and passed back by ciliary action along the base of the gills to be washed out through the upper of the two siphons. Sorting at the labial palps selects the finest particles, not necessarily the most nutritious. Large, coarse particles are rejected for bivalves have no masticating radula to break up food. Food particles are swept down a short gullet to the stomach. Cilia in the stomach further sort the particles and useless material is swept straight into the intestine.

Some preliminary digestion does take place in the stomach. Digestive enzymes, for breaking down carbohydrates, are secreted there by a very strange method. Inside a diverticulum of the stomach is embedded a tough, rod-like structure called a crystalline style which contains the digestive enzymes. The style gradually dissolves, releasing the enzymes but cells lining the diverticulum continually secrete new material behind. The style rotates and acts as a stirring rod and also as a windlass; threads of mucus bearing food are drawn from mouth into stomach.

Minute food particles are next taken via a pair of ducts to the digestive gland whose cells actually absorb the particles and digestion is completed inside them.

Bivalve molluscs, like snails, retain a muscular foot lying between the two sets of gills on the ventral side of the body. Its shape and position is altered by muscular contraction and can be protruded through the gape of the shell.

In one group of bivalves – the so-called Normal bivalves – the foot is well developed and the creatures use it to move about at the surface (e.g. cockles) or in some instances to burrow (e.g. razor shells). The giant clams of the Pacific and Indian Oceans belong to this group. They may grow to be more than a yard in length.

The Sessile group of bivalves have, in general, lost their mobility in the adult animal. Instead, they have become firmly attached to the surface. Modifications have accompanied this stationary mode of life. The ventral foot has tended to move more and more towards the front of the animal. As a direct result the anterior adductor muscle has become small or is lost; usually each valve becomes highly asymmetrical in shape.

A byssus nearly always appears at some stage in the life history. A byssus is a mass of sticky, diverging threads arising from a pit at the back of the foot. In the mussel the byssus protrudes through the gape in the valves. The pearl oyster has come to lie on its right valve and the byssus emerges through a notch.

The common oysters have lost the foot and byssus altogether; the right valve becomes cemented to the ground.

Pecten, the scallop, is structurally a sessile bivalve. The front adductor muscle has been lost by the forward migration of the foot. But the remaining muscle has become enlarged. By rapid contraction the valves are clapped together and water is violently discharged. This is an efficient mechanism for swimming and *Pecten* has given up its sessile habit.

The last division of the bivalves is the deep-burrowers. Unlike the burrowers of the Normal group, the deep burrowers have become extremely modified to their mode of life. The valves are only weakly hinged; often they have completely

PLATE 66

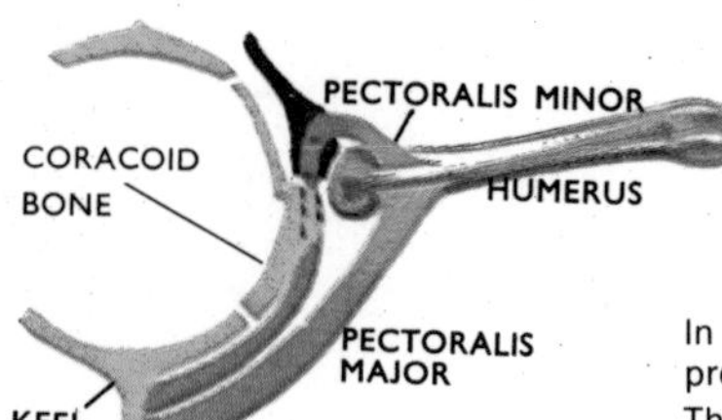

KEEL

In flying birds, there is a large process (Keel) on the breast bone. The large flight muscles are attached to this. Non-flyers have only a tiny keel or none at all.

KIDNEY

Human kidney partly cut away.

FATTY CAPSULE
CORTEX
RENAL ARTERY
RENAL VEIN
MEDULLA
URETER

PLATE 67

ISOPTERA

These insects live in large colonies, often making huge mounds of earth. There are worker and soldier castes as well as reproductive males and females. The colony is founded by a king and queen not just by a queen as in bees, wasps and ants.

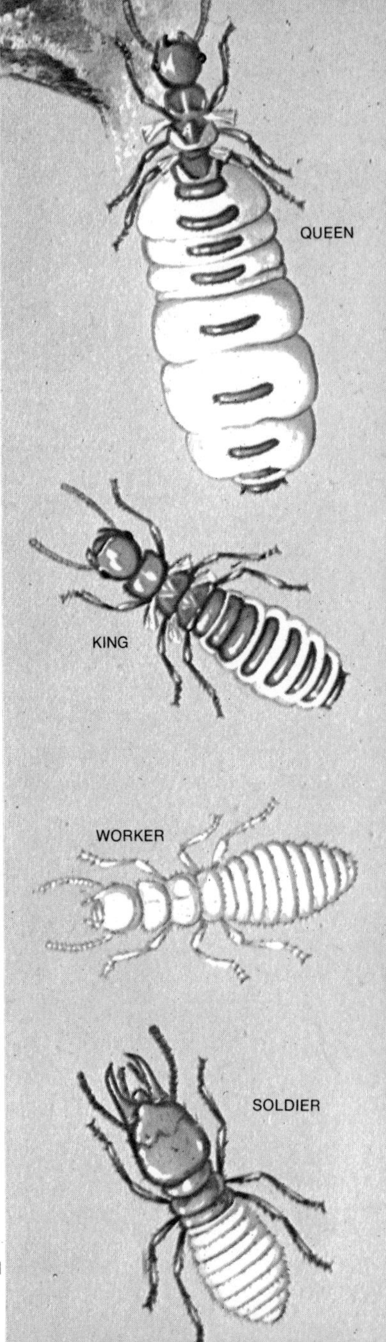

lost their ligament and the valves permanently gape. The siphons are enormous, often dwarfing the rest of the body. (E.g. *Teredo; Pholas*). (See Plates 68, 69, 70 and 115).

Lamp Shells (See *Brachiopoda*).

Larva. Young form of an animal that is very different from the adult. Examples include caterpillar (adult is butterfly), tadpole (frog), and the various crustacean larvae. Some animals pass through more than one larval form before reaching maturity. (See *Nymph*) and (Plates 63 and 78).

Larynx. Expanded upper region of the windpipe – the voice box. (See *Voice*) and (Plate 105).

Lateral Line System. A remarkable system of sense organs found only in fishes and in the young stages of amphibians. It is better developed in bony fishes than in shark-like fishes. The lateral line can clearly be seen running along the sides of both sharks and bony fishes from the back of the head to the tail. A pattern of similar lines can be seen on the head. They consist of distinct groups of sensory cells arranged in long rows and supplied with nerve endings.

The cells are protected either in an open groove running just beneath the surface of the skin or in a tube which opens to the exterior (through the scales in bony fishes, between them in sharks) at intervals by a series of pores.

Each cell has a hair-like process projecting into the water in the groove or tube. Movements and vibrations in the water round the fish move the hairs and the disturbance of the sense cell results in signals passing along nerve fibres to the brain.

The lines on the head are particularly well developed in the herring and other plankton-feeding fish. The system may play an important part in the detection of food. A certain deep-water fish has lateral line organs on stalks projecting from the sides of the body. Food is scarce in the abyssal regions of the sea: is it possible that this extraordinary development of the lateral line system helps the fish to detect prey? Alternatively, of course, it would be equally valuable in detecting disturbances of the water due to enemies. (See Plates 35 and 70).

Leech (See *Hirudinea*).

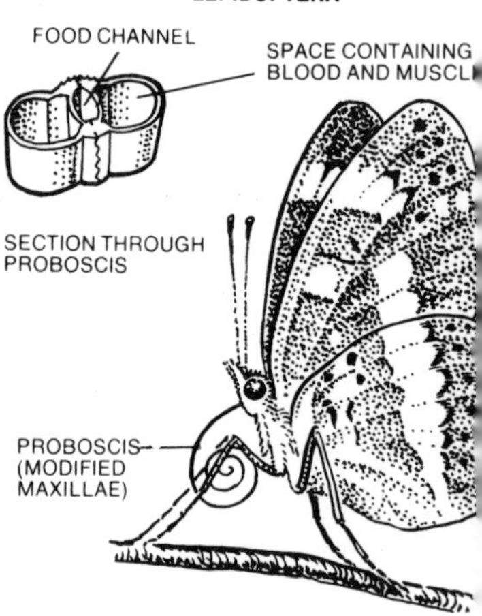

Lepidoptera. Order of *Insecta* (q.v.), containing the butterflies and moths. The characteristic feature is the clothing of body and wings with tiny scales which are responsible for the many bright colours to be found in the order. The adults are typically nectar-feeders, sucking up the liquid through a long tongue or proboscis which, when not in use, is coiled up underneath the head. Metamorphosis is complete, the larvae (caterpillars) have biting mouths and often possessing stumpy prolegs on the abdomen. (See Page 268).

Leucocyte. Name given to the various white blood cells. (See *Blood*).

Life Cycle. The series of changes undergone by an organism during its life time from fertilisation to death.

In most animals this is a simple cycle but where there is an *alternation of generations* (q.v.), the cycle includes both forms and does not end with the death of any one of them. (See Plate 63).

Ligament. Tough strip of collagen fibres that joins bones together at a joint. Also the horny hinge of a bivalve shell.

Linkage. The association of *genes* (q.v.), on one chromosome so that the features they produce in the organism will always tend to appear together. This is because complete chromosomes are normally passed on to the next generation and if ones gene goes, so will those linked to it. (See *Heredity*).

Littoral. Inhabiting the shores and surrounding regions of the sea bed.

Liver. An exocrine gland associated with digestion but also performing many other functions in vertebrate animals. Digestive glands of invertebrate animals are also often called livers.

The vertebrate liver is the largest gland in the body. It arises as a pouch-like outgrowth from the gut, and in the ancestors of the vertebrates it is likely that the liver was solely a producer of digestive enzymes. Though it still retains something of this activity in producing bile, its main functions concern the management of food-stuffs – fat, carbohydrate and protein – storing them and/or converting them into the molecules required by the tissues. Protein in excess of the body's requirements is broken down (deaminated), the nitrogen is converted into urea which is carried by the blood to the kidneys, and the remaining molecules are burnt to provide energy. Its other roles include the breakdown of harmful substances, such as alcohol, the metabolism and storage of iron and copper, and the making of vitamin A (an activity that accounts for the rich supply of this vitamin in oils obtained from fish livers). Special cells remove dead bacteria and the like from the blood. A recently discovered role is the storage of vitamin B_{12} (cobalamine) a substance necessary for the proper formation of red blood cells. Lack of this vitamin causes pernicious anaemia. It is thought that the liver releases vitamin B_{12} when the level in the diet is low. It circulates in the blood, reaching the sites where red blood cells are manufactured.

The liver consists essentially of a series of five – or six-sided columns (lobules), each made up of chains of cells (trabeculae) radiating from the centre. Between the trabeculae are blood-filled spaces (sinusoids) and other 'spaces' (canaliculi) into which bile is released. A blood vessel passes through the centre of each lobule. It collects blood from the sinusoids which are supplied by branches of the hepatic portal vein around the edge of the lobule. The central veins join to form the hepatic vein that carries blood back to the heart.

The liver is strategically placed in relation to the gut and the blood supply it receives from there. The gut itself has a rich blood supply to absorb the digested food material. Blood rich in food molecules is conveyed by way of the hepatic portal vein to the liver before it joins the main circulation. The liver, by a multitude of chemical processes, is then able to act on the food, before releasing to the tissues the substances that they require. This is also part of the activity by which the liver controls the composition of the blood.

The food materials arriving in the liver from the intestine obviously vary from one part of a day to another, and from day to day, depending on the quality of the food eaten. The activities of the liver will also vary, therefore, but not merely because of the food intake, for the demands of the tissues also vary from time to time. The muscles require little fuel while the body is resting, but, at a time when they are working rapidly, enormous supplies of fuel will be

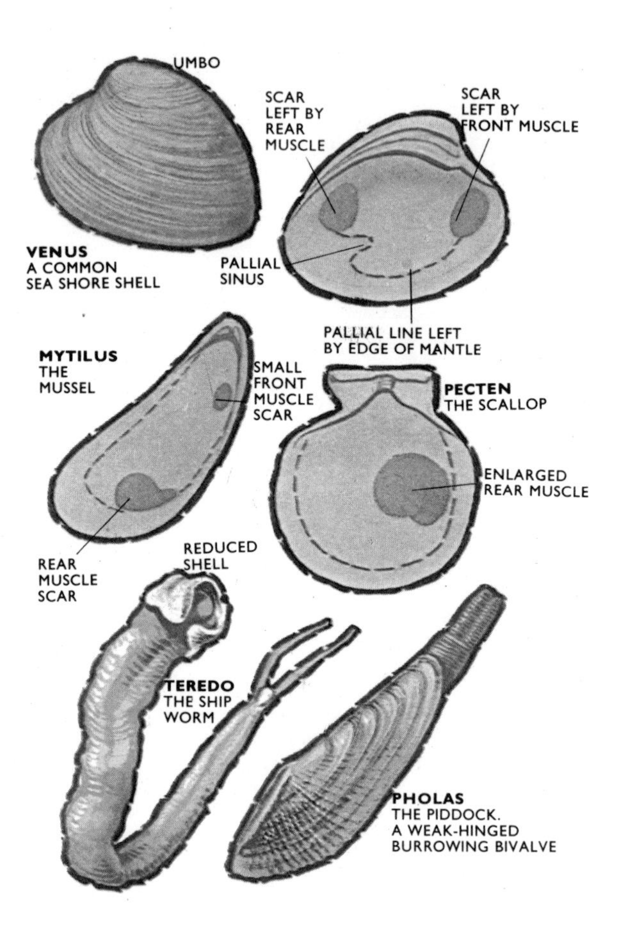

LAMELLIBRANCHIATA

(Top) Shell of Venus. Where the muscles abut against the shell, scars are left. The *pallial line* marks the edge of the mantle lobe. An insertion of the pallial line marks the position of the syphons. (Middle) Mussels, sessile bivalves, have a reduced forward muscle, the scallops have lost it altogether. (Below) Specialized burrowing forms.

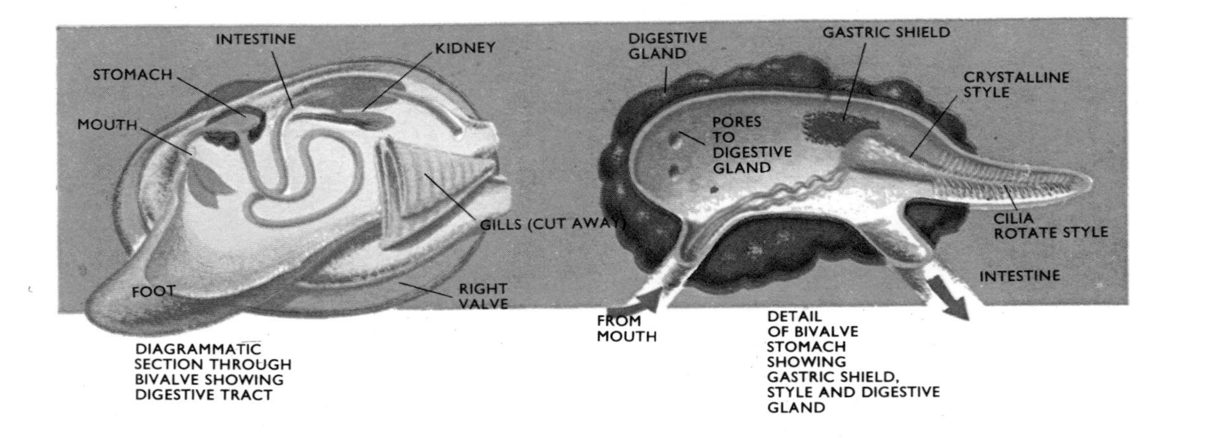

LAMELLIBRANCHIATA

The lamellibranchs are filter-feeders. Tiny particles are caught on the gills and swept into the mouth. A crystalline rod (*style*) in the stomach secretes digestive enzymes. Digestion is completed inside the cells of the digestive gland.

required. One of the principal activities of the liver in this respect is the storage of glycogen – a starch-like compound whose molecules are made up from numerous glucose molecules. When the blood contains more glucose than the tissues require, the liver cells join the glucose molecules together to form the larger glycogen molecules, and in this form they are stored. The liver is prompted to do this under the influence of insulin produced by the pancreas. When the tissues require further supplies of glucose, the glycogen molecules are broken down and glucose is released into the blood stream.

The liver also stores fat. The latter can be broken down to release the energy needed to power chemical processes or to produce heat. The smaller molecules produced can be reassembled to form glycogen. Thus fats can be converted into carbohydrates.

In a similar way the liver cells can break down amino acids and convert them into carbohydrates.(They cannot build up amino acids from simpler units. Most of the amino acids that the body requires have to be taken in with the food.) The amino ($-NH_2$) groups remaining are incorporated into urea molecules and this waste product is passed in the bloodstream to the kidneys for removal to the bladder. The liver breaks down only those amino acids that are surplus to the body's requirements for building up proteins and other molecules containing them. It normally passes on the amino acid molecules that it receives from the gut to the tissues that need them.

The liver cells release bile into the spaces (canaliculi) between the chains of liver cells. The tiny bile canaliculi join to form large bile channels that eventually join and enter the gall bladder. This is a 'pocket' that stores bile. Leading from the gall bladder is the bile duct which carries the bile to the intestine.

Bile is an alkaline secretion containing certain organic salts – the bile salts – the bile pigments, and such substances as cholesterol and lecithin. The bile salts reduce the surface tension of fats in the food, breaking them down into tiny droplets. This increases their surface area to such an extent that the fat-splitting enzymes in the pancreatic juice can act upon them. The bile pigments are breakdown products of haemoglobin from dead blood cells. They are removed from the body with the faeces.

Apart from the production of bile and the management of food substances, a most important function of the liver is detoxication – the conversion of harmful substances into harmless ones. This may be carried out in a number of ways. Thus ammonia, a highly toxic substance, formed in the process of deamination, is converted into urea for excretion by the kidneys. A substance such as benzoic acid is combined with an amino acid – glycine – and converted to the harmless hippuric acid. Other substances are acetylated, that is, $-COCH_3$ groupings are added to the molecules. This is how the body gets rid of sulphonamides (a group of drugs). Associated with these processes is the removal of dead bacteria and other foreign matter by special cells – Kupffer cells. All may be considered .protective functions of the liver.

The liver stores both iron and copper. It obtains iron from the food and also retains that released during the breakdown of haemoglobin. Copper is not itself part of the haemoglobin molecule, but in some way it enables the iron atoms to be incorporated into the haemoglobin molecules. (See Plate 71).

Lizard. (See *Squamata*).

Lumbar Vertebra. *Vertebra* (q.v.) of the waist region – between the ribs and the sacrum. (See Pages 217 and 244).

Lung. Air-breathing organ of vertebrates but also applied to the modified mantle cavity of slugs and snails (See

Gasteropoda). The vertebrate lung arises as a pouch in the ventral gut wall and it was present in some of the earliest fishes. It remains in many modern fishes as the swim bladder (q.v.), but it lies above the gut and has normally lost its connection with the gut. In the air-breathing vertebrates the lungs open into the pharynx by way of two bronchi and the trachea. Amphibians obtain much of their oxygen through their skin and the surface area of their lungs is small. The reptile lung is considerably more complicated while the surface area of man's lungs may equal about half a tennis court. In the mammalian lung the bronchi break up into smaller tubes called bronchioles which end eventually in tiny blind pockets called alveoli. Each alveolus is surrounded by blood vessels and oxygen from the air taken into the lungs passes through the alveolus wall and into the blood stream. The lungs of a bird do not have nearly such a complicated lining but there are a number of accessory air-sacs which act as pumps and ensure that a fresh supply of air reaches the absorbing surfaces of the lungs at each breath. This does not happen in mammals: the alveoli retain a certain amount of 'stale' air all the time and oxygen has to diffuse through this stale air before reaching the blood. The enormous number of alveoli makes up for this drawback in mammals. (See *Respiration; Respiratory Movements*) and (Plates 71, 72, 73 and 94).

Lung Book. Respiratory organ of spiders and scorpions, consisting of numerous sheets of tissue, well-supplied with blood, suspended in a pocket of the body wall, opening to the outside by a small pore.

Lung Fish. (See *Dipnoi*).

Lymph. Fluid that bathes the cells and tissues of the body, providing them with food and oxygen. Lymph is actually blood plasma minus its proteins and cells that cannot diffuse out from the blood capillaries. The lymph is returned to the heart via the *lymphatic system* (q.v.).

Lymphatic System. A special set of vessels returning lymph from the tissues to the heart. Its vessels reach nearly all parts of the body. The lymph capillaries are blind tubes – a little larger in diameter than the blood capillaries. They are in close contact with the tissue cells or the spaces round them. Although the tubes are blind, molecules of all shapes and sizes (even bacteria) can squeeze through the walls between cells. The smaller vessels join up to form larger ones in much the same way as veins. At intervals along the lymph channels are swellings – the lymph nodes. These are essentially networks of connective tissue that contain phagocytes and also other white blood cells called lymphocytes. The lymph nodes are particularly important at times of infection when the phagocytes actively consume bacteria. They are the 'swollen glands' that we feel in the armpits from an infected finger or in the neck from a bad tooth. Thus a major function of the lymphatic system is as a filter for bacteria and other foreign particles.

The lymphatic system is also concerned with maintaining the fluid balance of the tissue cells and the spaces round them. When channels become blocked by disease the affected part may swell considerably, a condition called oedema. The lymph vessels (lacteals) of the intestine transport fat away from the intestine. Lymph is moved very slowly through the lymph vessels as a result of body movements. Valves similar to those of veins prevent its backward flow. (See Plate 73).

Lymph Node. (See *Lymphatic System*).

Lymphocyte. Large type of white blood cell possibly concerned with the formation of *antibodies* (q.v.).

Macro- (=Large).

PLATE 70

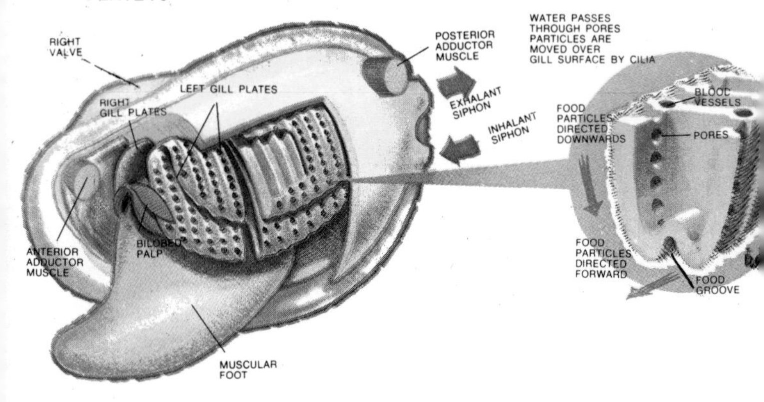

LAMELLIBRANCHIATA

The left valve and mantle lobe has been removed leaving the gill plates and the palps exposed. A section of the gill plate has been cut away, showing the structure of the gills more closely. Inset: detailed section of the gills showing cilia, pores and food grooves.

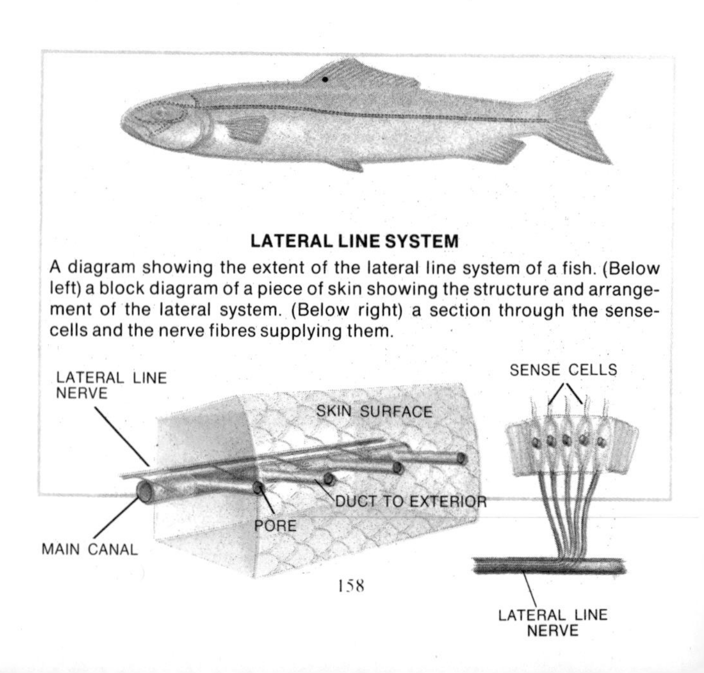

LATERAL LINE SYSTEM

A diagram showing the extent of the lateral line system of a fish. (Below left) a block diagram of a piece of skin showing the structure and arrangement of the lateral system. (Below right) a section through the sense-cells and the nerve fibres supplying them.

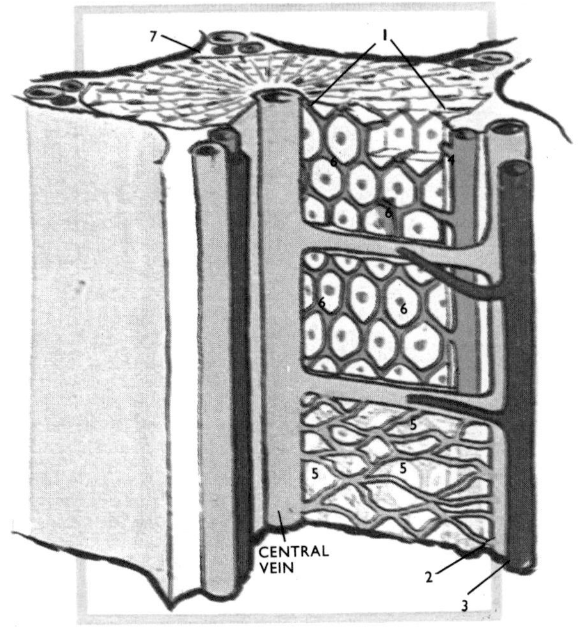

DIAGRAMMATIC
STRUCTURE OF LIVER
KEY TO DIAGRAM

LIVER

1. CHAIN OF LIVER CELLS OR TRABECULA
2. BRANCH OF HEPATIC PORTAL VEIN
3. HEPATIC ARTERY (carries oxygenated blood to liver)
4. BRANCH OF BILE DUCT
5. LIVER SINUSOIDS – filled with blood
6. BILE CANALICULI
7. CONNECTIVE TISSUE ROUND LOBULE

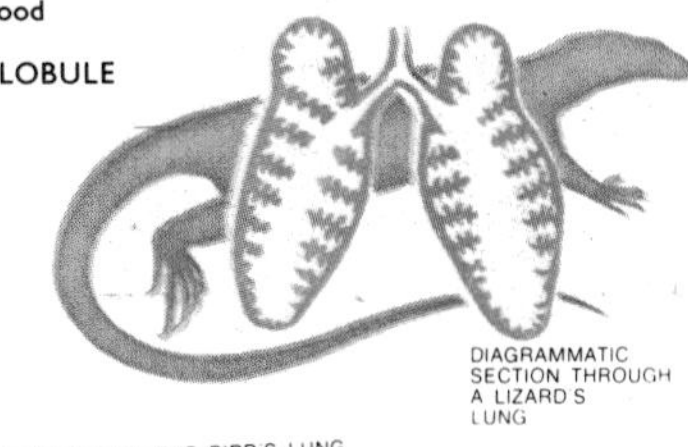

DIAGRAMMATIC SECTION THROUGH A LIZARD'S LUNG

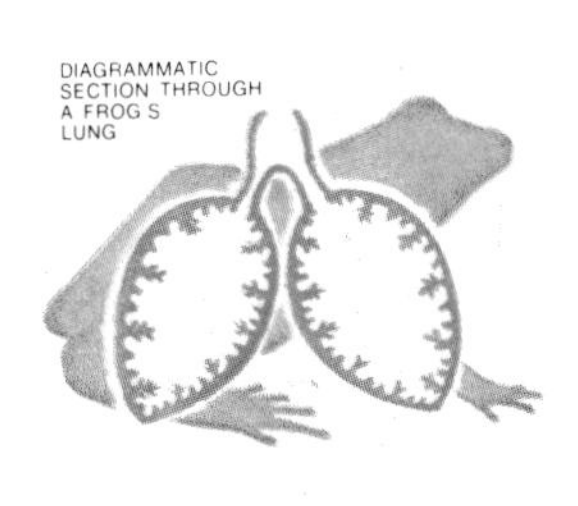

DIAGRAMMATIC SECTION THROUGH A FROG'S LUNG

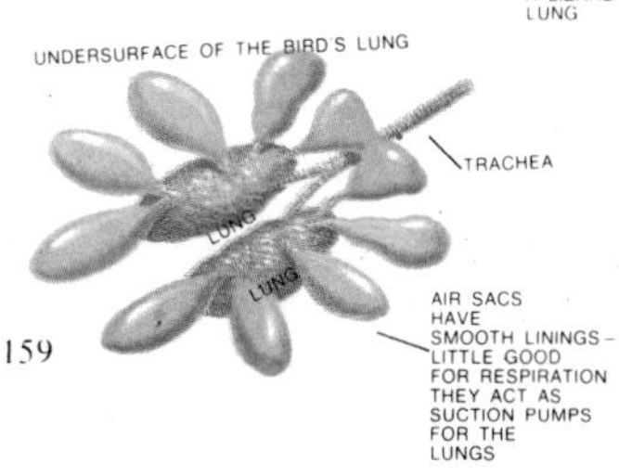

LUNG

Macrophagous. Feeding at intervals on relatively large items of food when compared with the size of the body. All land animals are macrophagous. (See *Microphagous*).

Malacostraca. Sub-class of *Crustacea* (q.v.) containing woodlice, crabs, lobsters, shrimps, and others whose eyes are typically stalked. (See Page 264).

Malleus. One of the mammalian ear ossicles (See *Ear*), derived from the articulate bone of the lower jaw of the reptilian ancestors.

Mallophaga. Order of *Insecta* (q.v.) – biting lice, ectoparasites of birds. (See Page 268).

Malpighian Body. Unit of vertebrate *kidney* (q.v.) consisting of Bowman's capsule and glomerulus.

Malpighian Layer. Basal layer of epidermis where new cells are made. (See *Skin*).

Malpighian Tubules. Excretory organs of insects. (See *Excretion*) and (Plate 62).

Mammalia. Large class of vertebrates including among many others; kangaroos, bats, whales, dogs, horses, monkeys, and men. The diagnostic characteristics are the possession of hair, the suckling of the young on milk produced by the mother, a single bone only (the dentary) in each half of the lower jaw, and several other internal features. Mammals share with the birds the ability to maintain a constant high body temperature. There are three groups of living mammals: *Monotremata* – primitive egg-laying mammals; *Marsupialia* – the pouched mammals; and *Placentalia* or *Eutheria* – the placental mammals which are the most advanced. (See Plates 122 and 123).

Mammary Gland. Milk-producing gland of female mammal. Thought to be modified sweat glands, the mammary glands consist of clusters of gland cells that extract material from the blood and convert it to milk. The activity of the gland is controlled by hormones and milk is produced only after the animal has given birth to young. (See Plate 74).

Mandible. The lower jaw of vertebrates. Also the paired biting and crushing appendage near the mouth of insects and crustaceans. (See Plate 64).

Mantle. Thick fold of skin covering all or part of the mollusc body. The mantle cavity between mantle and body contains the gills while the outer edge of the mantle secretes the shell. (See *Mollusca*) and (Plate 70).

Marsupialia (=*Metatheria*). Sub-class of *Mammalia* (q.v.) containing the pouched mammals living representatives of which are confined largely to Australasia, although a few live in the Americas. The kangaroo is probably the best-known marsupial. Others include the wombat, koala, Tasmanian devil, wallaby, and banded ant-eater.

In the placental mammals (e.g. rabbit), the developing embryo obtains its nourishment from the mother by way of a placenta – a specialised organ formed by the union of the womb lining and certain embryonic tissues. Such a device permits a long period of development and consequently the young are well developed at birth. In marsupials, however, the young are not nourished by a placenta, except in the bandicoot, but even here the placenta is relatively simple in structure. As embryos, the only nourishment they have is in the store of yolky material in the egg and a supply of 'milk' from the lining of the uterus. The yolk is quickly exhausted and consequently the young are born at an early stage in their development – in the opossum from only eight to thirteen days after fertilisation has occurred. They then crawl to a pouch on the abdomen of the female where they spend the early part of their lives, being suckled on milk from the mammary glands.

At birth, the offspring of the Virginia opossum are no larger than a honey bee. Even those of the great grey kangaroo are merely an inch or so long and weigh only an ounce.

The female does not pick up the new-born youngsters and place them in her pouch. They find their own way there, a quite remarkable feat for such immature creatures. Associated with this, the forelimbs and their nervous supply are well developed at birth. The hind limbs are relatively under-developed at this stage. The mother may lick the fur on her abdomen to assist the youngsters' journey to the pouch.

The length of time that the young spend in the pouch varies from about seven weeks in the marsupial cat to four months in the rat kangaroo. Young of the Virginia opossum are nursed for nearly two months and they do not become independent of the mother for at least three months.

Generally, a large number of young are produced. Ten is an average litter for the Virginia opossum, though ones of fifteen to eighteen are not uncommon, but the rat kangaroo produces only one. This is a curious situation, for the latter has four teats, – three are usually unoccupied therefore whilst the opossum has 13 teats (11 that actually produce milk), which means that in litters of 12 or more, surplus young die because they are unable to obtain nourishment.

From a study of marsupials, both in the wild and in captivity, it seems that they are able to breed at any time of the year, though strict breeding seasons are normally observed. A Virginia opossum female usually has two litters a year and becomes pregnant again after the first litter has been weaned.

Not all marsupials have a pouch or marsupium as well-developed as that of the kangaroo. Some merely have two flaps of skin whilst others, for example the woolly opossum, have no pouch. In this case the youngsters hang on to the nipples of the female as she moves around. Animals with a well-developed pouch have special processes – epipubic bones – on the pelvic girdle. These help to support the pouch. (See Plates 41, 122).

Mastigophora (=*Flagellata*).

Maxilla. A bone of the upper jaw in vertebrates, carrying most of the upper teeth. (See *Skull*). Also one of the pair of appendages behind the jaws (mandibles) of insects and crustaceans. (See Plate 64).

Mayfly. (See *Ephemeroptera*).

Meckel's Cartilage. Piece of cartilage forming the lower jaw of elasmobranch fishes, also of other vertebrate embryos. Becomes articular bone in adults.

Medulla. Central part of an organ where it differs from outer part (cortex). E.g. of kidney, adrenal gland.

Medulla Oblongata. Hind part of brain merging into spinal cord. A centre for the senses of taste and hearing, it also unconsciously controls the rate of breathing. (See *Brain*).

Medusa. Free-swimming saucer-shaped stage of coelenterate life-history. Larger ones are the typical jellyfish. They almost always reproduce by producing sex cells although they are themselves formed by budding. (See *Alternation of Generations; Coelenterata; Scyphozoa*) and (Plates 3, 23 and 107).

Meiosis. A type of nuclear division during which the number of chromosomes per nucleus is halved. This division occurs at some time during the life cycle of any organism that reproduces sexually – normally during the formation of sex cells. Without meiosis, the number of chromosomes

PLATE 72

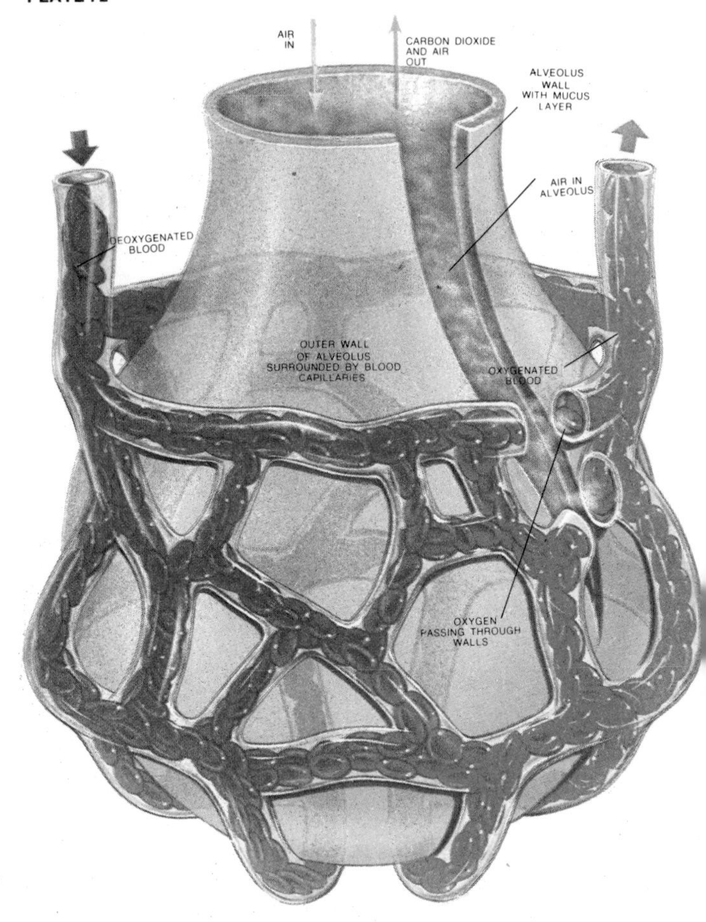

LUNG

Highly magnified diagram of a lung alveolus and its blood supply. Millions of these tiny pockets give the mammalian lung a huge surface area for the absorption of oxygen.

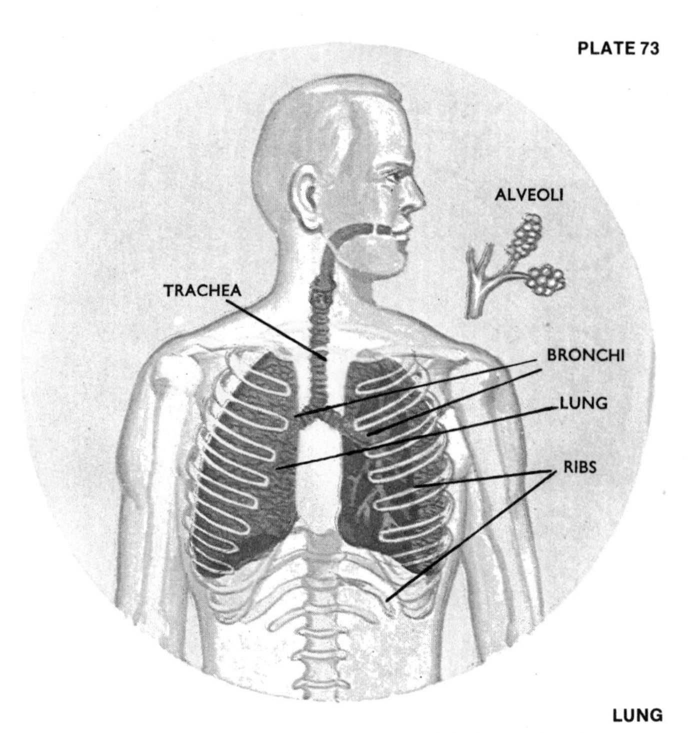

LUNG

The position of the human lungs.

LYMPHATIC SYSTEM

Bacteria in the body are carried along by the lymph into lymph nodes where they are destroyed.

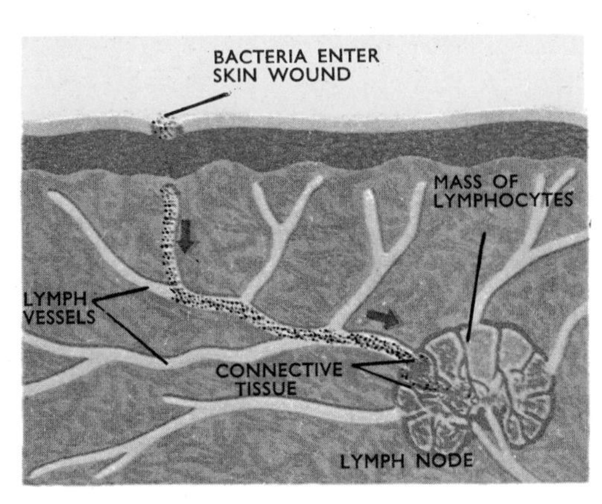

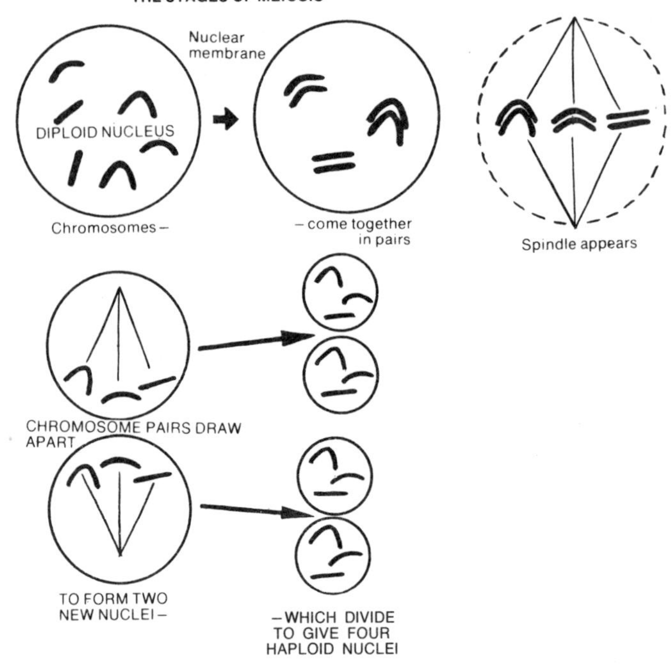

in a cell would double with each new generation, giving rise to an impossible state of affairs. In meiosis the pairs of *homologous chromosomes* (q.v.), come together. They then separate, one of each pair going to each end of the cell. A new nuclear membrane forms around the chromosomes and the cell divides into two. The two new cells then divide again but this time the chromosomes themselves divide into two identical halves so that the number is not reduced further in the four new cells. Thus, one original cell gives rise to four sex cells. (See *Mitosis*).

Meissner Corpuscle. Pressure receptor, hundreds of which are found in the skin of the hands and feet, especially on the tips of fingers and toes. Consists of a capsule of connective tissue surrounding a coiled nerve fibre.

Melanin. Dark brown pigment of many animals. Brown and yellows are produced by different concentrations of melanin.

Melanism. Excess of melanin in the tissues. Several moth species are known to produce occasional black individuals. The gene or genes controlling colour occasionally change so that the black (melanic) form appears. Under normal conditions the black form was easily seen by enemies and was eaten but in the last hundred years or so melanic forms have increased in industrial areas. Smoke pollution has blackened buildings and so the occasional mutation was valuable: the black moth was protected by camouflage and gradually increased its numbers as the black gene was passed on to the offspring. The normal form then declined in these areas. This is a good example of Darwin's idea of natural selection – the changing environment leading to the increase of new forms. The new form was not, however, caused by the changing environment. (See *Darwinism; Evolution; Natural Selection*) and (Plates 74 and 75).

Melanophore. Pigment cell containing melanin.

Membrane Bone (=*Dermal Bone*). (See *Bone*).

Mendelism. (See *Heredity*)

Meninges. The membranes covering the brain and spinal cord.

Menstrual Cycle. Cycle of changes in the female reproductive system found only in apes, man, and the old world monkeys, and which ends in the sloughing of the uterine lining with some loss of blood.

The uterus lining thickens as the egg cell develops in the ovary. It becomes more muscular and richer in glands and blood vessels. If fertilisation does not occur when the egg-cell is released, the growth of tissue continues for a time and then breaks down with the loss of blood characteristic of menstruation. Growth of the uterus lining and subsequent menstruation takes place regularly during approximately 28-day cycles in Man. (See *Oestrus Cycle*).

Mesentery. Fine tissues suspending stomach and other organs in the body cavity. Also the vertical partition found in some numbers in the gut cavity of corals and sea-anemones. (See Plate 1).

Mesoderm. Middle layer of triploblastic animal embryo and all the tissues to which it gives rise – muscle, blood, cartilage, and connective tissue. (See Plate 24).

Mesogloea. Jelly-like substance in body wall of *Coelenterata* (q.v.). (See Plate 23).

Mesozoic. Geological era. (See *Geological Time Scale*).

Metabolism. The sum total of the chemical processes going on within an organism.

Metacarpal Bones. Bones of the palm region of hand or front foot. (See Page 217).

Metameric Segmentation. (See *Segmentation*).

Metamorphosis. A transformation during the life history of an organism especially from larval to adult form – e.g. the change from caterpillar to butterfly or from tadpole to frog. (See Plate 63).

Metatarsal Bones. Bones of the sole of the hind foot – between ankle and toes.

Metatheria. (See *Marsupialia*).

Metazoa. Term used to cover all animals other than protozoans – i.e. the many-celled animals. Sponges, however, are sometimes excluded from the metazoa because their structure is so very different from that of other animals. (See *Porifera* and *Protozoa*), and (Page 253).

Micro- (=Small).

Microphagous. Feeding on particles that are relatively tiny when compared to the size of the animal's body. Filter feeders such as bivalve molluscs and whalebone whales are of this type. In contrast to *macrophagous* animals they tend to feed continuously.

Migration. Fairly regular, instinctive movement of animals. There is normally a seasonal basis and the animals move one way in winter, the other in summer. Fishes going to the spawning grounds, swallows moving north in summer, reindeer moving

MAMMARY GLAND

The structure of a cow's udder.

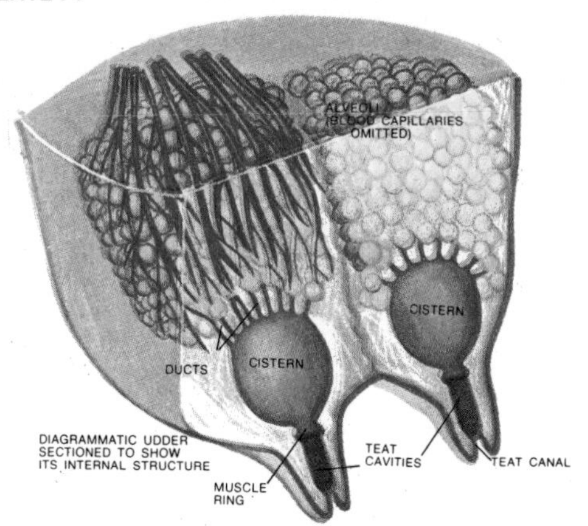

NORMAL PEPPERED MOTH

MELANISM

Many moths occasionally produce black (melanistic) individuals through genetic mutation. These are becoming relatively more common now because the blackening of trees and buildings favours the survival of these black forms (see opposite).

MELANIC PEPPERED MOTH

PLATE 75

1850 A.D.

MELANISM

Under agricultural conditions, the black forms were easily spotted and rarely had a chance to breed.

Industrial conditions favour the survival of the melanic forms. This is an example of natural selection.

1950 A.D.

south into the forests in winter, are all examples. Random mass movements with no later return are called *emigrations* and are normally brought about by overcrowding. The arctic lemmings are famed for their emigrations. Butterfly and locust swarms are also emigrations.

Milk Teeth. The first, deciduous teeth of mammals. Later replaced by permanent teeth. (See *Tooth*).

Mimicry. Phenomenon whereby an animal derives benefit from resembling another species. It can be explained by the Theory of Natural Selection. Among so many species of insect it is not unreasonable to assume that a number of them will look alike, and if one species is protected by evil smell, sting or warning colours—other similar-looking ones will also derive benefit. The resemblance will then be continued and improved by natural selection over many generations.

In 1861 a naturalist named H. W. Bates was travelling along the Amazon and observed that large numbers of black and brown butterflies were protected by having a distasteful flavour but occasionally there appeared specimens of a very different kind. They looked like the common ones but lacked the distasteful flavour. Bates realised that the edible species were protected from enemies by virtue of their resemblance to the other butterflies and that here was an example of mimicry. This type of example, where a harmless species imitates a harmful one, is known as Batesian mimicry.

The animals that are 'copied' are called the models and the others, the mimics. Predators soon learn that certain types of insect or certain colour patterns are associated with stings or vile taste and they leave all such insects alone. The mimic thus gains protection. Even if only one per cent of the mimics are saved, there is a great advantage. The model and mimic must obviously live in the same areas and mix freely. They must also behave in a similar fashion. For example, many spiders mimic ants. The spiders have dark marks on their sides that give the appearance of a narrow thorax while the front legs are held out rigidly in front as if they were antennae. All this would be useless if it were not accompanied by the correct behaviour, and so they dash to and fro in the urgent manner of ants, mingling with them so well that even trained entomologists have captured them thinking they were ants.

Obviously, for this type of mimicry to be effective, the models must be much commoner than the mimics. If this were not so, the predators would be quite likely to associate good food with the colour pattern and both mimic and model would decline.

There are, however, many instances, notably among tropical insects, in which both models and mimics are common, and both are distasteful to predators. This type of mimicry is called Müllerian, after the Brazilian naturalist Müller who described it in 1879. There may be two or more similar species. The advantage of the system is seen in the training of would-be predators. Suppose a bird requires 150 attempts before it realises that certain insects can sting. If a second species is also distasteful, three hundred insects will die before one bird learns to avoid these two species.

However, if the two insect species share a common colour pattern, only seventy-five of each will perish. Thus the mimicry is effective and the more species sharing the pattern the better. But mimicry helps some predators too. The most remarkable examples are the assassin bugs which feed upon other insects. They are remarkably like their prey, even to the smallest detail so that some species resemble stick insects while others look like mosquitoes or even, in one case, the Praying Mantis. The Assassin bugs can deceive even human collectors. (See *Protective Resemblance*) and (Plates 76 and 77).

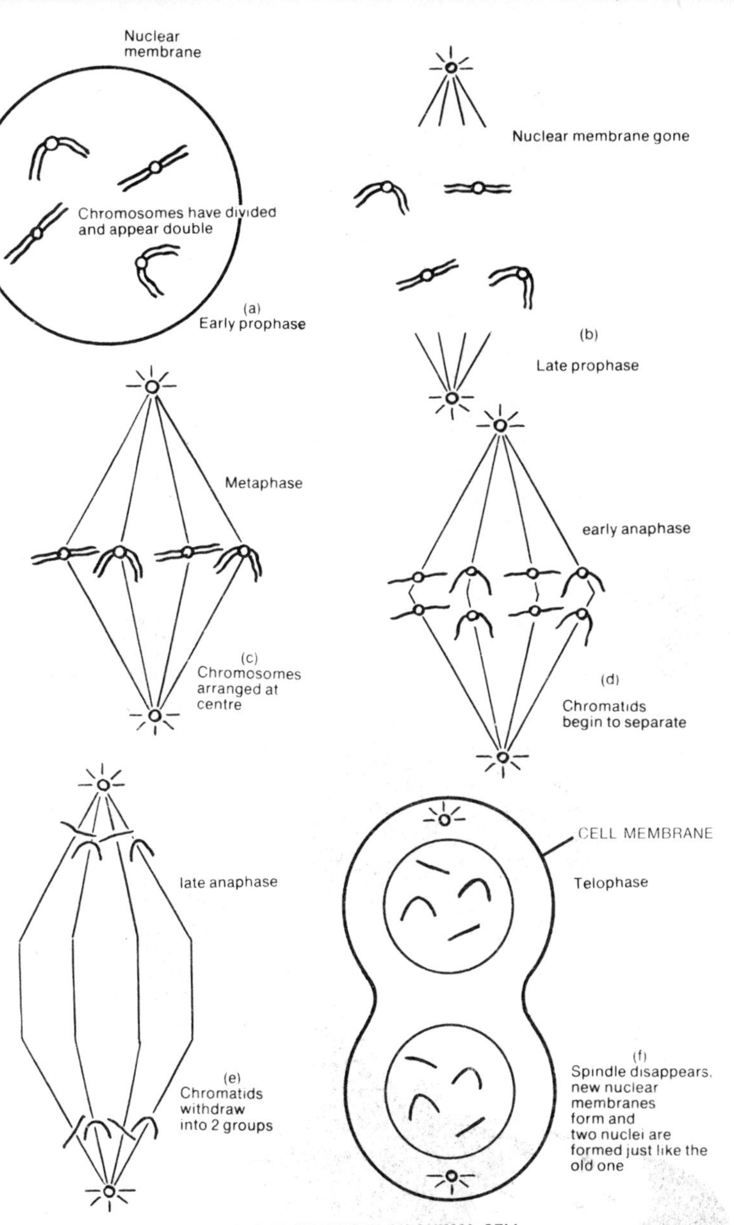

THE STAGES OF MITOSIS IN AN ANIMAL CELL

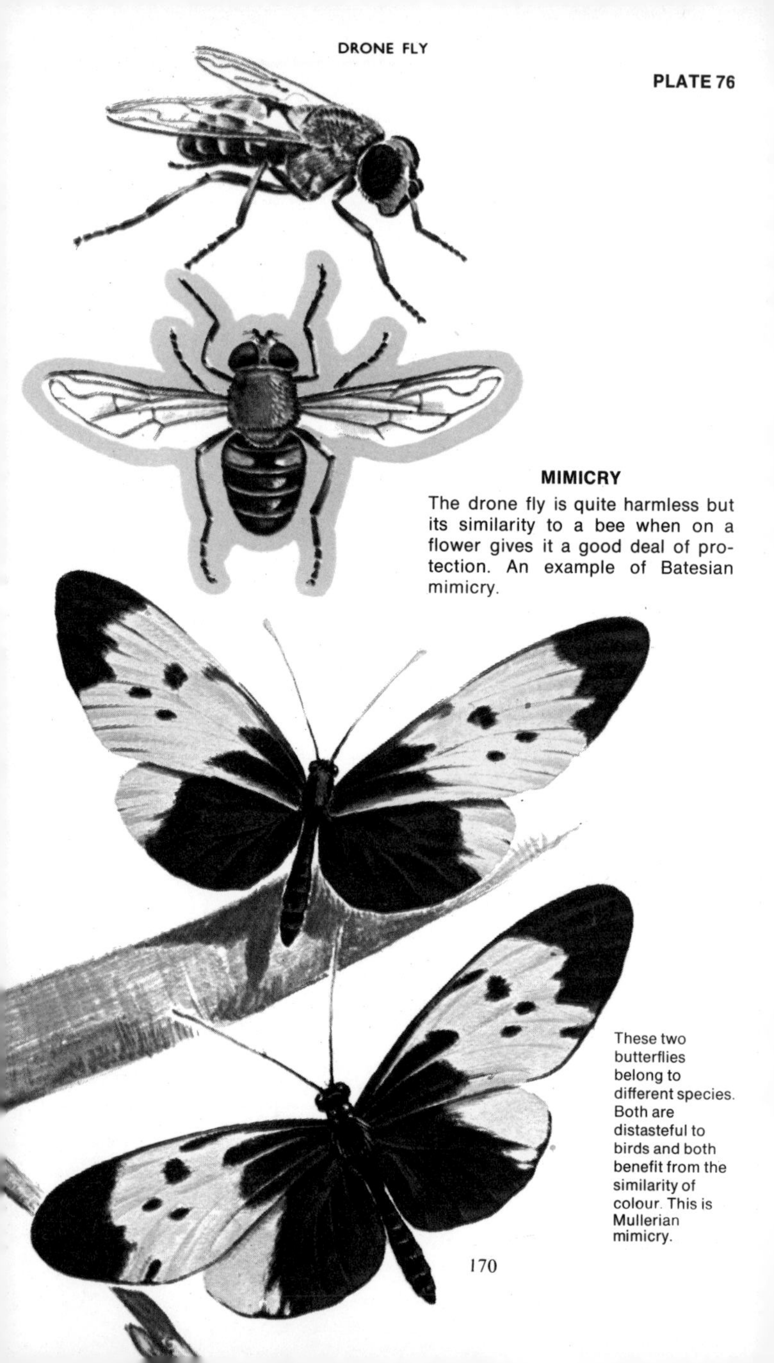

MIMICRY

The drone fly is quite harmless but its similarity to a bee when on a flower gives it a good deal of protection. An example of Batesian mimicry.

These two butterflies belong to different species. Both are distasteful to birds and both benefit from the similarity of colour. This is Mullerian mimicry.

MIMICRY

Many assassin bugs (lower insect) mimic their prey and can thus mingle with them without arousing fear.

Miocene Epoch. Division of geological time. (See *Geological Time Scale*).

Miracidium. A stage in the life-cycle of liver fluke. (See *Trematoda*).

Mite. (See *Acarina*).

Mitochondria. Tiny particles in *cells* (q.v.), that appear to be concerned with respiration.

Mitosis. Nuclear division chief feature of which is that the new nuclei receive identical chromosomes and genes to those of the parent cell. This is the normal process of division that takes place every time new cells are formed in the body. Before the nucleus begins to divide the chromosomes duplicate themselves exactly, forming pairs of *chromatids,* and then during the dividing process one of each pair of chromatids goes to each new nucleus. After the nucleus has divided, the cell itself divides.

Molar. Crushing and grinding tooth in the cheek region of mouth. (See *Tooth*).

Mollusca. A large phylum of soft-bodied, unsegmented animals, normally covered with a calcareous shell. The head is usually well-developed and there is a muscular 'foot'. All or part of the body is covered by a thick sheet of skin – the mantle – which secretes the shell outside it. The animals have a coelom but it is reduced and largely replaced by a haemocoel. Living forms include the slugs and snails, bivalves such as cockles and mussels and oysters, and the squids and octopuses. Among the many extinct forms the ammonites are the most important. The three main classes: *Gasteropoda, Lamellibranchiata;* and *Cephalopoda* (q.v.), have diverged considerably from the ancestral form which must have resembled the present-day chitons somewhat. These animals (Class *Amphineura*) creep about the sea bed on their muscular feet, their bodies protected by a shell consisting of eight plates. The remaining class (*Scaphopoda*) contains a few creatures that are in some respects part way between gasteropods and lamellibranchs. They have a tubular, open-ended shell and burrow in the sea-bed. Like the gasteropods they have a radula. (See Plates 78 and 115).

Monotremata. Order of mammals showing many primitive features that indicate the reptilian ancestry of mammals, although the monotremes – the echidnas and the duck-billed platypus – are only distantly related to the other living mammals. The affinities of the monotremes with the reptiles are especially obvious through similarities in the bones of the skull, the back-bone, and the limbs and limb girdles. The gut, reproductive and excretory systems open into a common chamber, the cloaca, and, perhaps the most striking characteristic of all, they lay large, yolky eggs that have shells. The young are suckled by the female, however, and feed on milk produced by specialised sweat glands on the abdomen. These open as slits; the ducts do not form nipples as in other mammals.

The female echidna grows a pouch during the breeding season. She lays only one egg and, with her beak-like muzzle places it in the pouch to incubate it. The youngster hatches in the pouch and feeds there on milk. After a period of weaning, the young are left to fend for themselves. (See Plate 122–1, 2).

Morphology. The study of the external form of animals and organs.

Mosquito. An insect of the order *Diptera* (q.v.) – family Culicidae. Mosquitoes are extremely important because the females are blood-feeders and transmit a number of serious diseases including malaria and yellow fever after feeding on infected persons. The mouthparts are modified into sharp 'needles' which puncture the skin and which enclose two channels—one up which blood is sucked, the other down which saliva and infectious parasites enter the wound. The eggs of mosquitoes are laid in water and the larvae develop there. Unlike the pupae of most insects, the mosquito pupa can move about, although it does not feed in this stage. (See Plate 78).

Moth. (See *Lepidoptera*).

Motor. Motor nerve fibres are those that carry impulses to muscles and glands, stimulating them to action. *Sensory* fibres are those that carry messages to the brain from sense organs.

Muscle. A highly contractile tissue that is responsible for the majority of animal movements. Muscle is composed of fibres of which there are three main types. *Striped,* or *skeletal* muscle fibres, which make up the bulk of the body's muscles, are about 1/10th millimetre in diameter but they may be several centimeters long. Each contains hundreds of nuclei and is made of long, thin strands (fibrils) which are striped with alternate light and dark bands. The width of these bands alters when the muscle contracts. Striped muscle is under conscious control and can contract very rapidly. *Unstriped* muscle is found in the lining of the gut and the blood vessels and certain other places in vertebrates. It is controlled by the nervous system but not consciously (See *Autonomic Nervous System*). Each fibre is about 1/5th millimetre long and 1/150th millimetre wide and contains only one nucleus. Unlike striped muscle, it can maintain a state of contraction for long periods without fatigue. Also called smooth or involuntary muscle. *Cardiac muscle* is found only in the heart. Its fibres branch and form an elaborate network well-suited to the continual contraction and relaxation of the heart. Its fibrils are similar to those of ordinary striped muscle. (See Page 176).

Musculo-epithelial Cell. Characteristic cell of *Coelenterata* (q.v.) (See Plate 22).

Mutation. A sudden change in a gene or chromosome that leads to the appearance of new features in the organism possessing it. Because they are controlled by genes, these new features can be inherited. Most mutations are harmful and the animals do not normally survive, but some are useful and make the animal more successful. These useful mutations will be passed on to succeeding generations. (See *Natural Selection*).

Myelin. Fatty substance sheathing nerve fibres of vertebrates and some other animals.

Myriapoda. Class of *Arthropoda* (q.v.), containing the centipedes (*Chilopoda*) and millipedes (*Diplopoda*). They have one pair of antennae, many pairs of legs and breathe by means of tracheae. Centipedes have one pair of legs per segment while millipedes have two pairs per segment. Among many other differences, centipedes are carnivorous while millipedes feed on vegetable matter. Although included in one class, the two groups are not closely related. (See Plate 111).

Nares. Nostrils—the openings of the nasal or olfactory cavity. In most fishes the only openings are on the outside of the head—external nares—the olfactory organs being merely sunk into pits in the head. In lungfishes and all higher vertebrates, however, there are also internal nares opening into the mouth. (See Plates 82 and 83).

Natural Selection. A naturally occurring mechanism which Darwin suggested as the basis of evolution and which is now widely held to be so.

Darwin's theory appeared in print in 1859 as the famous 'Origin of Species' although he had previously lectured on his findings and those of Wallace who arrived independently

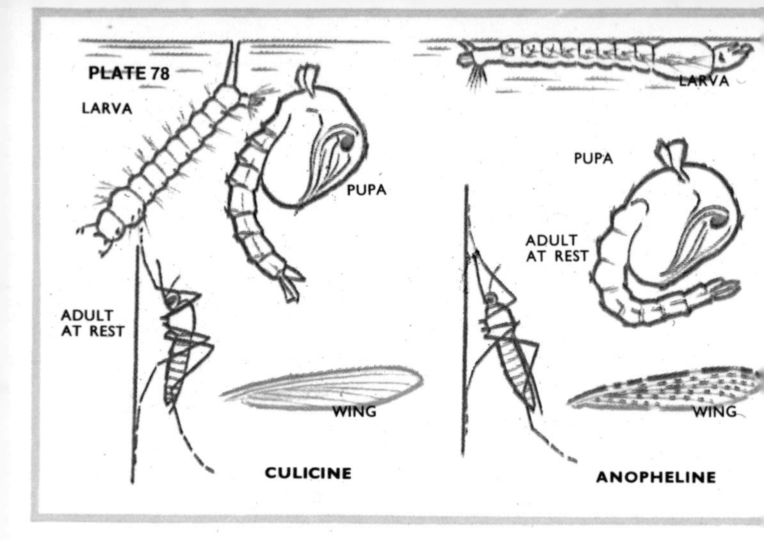

MOSQUITO
The differences between the two main groups of mosquitoes.

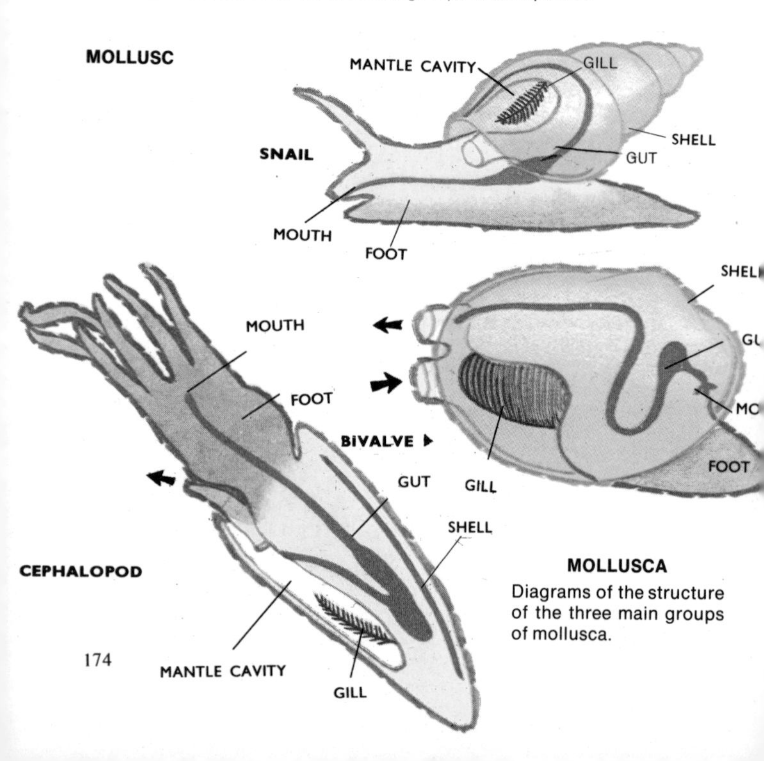

MOLLUSCA
Diagrams of the structure of the three main groups of mollusca.

NEOTENY

The mud-puppy, one of many salamanders that retain larval characters throughout life.

NERVE CELL

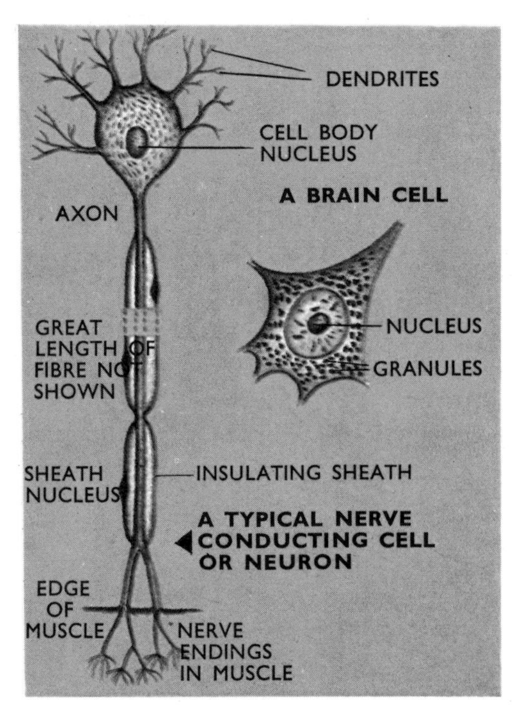

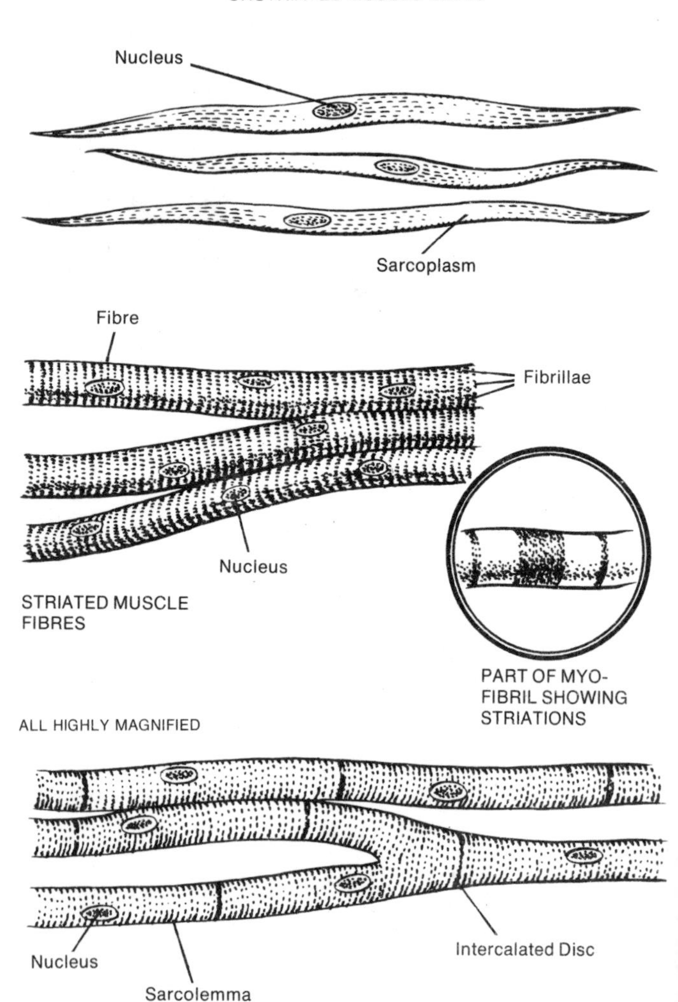
UNSTRIATED MUSCLE CELLS
Nucleus
Sarcoplasm
Fibre
Fibrillae
Nucleus
STRIATED MUSCLE FIBRES
PART OF MYO-FIBRIL SHOWING STRIATIONS
ALL HIGHLY MAGNIFIED
Nucleus
Sarcolemma
Intercalated Disc
CARDIAC MUSCLE FIBRES

at a similar theory at about the same time. Darwin witnessed the 'struggle for existence' among animals. Most of them produce many offspring but only a few survive. The others succumb to predators and disease: in other words there is 'survival of the fittest'. Darwin also noticed that individuals of a species all vary slightly. Such variations make some animals more suited to their surroundings than others. Those best suited are more likely to survive and to reproduce and therefore the favourable variations will be passed on to the next generation. In this way an animal species gradually changes and becomes ideally suited to its surroundings. The latter are always changing however and so natural selection works continuously to produce new forms and, eventually, new species.

Darwin's theory of Natural Selection can explain the evolution of the giraffe's neck quite easily. The early giraffes competed with other animals for food. The giraffes with the longest necks were able to get better food and thus survived better and produced more offspring. These offspring too, had long necks but, more important, they varied among themselves. Selection again acted in favour of those with the longest necks. Over many generations the average neck length increased until the present-day giraffes appeared. Lamarck (See *Lamarckism*) would have argued that by stretching to reach the higher branches, the giraffes gradually grew longer necks.

Although Darwin's theory showed clearly how natural variation could be the basis of evolutionary change, there was no explanation of how the variations occurred or how they were inherited. Later work on genetics, however, has shown how the natural variation can come about and also how sudden changes may lead to the appearance of new characteristics (See *Heredity; Mutation*).

Nekton. The free-swimming life in the sea as opposed to the floating plankton and the bottom-living benthos. Fishes, squids, and whales make up most of the nekton. There is no sharp division between nekton and plankton for some animals which can swim actively spend much of their time floating with the plankton.

Nematocyst. Stinging capsule of *Coelenterata* (q.v.). (See Plate 23).

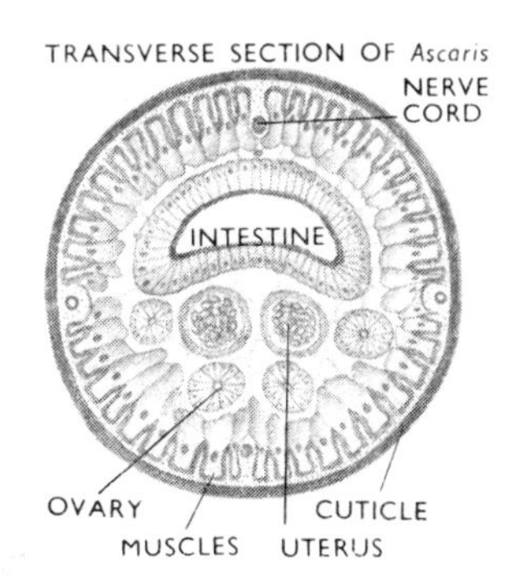

Nematoda. Roundworms or eelworms. Members of this phylum have cylindrical, unsegmented bodies, pointed at both ends. There is no coelom but a fluid-filled space surrounds the gut and other organs of many species. Nematodes are found in every conceivable habitat and as individuals are extremely numerous. Many are parasitic and cause severe damage to crops (e.g. potato eelworm) or to animals, including man. *Ascaris lumbricoides,* found in the intestine of man and pigs, may reach a length of nine inches but the majority of nematodes are very much smaller. (See Plate 109).

Nematomorpha. Small phylum of very fine worm-like creatures (hairworms) which in their young stages parasitise insects. (See Page 260).

Nemertea. Proboscis worms – a small phylum of free-living, unsegmented worms most of which are marine. In

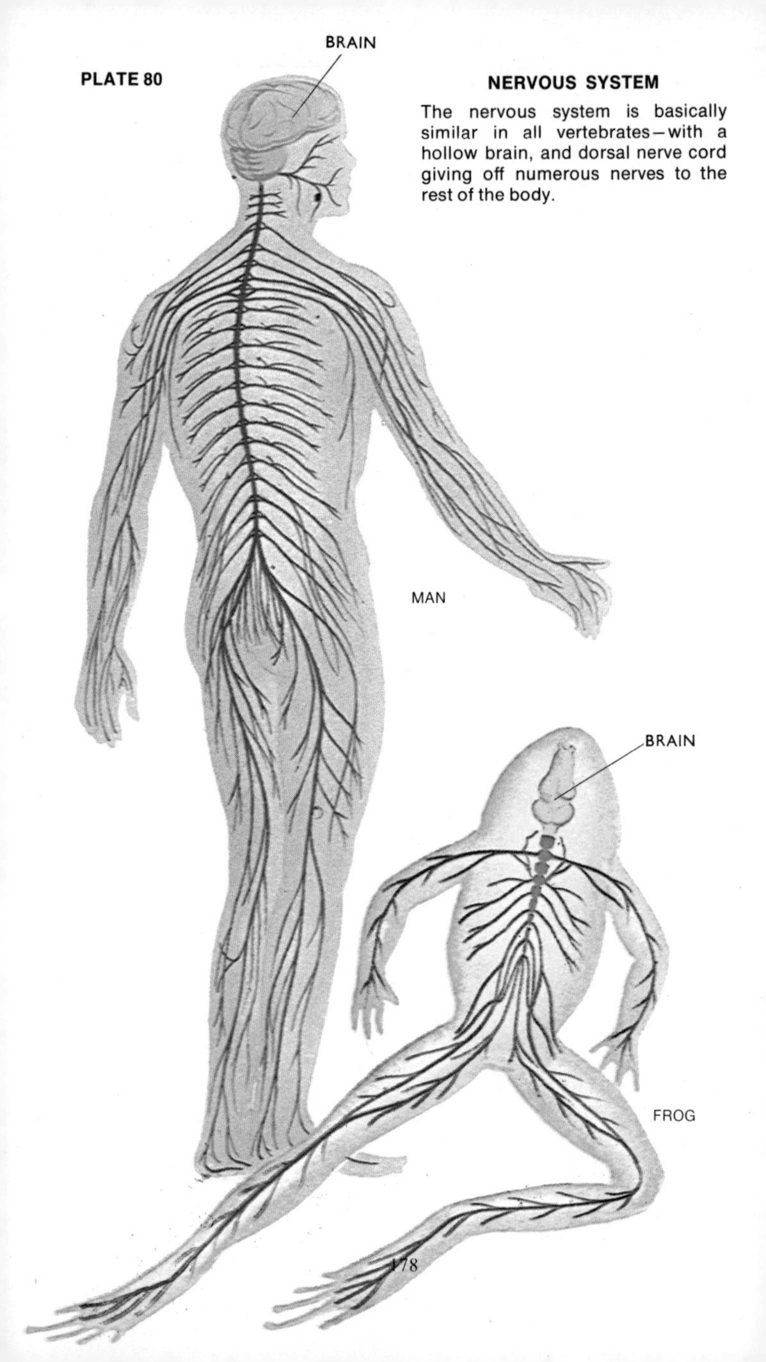

NERVOUS SYSTEM

The nervous system is basically similar in all vertebrates—with a hollow brain, and dorsal nerve cord giving off numerous nerves to the rest of the body.

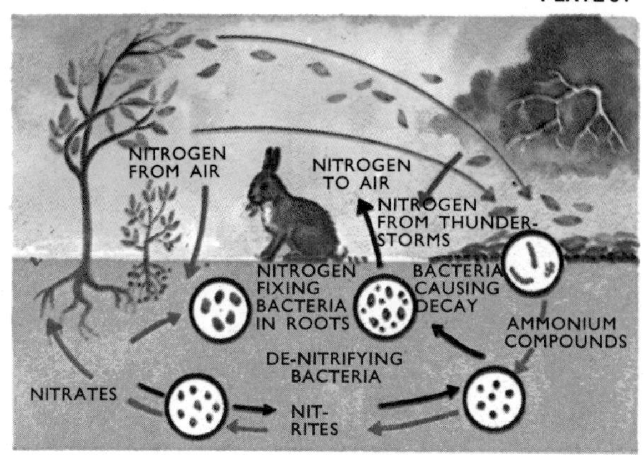

NITROGEN CYCLE

A simplified diagram showing the circulation of nitrogen.

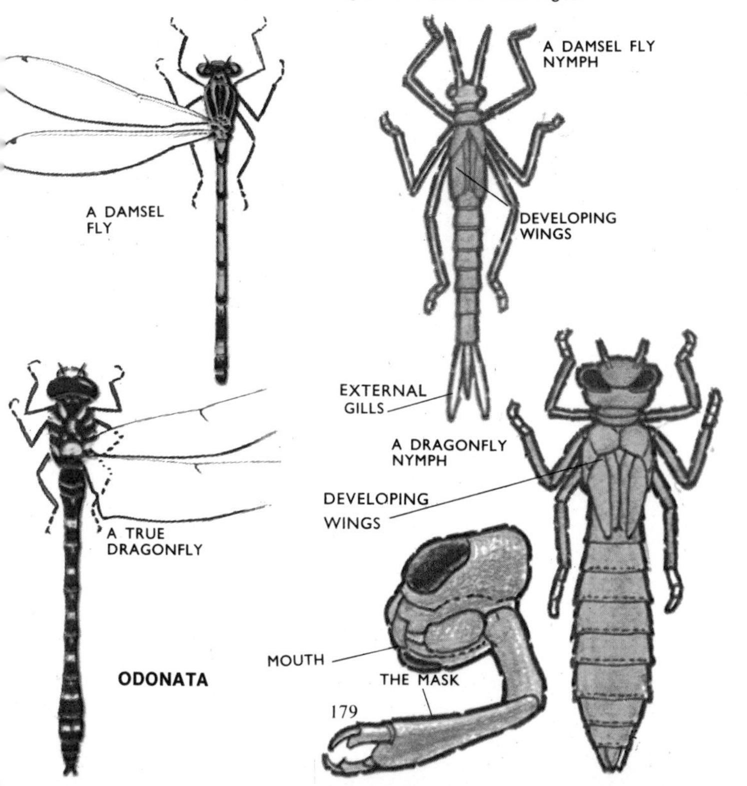

ODONATA

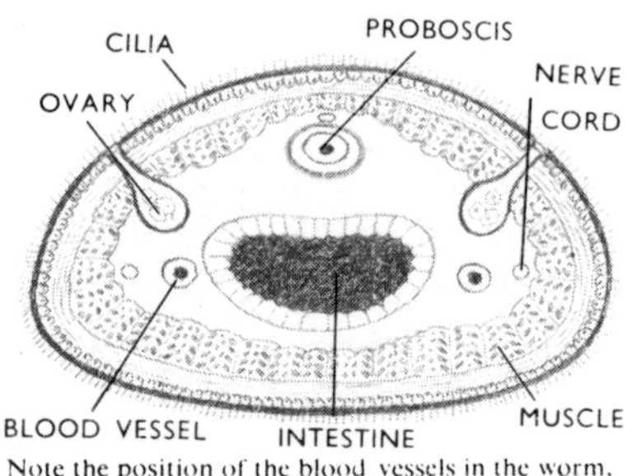

Note the position of the blood vessels in the worm, the lateral nerve cords and the proboscis

Micrura

CIRCULATORY SYSTEM

BASIC MORE COMPLEX

1. PROBOSCIS EXTENDED
2. CONTRACTED

The basic circulatory system consists of three blood vessels running alongside each other (see above). Sometimes the blood is coloured by an oxygen carrying pigment, haemoglobin. The PROBOSCIS is sticky and traps prey.

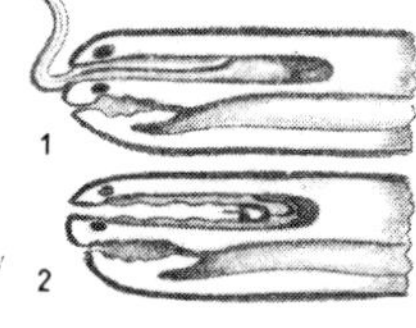

being flattened and possessing flame-cells (q.v.), they resemble the platyhelminthes, but they show certain advances over the latter – notably the possession of a blood system and two openings to the gut. The most characteristic feature is the proboscis which lies in a cavity above the gut. It is rather like the finger of a glove that has been pulled into the hand by a muscle attached to the tip. It may be sticky or armed with spines and it can be shot out by muscular action to catch food. (See Plate 109).

Neoteny. The persistence of larval features in an animal beyond the normal larval period. It may be temporary – caused by unsuitable conditions for further development – or it may be a permanent retention of larval characteristics in an otherwise adult animal. In permanent neoteny – called paedogenesis – the animal breeds in its larval form. Many salamanders show neoteny and paedogenesis. The phenomenon may have played a large part in evolution. (See Plate 79).

Nephridium. Excretory organ of many invertebrates consisting of a tube opening to the exterior. The inner end may be closed as in the flatworms and other acoelomates (See *Flame Cell*), or open as in annelid worms. (See *Oligochaeta*) and (Plates 84 and 85).

Nerve. Group of nerve fibres, together with their surrounding membranes, running to or from a particular region.

Nerve Cell (=*Neurone*). Cell of the nervous system that actually conducts impulses. Typically the cell body is rounded and gives off one long axon and several short dendrites. The axon is not always present, however: brain cells and cells of primitive nerve nets give off a number of fairly equal processes and pass signals in all directions. The axon, together with the surrounding membranes and fatty sheath, forms the nerve fibre and it may be nearly as long as the animal itself. The impulses pass from the cell-body along the axon which ends in a muscle or gland or makes a synapse with the dendrites of another neurone. A *synapse* is a junction between neighbouring nerve cells. The cells do not join but impulses are able to 'jump' the gap and continue their way. Nerve fibres or axons can normally conduct impulses in only one direction – towards the central nervous system in the case of sensory nerves, and away from it in the case of motor nerves. The majority of cell bodies lie within the central nervous system so that the nerves running through the body are composed almost entirely of axons and their sheaths. (See Plate 79).

Nerve Cord. Any major nervous pathway, such as the spinal cord.

Nerve Fibre (See *Nerve Cell*).

Nerve Net. Simple nervous system found in *Coelenterata* and *Echinodermata* (q.v.). The cells branch out in all directions and connect up to form the net but there is nothing that can be called a brain.

Nerve Root (See *Spinal Nerve*).

Nervous System. The whole system of nerves in an animal. A nervous system is found in all many-celled animals apart from the sponges. Every action involves the nervous system to some degree. (See Plate 80).

Neurone (=*Nerve Cell*).

Neuroptera. Order of *Insecta* (q.v.), containing the lacewing flies and related insects. The delicate wings are criss-crossed by many tiny veins. Metamorphosis is complete and the larvae generally feed on other insects, notably aphids. (See Plate 113).

Nictitating Membrane. 3rd eyelid – a transparent fold of skin found in many birds and reptiles and some amphibians. Only a few mammals have one.

Nidicolous Birds. Those hatching at an early stage of development and remaining in the nest for a relatively long period.

Nidifugous Birds. Those that hatch at a relatively advanced stage and leave the nest almost immediately – e.g. ducks.

Nitrogen Cycle. Nitrogen is one of the essential elements of life, being a major constituent of protein. In the form of nitrates, nitrogen is absorbed by plants and used to build up proteins. These are consumed by animals and converted to other proteins in the body. Upon the death of the organisms, the organic substances decay and bacteria convert the proteins back to nitrites and nitrates which can be used again by plants. This is the basis of the nitrogen cycle. A few bacteria, notably those forming nodules in the roots of leguminous plants, can convert free nitrogen into nitrates. Nitrates are also formed during thunder-storms: the energy of lightning causes oxygen and nitrogen to combine. The compound so formed dissolves in the rain water and falls to earth as a very dilute solution of nitric acid. This acts on minerals in the soil to form nitrates. But the formation of nitrates in this way is offset by the activity of certain bacteria that break down protein and release free nitrogen to the air. (See Plate 81).

Notochord. A flexible skeletal rod found at some stage during the life of all chordates. In most vertebrates it is found only in the embryo and is later replaced by the vertebral column. (See Plates 21 and 30).

PLATE 82

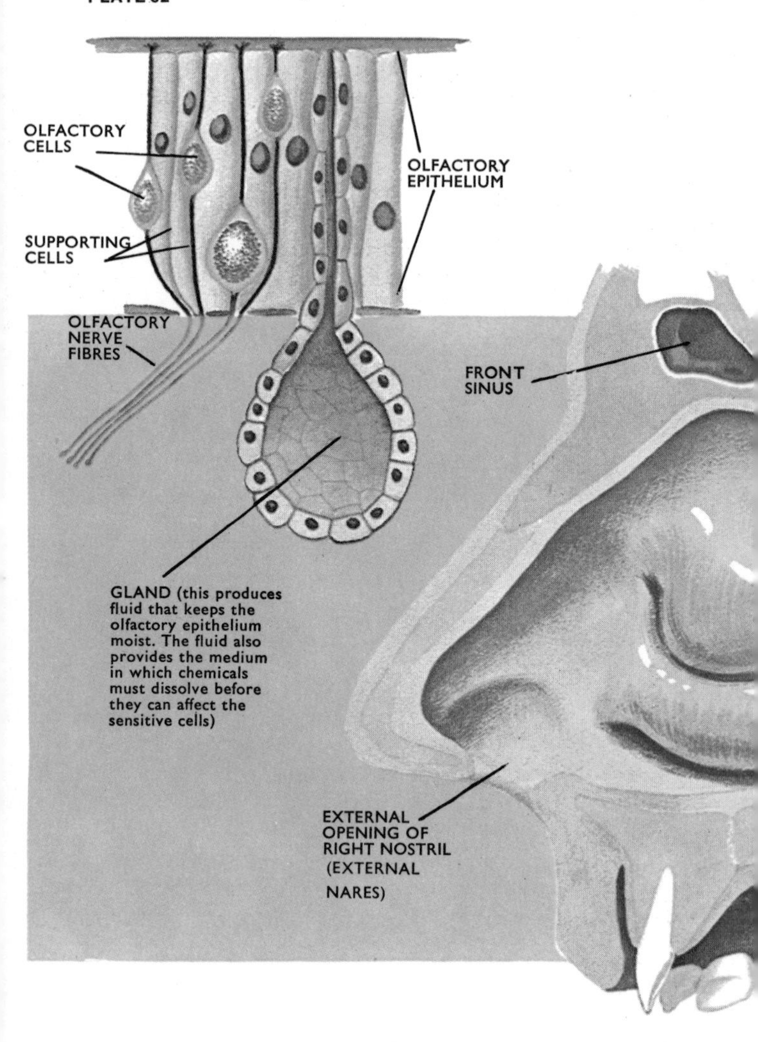

OLFACTORY SENSE

A diagram of the human nasal cavity showing the olfactory area and the false palate which grows in from the jaw-bone and divides the mouth cavity from the nasal cavity.

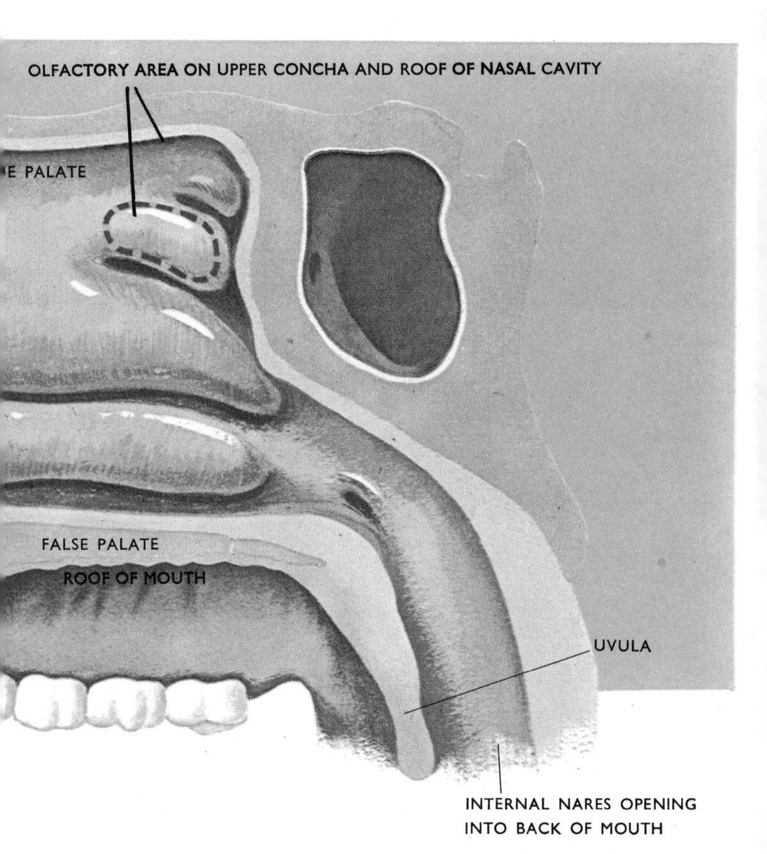
OLFACTORY AREA ON UPPER CONCHA AND ROOF OF NASAL CAVITY
E PALATE
FALSE PALATE
ROOF OF MOUTH
UVULA
INTERNAL NARES OPENING
INTO BACK OF MOUTH

Nucleic Acid. A complex compound made up of chains of pentose sugar molecules linked to molecules of phosphate and nitrogen-containing molecules called bases. Nucleic acids occur in the chromosomes and in the cytoplasm of the cell. The genes are, in fact, chains of nucleic acid put together in various ways, and they control the features of the cells by controlling the types of protein that are made in the cells.

Nucleolus. Dense region of cell nucleus. (See *Cell*).

Nucleus. A feature of nearly all *cells* (q.v.) which contains the chromosomes and appears to be the controlling influence of the cell.

Nymph. Young stage of an insect that differs from the adult mainly in size and the absence of fully developed wings and sex organs. The wings develop gradually on the outside of the body (exopterygote condition). (See *Insecta; Larva*) and (Plates 63 and 81).

Ocellus. Simple eye of many invertebrate animals, capable only of distinguishing light and dark.

Oculomotor Nerve. 3rd *cranial nerve* (q.v.) of vertebrate head supplying four of the six *eye muscles* (q.v.).

Odonata. Order of *Insecta* (q.v.) including the dragonflies and damsel flies. Nymphs are aquatic and, like the adults are carnivorous. There are two main sub-orders – Anisoptera, containing the true dragonflies, and Zygoptera, containing the more slender and weaker-flying damsel flies. Nymphs of the latter have external gills at the hind end, whereas the gills of the anisopterans are inside the rectum. The labium (lower lip) of the nymph is modified to form the *mask* which is shot out from under the head to capture food in its pincers. (See Plate 81) and (Page 268).

Oesophagus. Part of *alimentary canal* (q.v.) leading from throat to stomach.

Oestrus Cycle. Cycle of changes in the female reproductive system of many mammal species. The cycle starts with the growth of the eggs in the ovary and the growth of the wall of the uterus. The eggs are then released and this is accompanied by a short period of oestrus or 'heat' during which the female is prepared to mate. She will not mate at any other time. If the eggs are fertilised, the cycle is suspended while the embryo(s) develops and there is a great deal of hormone secretion by the corpus luteum in the ovary. If fertilisation does not occur, the corpus luteum soon degenerates and the lining of the uterus returns to its normal thickness. The cycle varies in time from a few days to several weeks. In many animals the cycle starts again immediately but some have definite breeding seasons and the oestrus cycle is active only at these times. Some animals have one oestrus cycle per year. The *menstrual cycle* (q.v.) is a variation of the oestrus cycle.

Olfactory Sense. The sense of smell. It is a chemical sense, the olfactory cells being stimulated by actual molecules of the substance concerned. The smell receptors are carried on the antennae of many arthropods, being extremely well-developed in many moths. In fishes they occur in pits on the snout; in other vertebrates they are embedded in the lining tissue of the nose, on the roof of the nasal cavity, on the upper part of the wall that divides the nose into two halves and on the upper fold (concha) in each half.

The olfactory cells are unique in that their axons pass to the central nervous system. (Generally nerve processes grow out from the central nervous system.) They are surrounded by supporting cells and glands. The latter produce a yellowish-brown fluid which moistens the ends of the olfactory cells. The chemicals to which the receptors are sensitive dissolve in this fluid. Its continuous production washes away chemicals that have already stimulated the receptors and so leaves them clean and prepared for further substances. All the olfactory cells have the same structure yet we can appreciate a wide range of smells. There are many smell receptors and numerous nerve fibres carrying signals to the brain. Within the olfactory parts of the brain the nerve fibres interweave and connect up with others in a most complicated way. It is possible that there are several different sorts of receptors sensitive to different smells. Since each part of the olfactory lobe receives impulses from a variety of receptors because of the elaborate interconnections, a whole range of different smelling substances can be distinguished. (See Plates 82 and 83).

Oligo- (=Few).

Oligocene Epoch. Division of Tertiary Period. (See *Geological Time Scale*).

Oligochaeta. Class of *Annelida* (q.v.), containing the earthworms such as *Lumbricus* and a number of freshwater forms. The following account is of *Lumbricus terrestris* but the main features are the same in the whole class. (See Plates 5, 84 and 85).

There are about 150 segments—all basically alike. The most noticeable external feature is the clitellum or 'saddle' which is a thicker region between segments 32 and 37 and which is concerned with reproduction. Each segment other than the first and last has four pairs of small *chaetae* that assist movement and are responsible for the roughness of the worm.

The movement of a worm can be studied by allowing it to crawl over a piece of rough paper. The bristles at the front end are withdrawn and the front end is pushed forward. Circular muscles in the body wall contract and the pressure on the body fluids causes the body to lengthen. Then the bristles are extended again and grip the surface. Bristles at the hind end are withdrawn and, by contraction of the longitudinal muscles, the hind region is drawn up towards the front. The bristles are again extended to anchor the hind end and the front moves forward once more.

This type of movement is rather slow but the worm can also move very fast. If it is disturbed when partly out of its burrow it can withdraw very rapidly. Some large nerve fibres running the whole length of the body carry messages rapidly to all the muscles and they contract quickly. As the hind end of the worm is fixed in the burrow by means of the bristles, the result is that the whole body shortens and retreats into the hole. The worm makes use of the two muscle layers in burrowing too. The circular muscles contract, making the body thin. It can then squeeze into cracks between soil particles. Then the longitudinal muscles contract and the pressure on the body fluids makes the worm fatter, thus enlarging the hole and allowing the worm to pass in.

Internally, the most noticeable feature is the food canal extending the whole length of the body. It is generally surrounded by a mass of yellow *chloragogen cells* that are concerned with excretion. The mouth opening (in segment one) leads into the small *buccal cavity*. In segment three this passes into the muscular *pharynx* which occupies the next three segments. Glands in the pharynx secrete mucus and enzymes that mix with the food.

On the front of the pharynx there are two small masses of nerve tissue connected by a 'collar' of nerves (commissures) to the main nerve cord running underneath the gut. These masses of tissue form the 'brain' of the worm.

Behind the pharynx comes the *oesophagus*—a narrower part of the gut which is surrounded by five pairs of blood vessels called pseudohearts. These contract rhythmically and carry blood from the dorsal vessel to the vessel underneath the gut. Bulging out from the oesophagus are a number of small pouches which secrete calcium

N

PLATE 84

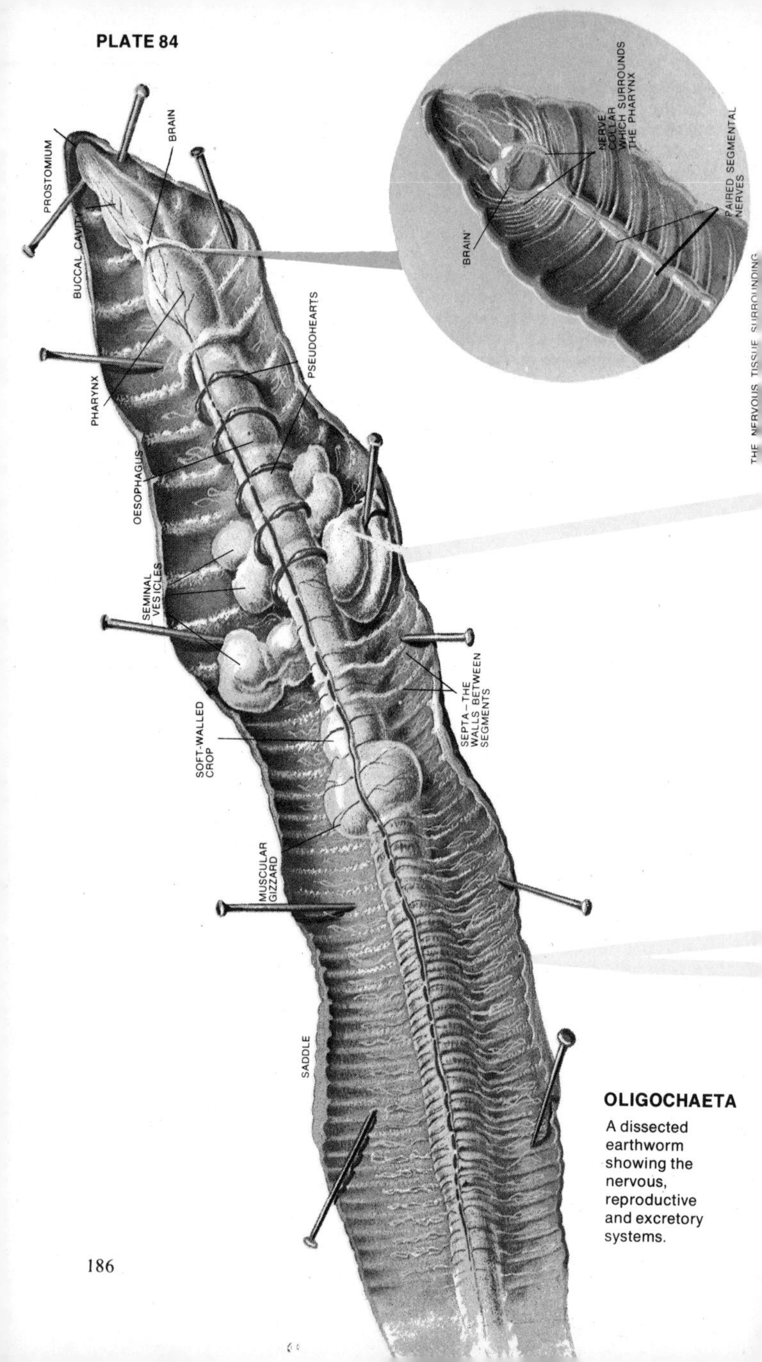

OLIGOCHAETA

A dissected earthworm showing the nervous, reproductive and excretory systems.

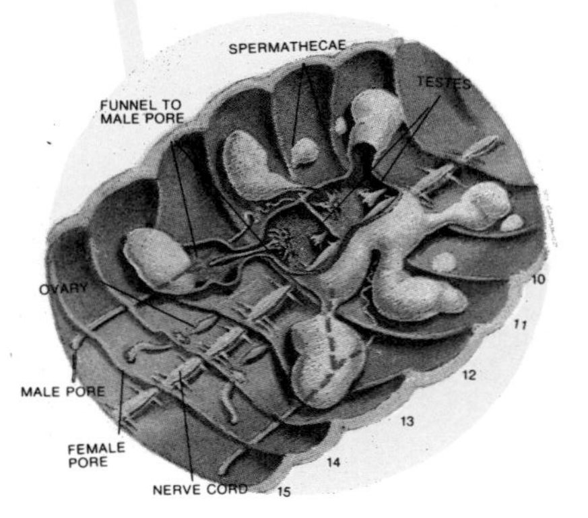

THE REPRODUCTIVE SYSTEM WITH THE SEMINAL VESICLES PARTLY CUT AWAY TO SHOW THE TESTES AND THE FUNNELS LEADING TO THE PORES. THE OVARIES AND SPERMATHECAE ARE ALSO SHOWN.

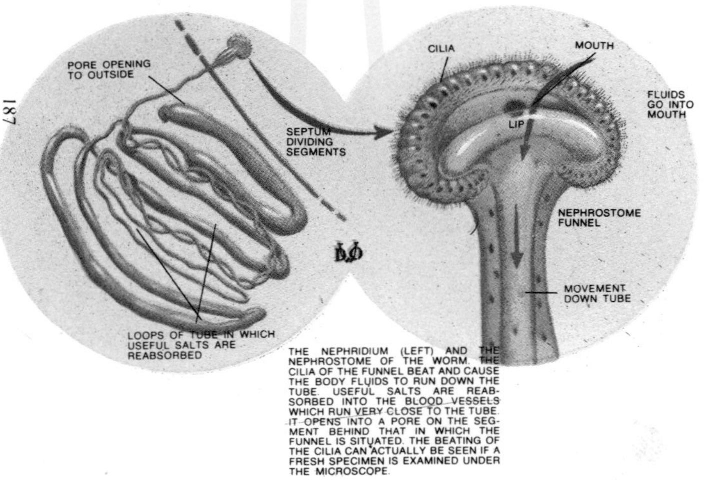

THE NEPHRIDIUM (LEFT) AND THE NEPHROSTOME OF THE WORM. THE CILIA OF THE FUNNEL BEAT AND CAUSE THE BODY FLUIDS TO RUN DOWN THE TUBE. USEFUL SALTS ARE REABSORBED INTO THE BLOOD VESSELS WHICH RUN VERY CLOSE TO THE TUBE. IT OPENS INTO A PORE ON THE SEGMENT BEHIND THAT IN WHICH THE FUNNEL IS SITUATED. THE BEATING OF THE CILIA CAN ACTUALLY BE SEEN IF A FRESH SPECIMEN IS EXAMINED UNDER THE MICROSCOPE.

carbonate. In this way the worm gets rid of unwanted calcium and carbon dioxide.

Worms feed by swallowing soil as they go through the earth. Much of their tunnelling is done by swallowing the soil as well as by forcing the particles aside. The soil goes through the oesophagus and into the soft-walled *crop* which probably secretes digestive juices. Behind the crop is the *gizzard* where the soil particles are crushed to release all digestible material (i.e. decaying plant and animal remains). From the *gizzard* it all passes to the *intestine* where the food is further digested and absorbed. The undigested soil particles, together with a fair amount of calcium carbonate pass out of the worm as *worm casts*. Most worms, including *Lumbricus,* deposit their casts under the surface but a few species make surface casts. This ploughing action of worms is of great importance and without it, soil would soon become compacted and sterile.

When disturbed, worms quickly begin to burrow again for although they have no eyes, they do not like the light. They often come to the surface at night and drag leaves or other material into their burrows. They return to their burrows when it gets light, hence the expression the early bird gets the worm. Worms rarely come to the surface in dry weather or when it is very cold.

Earthworms are *hermaphrodite* animals. When the worm is opened, the large white lobes of the *seminal vesicles* are clearly seen around the oesophagus in segments 9 to 13. This is where the male cells are stored while they mature. To examine the reproductive system fully, the food canal must be cut away carefully. In segments 9 and 10 there are two pairs of *spermathecae* and in segment 13 a pair of tiny *ovaries* where the eggs are produced.

If the mid-part of the seminal vesicles is opened, it may be possible to see the tiny testes where the male cells are actually produced and the funnels which lead to the outside. These funnels open to the outside in segment 15 while the funnels carrying the eggs open in segment 14.

Although both male and female structures are present in each worm, two individuals must come together to reproduce. This usually happens on damp nights when the worms leave their burrows. Two worms come together, each with segments 9 to 11 opposite the saddle of the other. They secrete a lot of mucus around themselves and then male cells are exchanged.

Sperms leave the opening on segment 15 and run into a groove that extends backwards to the saddle. A series of muscle ripples carries the sperms along to the saddle from where they pass into the openings of the spermathecae of the other worm. The two worms then separate.

In *each* worm the saddle then produces a cocoon made up of slime cells. A dozen or so eggs pass back along a groove into the cocoon which then becomes detached from the body and slides off towards the front. On the way it picks up sperms pushed out of the spermathecae (i.e. sperms from the other worm). These sperms fertilise the eggs. The brownish cocoon is shed into the soil and is about the size of a pea. Usually only one embryo survives in each *Lumbricus* cocoon but several cocoons are produced by each adult until all the sperms have been discharged from the spermathecae.

After a few weeks the young worms leave the cocoons and those that escape the attention of moles, birds and other enemies may live for two or three years.

Unwanted carbon dioxide produced in respiration is got rid of by combining it with excess calcium absorbed from the soil to form calcium carbonate ($CaCO_3$). This then passes out with the undigested soil. Waste nitrogenous material is excreted via the yellow cells surrounding the gut. These cells also store fats. The yellow cells secrete the nitrogen-containing substances into the body fluid. This then passes into the nephridia-paired tubes that occur in all but the first three and the last segments. The inner end of the nephridium is the *nephrostome*. It is a tiny funnel covered with cilia which beat continuously and help to move the fluid dowm into the tube. If a nephrostome is removed from a freshly killed worm and looked at under the microscope it may even be possible to see the beating of the cilia. The tubes open to the outside by tiny pores. Blood vessels are closely connected with the coiled tubes and as the fluid moves down towards the pore, useful salts are reabsorbed. Excess water and the unwanted materials then pass out of the body.

Ommatidium. Unit of compound eye (See *Eye, Compound*) and (Plate 46).

Onychophora. Primitive class of *Arthropoda* (q.v.) which, in the possession of cilia and some other features, resemble annelid worms. The class contains *Peripatus* and related animals which are caterpillar-like, having numerous stumpy but unjointed legs. They are found in most of the warmer parts of the world where they live under logs and in other damp places. (See Plate 111).

Operculum. The cover protecting the gill-slits of bony fishes. Also the horny plate with which many *gasteropods* (q.v.) close their shell when at rest.

Ophidia. Sub-order of *Squamata* (q.v.). Snakes. (See *Reptilia*).

Ophiuroidea. Brittle stars. (See *Echinodermata*).

Optic. Concerning the eye. Optic nerve is second *cranial nerve* (q.v.).

Oral. Concerning the mouth.

Orbit. Bony cavity housing the eye of vertebrates.

Order. Category used in *classification* (q.v.).

Ordovician Period. Period of geological time. Began about 420 million years ago. (See *Geological Time Scale*).

Organelle. Part of a cell, especially of protozoan, forming a distinct unit. E.g. a flagellum.

Ornithischia. (See *Dinosaur*).

Orthoptera. Order of *Insecta* (q.v.) containing crickets and grasshoppers. The hind legs are modified for jumping. Many produce sound by rubbing two parts of the body together. (See *Stridulation*) and (Plate 93) and (Page 268).

Osculum. Large opening through which water leaves the body of sponges. (See *Porifera*) and (Plate 88).

Osteichthyes. Bony fishes, as opposed to the cartilaginous sharks and rays. Divided into two classes—*Actinopterygii* and *Crossopterygii* (q.v.). (See Page 276).

Osteoblast. Bone-secreting cell. (See *Bone*).

Ostium. Small pore of sponge. (See *Porifera*) and (Plates 88 and 89).

Ostracodermi. Term sometimes used to refer to ancient jawless fishes which were heavily armoured.

Otolith. Calcium carbonate granule of vertebrate inner ear. By falling against various sensitive cells it informs the animal of its position with respect to gravity. (See *Ear*).

Ovary. Organ in which female sex-cells are formed. Also produces various female hormones. (See Plates 84, 85 and 86).

Oviduct. Tube carrying egg-cells to the outside. Fertilisation may occur at some point in the oviduct.

Oviparous. Laying eggs in which

PLATE 86

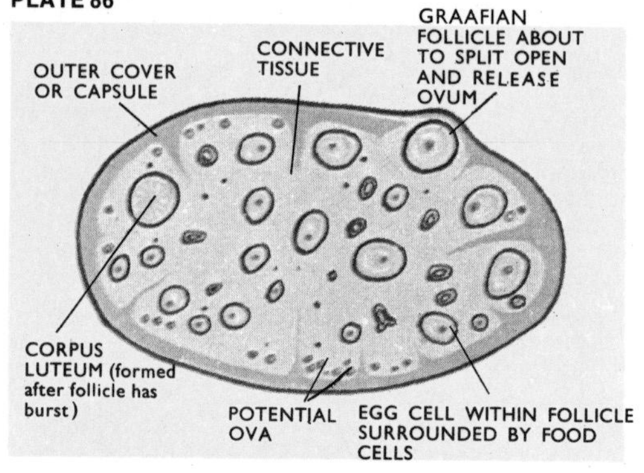

OVARY

Structure of the mammalian ovary showing ova at various stages of development.

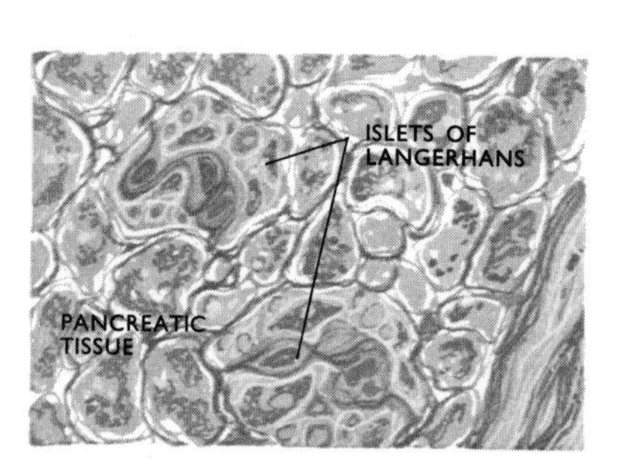

PANCREAS

Pancreas section showing pancreatic tissue that secretes digestive enzymes and Islets of Langerhans that secrete insulin.

PINNIPEDIA

Pinnipedia – a division of order Carnivora.

PLATE 87

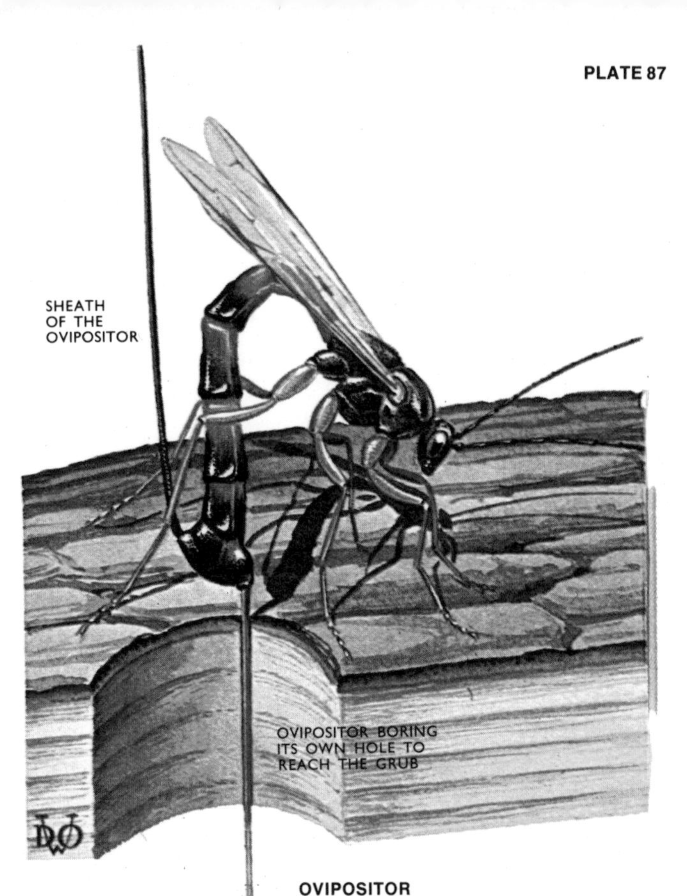

OVIPOSITOR

The ichneumon *Rhyssa* has a very long ovipositor with which it can bore into wood and lay an egg on a wood wasp grub deep in the wood.

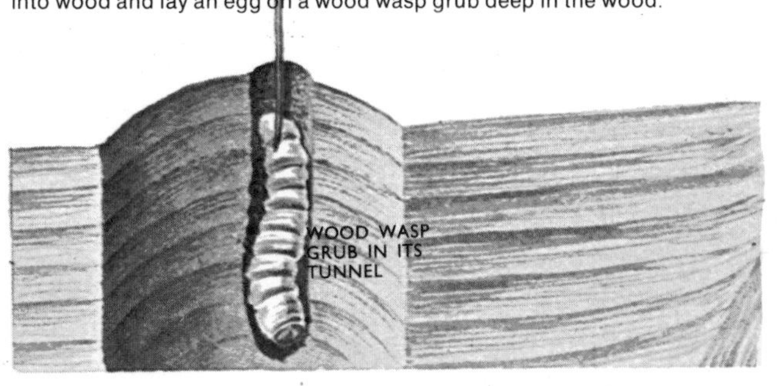

embryos are at a very early stage. (See *Ovoviviparous; Viviparous*).

Ovipositor. Organ possessed by many female insects for placing eggs in suitable position. It is made of several parts that interlock. The ovipositor of many hymenopterans is very long and in the ichneumon *Rhyssa* it can drill a hole in wood to reach the grub in which *Rhyssa* lays its eggs. The stings of bees and wasps are modified ovipositors and that is why the drones cannot sting – they have no egg-laying apparatus. (See Plates 10, 11, 63, 87).

Ovotestis. Organ of hermaphrodite animals such as snails that acts as both male and female gonad.

Ovoviviparous. Producing eggs that undergo all (or at least most) their development within the female parent. Although the young may hatch before the eggs are laid, they are never directly attached to the female parent as mammalian embryos are. (See *Oviparous, Viviparous*).

Ovulation. The release of a ripe egg-cell from the ovary.

Ovum (plural ova). Strictly an unfertilised egg-cell but the term is sometimes used for eggs – especially of insects.

Oxygen Debt. Energy for bodily activity is provided by the oxidation of substances in the cells. During vigorous exercise, insufficient oxygen may be able to reach the tissues and extra energy is obtained by other chemical reactions. But the substances resulting from these reactions must be removed afterwards by oxidation reactions and the oxygen deficiency in the tissues must be made up. The amount of oxygen needed to restore the balance is the oxygen debt and it is in order to pay off this debt that we breathe heavily for a time after exercise.

Oxyhaemoglobin. (See *Respiratory; Pigment*).

Pacemaker. Region of the heart where the contractions start.

Paedogenesis. (See *Neoteny*).

Palaeo- (=*Ancient*).

Palaeocene Epoch. Division of Tertiary Period. (See *Geological Time Scale*).

Palaeoniscoidei. Order of bony fishes abundant in Devonian and Carboniferous times and surviving to the present day in the form of *Polypterus*, the bichir of African rivers. This fish has thick, overlapping scales and many more bones in the skull than modern fishes have. The air-sacs are paired like the lungs of tetrapods but, although they may be used to aid respiration, *Polypterus* cannot survive out of water. (See Plate 117–4).

Palaeontology. The study of fossils (q.v.).

Palaeozoic Era. Large division of *Geological Time Scale* (q.v.).

Palate. The roof of the mouth in vertebrates. In most vertebrates (other than mammals) the palate is the floor of the brain case, but in mammals and crocodiles a bony plate grows inwards from the bones of the upper jaw and forms a false palate under the true palate. The space between the two becomes an extension of the nasal cavity and the internal nares (q.v.) open at the back of the mouth instead of at the front. (See Plates 82, 83 and 105).

Palp. Sensitive appendage on the head of various types of animal. They often play a part in feeding and are found especially in arthropods, although they are not always *homologous structures* (q.v.). (See Plate 64).

Pancreas. An important vertebrate gland, or strictly a combination of two glands, situated in the region of the intestine. The major part consists of a network of tubes which secrete pancreatic juice. This is a mixture of digestive enzymes which is released into the intestine by way of the pancreatic duct. (See *Digestion*). Scattered throughout the pancreas are patches of tissue known as Islets of Langerhans. These are actually endocrine glands and produce the important hormone *insulin* (q.v.) that controls the carbohydrate metabolism of the cells. (See Plate 86).

Paramoecium. Typical member of *Ciliophora* (q.v.). (See Plates 26 and 106).

Parapodium. Paired, muscular projection of body wall of *Polychaeta* (q.v.). (See Plate 5).

Parapsida. Extinct group of *Reptilia* (q.v.) including ichthyosaurs and pliosaurs.

Parasite. An organism that lives *in close association* with another – often inside it – and takes food from it without giving anything in return. The organism that is attacked is called the host but it is not normally killed – at least not until the parasite has completed that part of its life cycle that takes place in the host. Many parasites produce no apparent symptoms in the host and it is thought that in such cases the association has been in existence so long that the host has become completely adapted to the parasite's attack. In those cases in which severe symptoms are produced – such as sleeping sickness produced by infection with trypanosomes – it is believed that the association between parasite and host is relatively new.

Endoparasites are those that live inside their hosts. Examples include tapeworms, the organisms causing malaria and sleeping sickness, and the larvae of warble flies that burrow under the skin of cattle. Ectoparasites, such as fleas and lice, remain outside the host, although they may puncture the skin to suck blood. Many organisms are parasitic for only part of their lives but they nevertheless qualify as parasites because of the close association with the host during that period. Mosquitoes and various other blood-sucking insects, although they give nothing in return for their food, are not normally classed as parasites because they spend only a relatively short time on the so-called host. Ichneumon flies show a special form of parasitism in which the host – the larva of another insect – is killed when the parasites have finished with it. The female ichneumon lays her eggs in the larva of the host insect and the young ichneumons grow inside the host, feeding on its food stores and various non-vital organs. The vital organs are not touched at first and the host can go on providing food for the parasites. When the young parasites are almost fully grown they start to destroy the vital parts of the host and then they bore through the body and pupate outside what is now little more than an empty skin. Social parasitism is displayed by the cuckoo and various cuckoo bees: instead of raising their own families they lay their eggs in the nests of others and the young are reared by foster parents.

Parasympathetic System. Part of *Autonomic Nervous System* (q.v.).

Parathyroid Glands. Endocrine glands of vertebrates, usually associated with, though not connected with, the thyroid gland. There may be several pairs of parathyroids. They are particularly concerned with the metabolism of calcium, possibly also with that of phosphorus. Their removal leads rapidly to the continued contraction of the muscles (tetany), as a result of the disturbance of muscle and nerve fibres, and death ensues. Disruption of the normal working of muscles and nerves is largely due to the drop in the blood calcium level which follows parathyroid removal.

The parathyroid hormone (PTH) has not been purified yet and an accurate analysis of its role in the body is not possible as present, though many experimental data have been obtained. Injection of parathyroid extract or of calcium relieves the symptoms that follow the glands' removal. There

PLATE 88

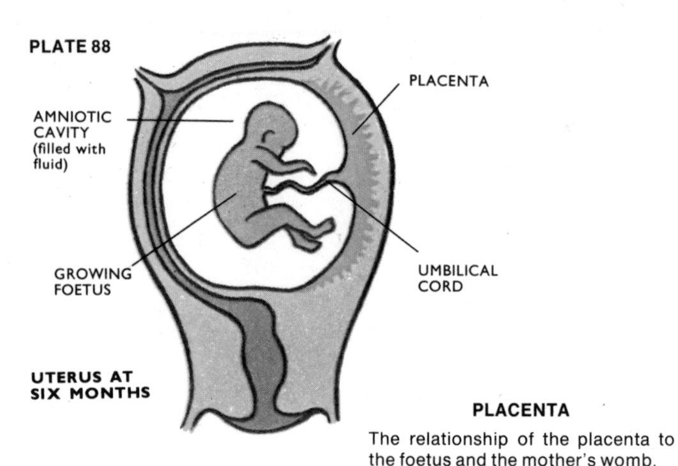

PLACENTA

The relationship of the placenta to the foetus and the mother's womb.

PORIFERA

Sponges are unlike any other animals. Water is drawn in through tiny pores (ostia) and goes out through a large osculum. Collar cells absorb food particles.

POLYCHAETA

PORIFERA

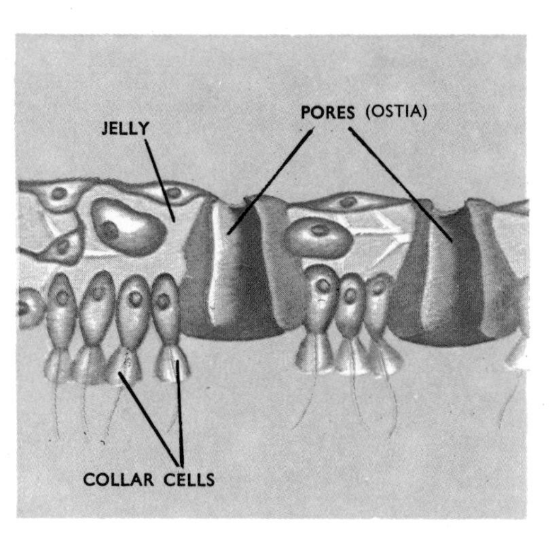

POLYCHAETA

← *Nereis*—the ragworm. The "rags" are in fact the projecting parapodia. The head of the ragworm is equipped with sensory organs and jaws.

▼ *Pomatoceros*, a serpulid worm, covers the rocks with its limestone tubes. It traps food in its tentacles.

is a relationship between the size of the parathyroids and the amount of calcium in the diet. A low dietary calcium level causes their enlargement and conversely an increase in the level of calcium produces a reduction in their size. Milk is rich in calcium, and so it is not surprising that the parathyroid gland of a female mammal increases in size whilst she is suckling her young.

PTH increases the absorption of calcium from the food through the wall of the intestine. It also has profound effects on bone. The injection of PTH causes calcium to be removed from the bone and there is a consequent increase in the blood calcium level.

A large part of the body's calcium is stored in the skeleton. Besides its structural role there and in teeth, and its part in the working of muscles and nerves, it is also necessary for the proper clotting of the blood. Calcium affects the passage of ions from one cell to another, particularly through the walls of the blood capillaries. Since calcium has so many functions it follows that the effects of the parathyroid are multiple, and hence abnormalities of them produce such far-reaching results.

Parazoa. Sub-kingdom of animals including Sponges (Phylum *Porifera*) differing considerably from other many-celled animals (*Metazoa*).

Parietal Bone. Bone of *skull*. (See Page 221).

Parthenogenesis. The production of fertile eggs and young without fertilisation. It is common in the aphids, stick insects, and also in water-fleas (*Daphnia*). The parthenogenetic eggs develop quickly and large populations are rapidly built up Normally the young are genetically identical with the mother and, therefore, all female. Males are rare and may be produced only at certain times of the year. Normal sexual reproduction then takes place. The drones of bees are produced from unfertilised eggs: when laying eggs in drone cells, the queen cuts off the flow of sperm from her *spermathecae* (q.v.).

Passerine Bird. Member of the order Passeriformes – the perching birds whose first toe (hallux) is directed backwards and adapted for gripping branches. About half the living birds are passerines, including all the common garden birds – thrushes, tits, robin, etc. The crows are the largest passerines. (See *Aves*) and (Page 284).

Patella. Knee-cap, a small bone in front of knee-joint. (See Page 217).

Pathogen. A disease-causing organism, e.g. many bacteria and protozoans.

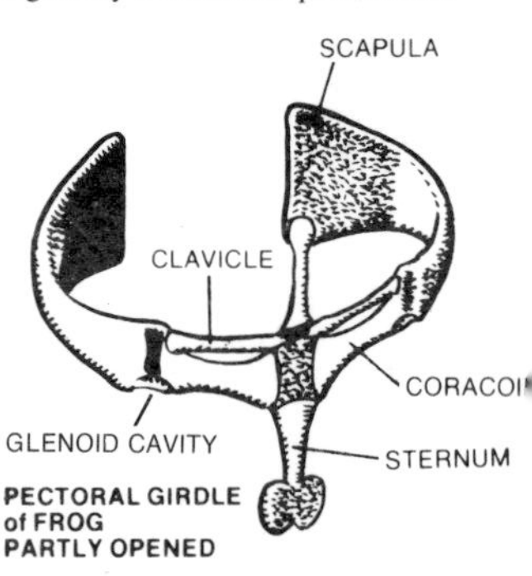

PECTORAL GIRDLE of FROG PARTLY OPENED

Pectoral Girdle. The shoulder girdle connecting the front limbs to the trunk. The primitive pectoral girdle consisted of a simple 'U'-shaped structure to the angles of which the limb bones were joined. The upper part of each side is the scapula (shoulder blade) and the lower part the coracoid. The coracoids normally join the breast bone in tetrapods but, unlike the hip girdle, there is no connection to the backbone. There is also another bone in most tetrapods – the clavicle. It forms the collar-bone of man and the two clavicles join to form the 'wishbone' of birds. The coracoid is very reduced in mammals and appears as a small knob on the scapula.

Pelagic. Inhabiting the open sea but not fixed to the bottom. Divided into free-floating plankton and actively swimming nekton. (See *Littoral*).

Pelvic Girdle. Hip girdle connecting hind legs to trunk. The dorsal region – the ilium – unites with one or more sacral vertebrae in tetrapods. The ventral region is the ischio-pubis and normally consists of two bones – the ischium and the pubis. The *acetabulum* – the socket taking the head of the femur – lies between the ilium and the ischio-pubis. In those animals where the bones all join up to form a single structure, each half of the pelvic girdle is called the innominate bone. (See Page 217).

Penis. Male organ used for transferring sperm to female.

Pentadactyl Limb. Basic limb structure of tetrapods named from the presence of five digits. Both front and hind limbs are of the same basic structure. (See Plate 61).

Pepsin. Protein-splitting enzyme secreted in vertebrate stomach. (See *Digestion*).

Pericardium. Wall of pericardial cavity surrounding the heart.

Periosteum. Connective tissue surrounding *bone* (q.v.).

Peripheral Nervous System. That part of the nervous system other than the *central nervous system* (q.v.). Consists of nerves running to and from the C.N.S. and the various muscles, sense organs, glands, etc. (See *Nerve*).

Perissodactyla. An order of hoofed mammals containing horses, rhinoceroses, and tapirs. The main axis of the foot runs through the 3rd toe which is normally larger than the others and may be the only functional one. (See *Artiodactyla; Ungulate*) and (Plate 123–15, 16).

Peristalsis. Rhythmic muscular contraction of the alimentary canal that causes food to pass along.

Peritoneum. Membrane lining the abdominal cavity and covering the organs within it.

Permian Period. Division of the *Geological Time Scale* (q.v.).

pH. An index figure denoting the degree of acidity or alkalinity. pH7 is neutral. Lower figures are acidic, higher ones, basic.

Phagocyte. A cell, especially of the blood, that engulfs particles from its surroundings in the manner of *Amoeba* (q.v.). Blood phagocytes are very important in defending the body against bacterial infection.

Phalanges. Bones of the fingers and toes. (See *Skeleton*).

Phalangida. An order of *Arachnida* (q.v.) containing the harvestmen or harvest-spiders. Unlike true spiders, they have no silk glands and the body is not divided into two regions. (See Plate 112).

Pharynx. Region at the back of the mouth into which the windpipe opens. In fishes the gill slits open into the pharynx.

Phenotype. The visible appearance of an organism with respect to one or more characters, as opposed to the genetic constitution (*Genotype*). A certain genotype may give rise to several phenotypes according to the environment in which they live. Also a given phenotype may be produced by different genotypes: an heterozygous organism will exhibit the same features as a homozygous one possessing dominant genes. (See *Gene*).

Pholidota. Order of mammals – Pangolins. (See Plate 123–1).

Photophore. Light-producing organ. (See *Bioluminescence*).

Phylogeny. The evolutionary relationships of a group of animals.

PLATE 90

RECEPTOR

(Left) A pit on an antenna containing smell receptors. *(Centre)* Sensory hairs of various kinds on an antenna. *(Right)* A simple touch-sensitive hair.

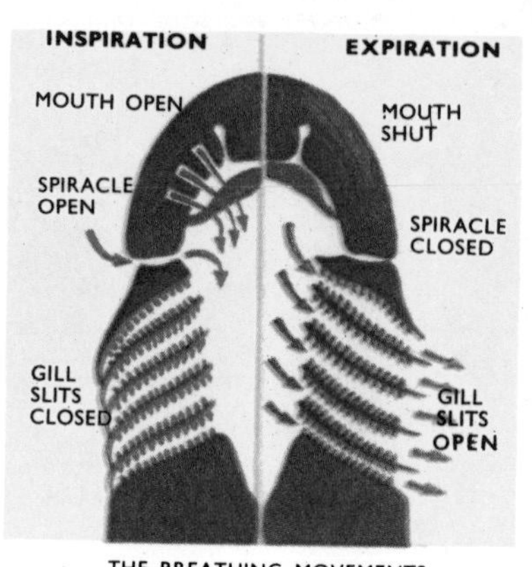

THE BREATHING MOVEMENTS OF SHARKS

RESPIRATORY MOVEMENT

SEGMENTATION

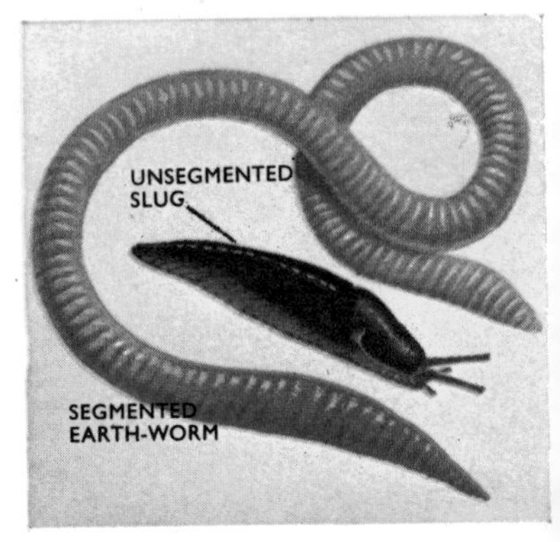

SEMINIFEROUS TUBULE

Section of one of the tubules making up the testis.

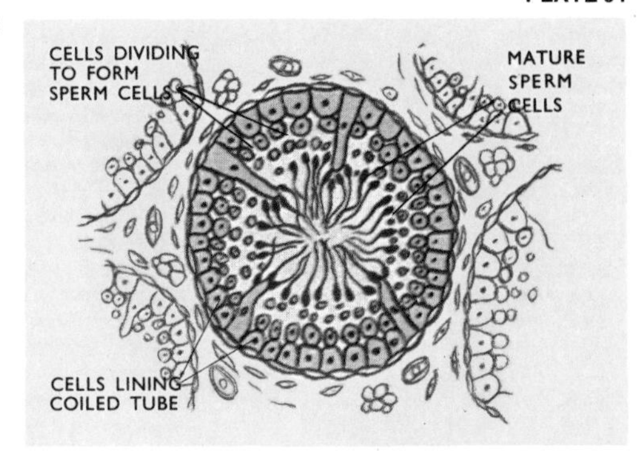

SIRENIA

Dugong and Manatee – marine and estuarine mammals.

SKIN

Temperature control by the skin is automatically controlled by the brain. If the blood is too hot, messages from the brain cause the skin blood vessels to expand and more heat is lost. When the blood is 'cold', the vessels contract.

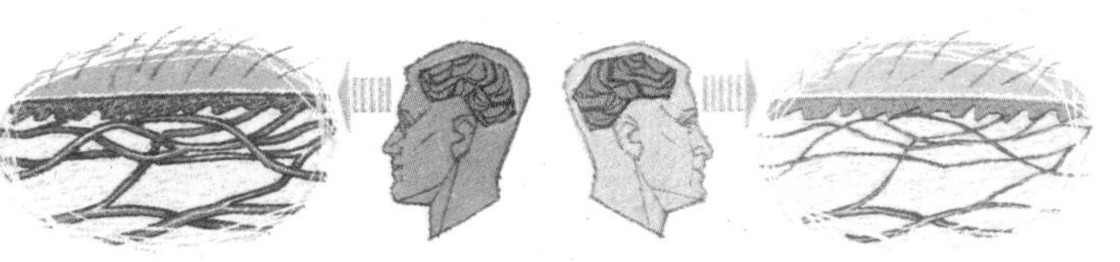

Phylum. The largest category used in *classification* (q.v.). All members of a phylum have a basic similarity of structure but may differ greatly in detail.

Physiology. The study of living processes such as digestion. (See also *Biochemistry*).

Pinnipedia. Group of aquatic carnivores with flippers instead of legs – seals and walruses. (See Plates 86; 123).

Pisces. An old term covering all types of fish. It is not a true classificatory grouping.

SECTION OF PITUITARY GLAND

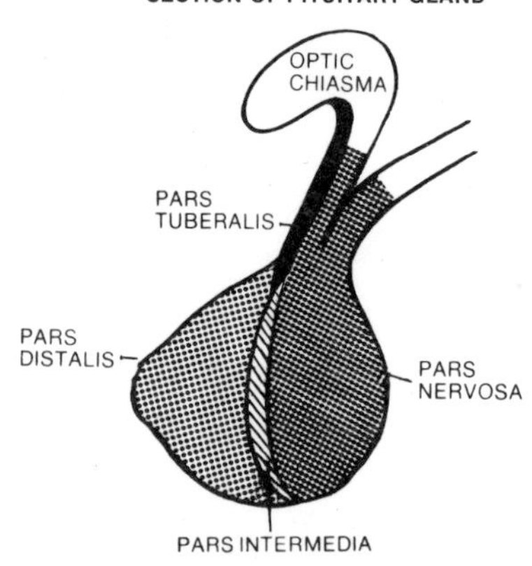

Pituitary Gland. A tiny structure attached to the underside of the vertebrate brain. It is formed partly from the floor of the brain and partly from the roof of the mouth. It weighs about 1/60 ounce in man. Yet the many hormones that it produces have such numerous and important effects that it is rightly called the *master gland*.

These hormones affect growth and metabolism, particularly that of proteins, fats, and carbohydrates; they control water and salt loss through the kidney, the sex glands, thyroid and adrenals, and have an effect on the smooth muscle in the walls of the blood vessels. Another important effect is that of stimulating the muscle in the wall of the uterus during the birth process. Most of the knowledge of the pituitary is based on mammals.

However, many of the endocrine glands are not under the control of the pituitary, while its control of others is only that of adjusting the rate at which they produce their own hormones. Removal of the pituitary does not prevent them from secreting these hormones. It must also be stressed that the pituitary is itself acted upon by other endocrines. For example the rate at which it produces the hormone that acts on the thyroid (the so-called *thyrotropic* hormone) varies with the rate at which the thyroid is working. Thus, when the thyroid is producing less hormone than it should be, the pituitary releases more of its thyrotropic hormone and so hormone production in the thyroid is speeded up. This 'see-saw' or reciprocal relationship between the pituitary and other structures is characteristic of many of the body processes ensuring that the 'steady state' is maintained.

Over-activity and enlargement of the pituitary causes gigantism and acromegaly. In young children such a condition results in the continued growth of the skeleton producing a giant. If the defect occurs after the long bones have stopped growing acromegaly results. The bones become very much thicker, the hands and feet broader, the chin protrudes and the skin becomes coarse. Abnormalities of the thyroid, pancreas and sex glands may also result.

The pituitary is divided into two main lobes – *anterior* and *posterior*. It may be sub-divided into a *pars distalis* (anterior) and *pars tuberalis, pars intermedia* and *pars nervosa* forming the posterior lobe.

The anterior lobe is quite distinct from the remainder of the gland. The hormones that it produces are all proteins which, between them, probably affect most of the other cells in the body. They fall readily into two main groups (1) those having an effect on *growth* and *metabolism,* (2) those that influence the *adrenals* and the *gonads*.

A *growth* hormone has been isolated. It plays an essential part in the normal growth of the body. Overproduction produces gigantism and acromegaly. Loss of function of the anterior pituitary in young mammals produces dwarfs. Growth hormone also affects the secretion of digestive enzymes. It opposes some of the actions of the adrenals, encourages the body cells to retain nitrogen, and speeds up the burning of fat.

Another hormone released by the anterior pituitary is the *thyrotropic* hormone which acts on the thyroid gland, stimulating its cells to secrete. Thyroid hormone governs the general metabolism of the body cells. *Prolactin,* another anterior pituitary hormone, causes the production of milk in the mammary glands after these have been 'prepared' by the action of hormones released by the ovary.

The other hormones released by the anterior pituitary affect either the sex glands or the adrenals. The *adrenal gland* (q.v.) plays a prominent part in preparing the body to cope with unusual conditions such as extensive heat or cold.

Two major hormones produced by the anterior lobe act on the sex glands. One stimulates the production of eggs in the ovaries of the female or sperm in the testes of the male. The other causes the development of a special tissue in the spaces left after the eggs have been discharged from the ovaries. This tissue – *corpus luteum* – is particularly important in producing *progesterone,* a hormone that stimulates the development of the womb lining and, if a fertilised egg is implanted there, in the later development of the placenta through which the growing embryo is nourished.

Our present knowledge indicates that the posterior part of the pituitary has three main activities produced by two hormones. One, *oxytocin* (*or pitocin*), causes the womb (*uterus*) to contract. It is thought that this action is extremely important at birth in assisting the passage of the young out of the uterus.

The second hormone produced by the posterior pituitary is vasopressin. Its effect on the blood system is slight, injections causing the smooth muscle of the blood vessel walls to contract. Its normal role in man is not certain. However, another effect is well established, that of controlling the loss of water and salt in the urine. Water loss is known as diuresis. Vasopressin acts on the kidneys causing them to reabsorb more water from the urine – it reduces water loss – and it is known therefore, as the antidiuretic hormone (ADH). It promotes the retention of water by the kidney tubules but at the same time it causes a greater loss of salt. Cells in the part of the brain above the pituitary (the hypothalamus) are sensitive to the salt concentration in the blood. Special nerve cells of the hypothalamus probably produce the ADH and it passes to the posterior pituitary along the nerve fibres, being released when required into the blood capillaries there. Such a transport of stimulating material along nerve fibres is called neurosecretion.

Failure of the pituitary to produce ADH in sufficient quantities causes the disease *diabetes insipidus* when as much as thirty-five pints of water may be lost per day in the urine. It is interesting that the level of ADH in the blood of the kangaroo rat, that lives in deserts, is eight times as high as that of a dog. Consequently the former produces very much more concentrated urine.

Placenta. A structure, found only in the higher mammals – not monotremes and marsupials – that is concerned with the nourishment of the embryo. The placenta is formed from the lining of the mother's uterus and certain of the embryonic tissues – the allantois. For this reason it is known as an allantoic placenta. The placenta is rich in blood vessels, partly supplied by the mother and partly by the embryo or foetus. Food materials and oxygen pass from the blood vessels of the mother into those of the foetus, and waste substances (e.g. urea and carbon dioxide) in the reverse direction. The placenta persists throughout the development of the young. (See Plate 88).

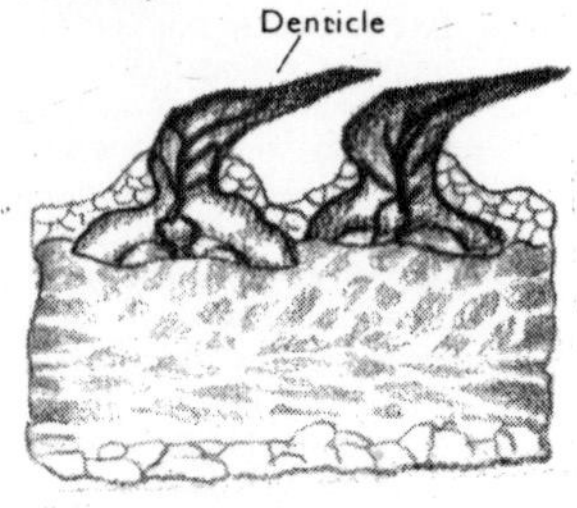

Section through the skin of a shark, showing the horny scales.

Placoid Scale (=*Denticle*). Characteristic tooth-like scale of sharks and other elasmobranchs. The skin over the jaws carries modified scales which act as teeth. The structure of placoid scales, with dentine, enamel and pulp cavity, is very like that of the teeth of higher vertebrates.

Planarian. One of the free-living flatworms. (See *Platyhelminthes; Turbellaria*).

Plankton. The free-floating organisms near the surface of the sea or lake. Includes many crustaceans, the young stages of fishes, jellyfishes, and the host of tiny organisms—plant and animal—on which they feed.

Plantigrade. Walking on the soles of the feet, as man and bears. (See *Digitigrade; Unguligrade*) and (Plate 30).

Plasma. The fluid of *blood* (q.v.).

Plasma Membrane. The very thin membrane covering the surfaces of all cells.

Platyhelminthes. Phylum of worm-like animals, many of which are important parasites. The flatworms are bilaterally symmetrical, slightly flattened animals with no body cavity—the space between body wall and gut is full of cells. If the gut is present it has only one opening—the mouth. The reproductive system is usually hermaphrodite. Excretion is by flame cells (q.v.). (See Page 257).

Pleistocene Epoch. Division of Quaternary period. (See *Geological Time Scale*).

Pleural Sac. Space surrounding the lungs of a mammal.

Pliocene Epoch. Division of Tertiary Period. (See *Geological Time Scale*).

Poikilothermic. (See *Homoiothermic*).

Polychaeta. A large order of annelid worms (See *Annelida*) which differ from earthworms (*Oligochaeta,* q.v.) mainly in the possession of many bristles and in the presence of a distinct head. The bristles arise in bunches from leaflike projections of the body wall called parapodia (side-feet). Each segment possesses a pair, one on each side of the body. Parapodia are well shown in one of the commonest shore-dwelling polychaetes, the ragworm (*Nereis*). Each individual parapodium consists of an upper half, the notopodium and a lower half, the neuropodium; both support a bunch of chaetae. Above and below each parapodium are flaps of skin, the dorsal and the ventral cirri.

Another feature in which polychaetes differ from oligochaetes is the formation of a distinct head. Earthworms have a segment or prostomium in front of the mouth but there are no features suggesting a concentration of sensory organs. In *Nereis*, however, the prostomium is equipped with a pair of sensitive tentacles above and a pair of palps below. The next two segments have become fused together. Of all the segments of *Nereis,* they alone lack parapodia; but the cirri are still there—modified as sensitive tentacles.

Nereis is an example of an errant polychaete, a worm which moves about, using its rows of parapodia as paddles for swimming or just undulating its body. Actually, most of its time is spent in shallow burrows. The sharp bristles which at other times probably protect the creature now enable the animal to grip the smooth walls of its burrow, while gentle undulatory movements of the body cause water to flow in and out, carrying oxygen and possible indications of food in the vicinity. When small animals do pass the burrow, the worm's pharynx is turned inside out so that it extends from the burrow. On the end are two horny jaws for gripping the prey.

Another group of wandering polychaetes are the scale worms. The upper surface of these creatures appears to be covered with armour plates, causing them to resemble the molluscan chitons. The plates are called elytra and are adaptations of the dorsal cirri; these structures have curved upwards and backwards on either side of the body and overlap on the top surface. Scale worms are usually small – rarely more than an inch or so in length. A notable exception, however, is the 'seamouse' (*Aphrodite*). Not at all like a worm in appearance, this creature, which burrows in muds in off-shore waters, is six inches or so in length and two inches across. Its scales are not visible, for a dense coat of matted hair covers the upper surface. The hairs are really modified chaetae formed from the notopodium. Short iridescent chaetae, projecting laterally, are used for locomotion. In the burrow, water is continually pumped through the space between the back and the covering of hairs. The scales probably absorb oxygen.

Nereis has been described as primarily a burrower. But, for reproductive purposes, a remarkable change takes place both in its habits and its structures. As eggs and sperm develop in the bodies of the male and female worms (unlike the earthworm *Nereis* has separate sexes), the parapodia become larger and the spiny chaetae become flattened – almost oar-shaped. The colours become richer and the males' eyes become enlarged. With the change complete, the worms take to the open waters where eggs and sperm are liberated into the sea. This sexual stage is known as the heteronereis; formerly heteronereids were thought to be different animals altogether – and not surprisingly so.

In the paddleworms, parapodia and dorsal cirri are paddle-shaped all the time and the animals swim as well as crawl. A remarkable pelagic worm is *Tomopteris*. Its parapodia have developed into enormous lobes. On the head are two very large 'antennae'. In fact these are really parapodia much modified and supported by very long chaetae.

Distinct from the wanderers and shallow burrowers are the tube-making polychaetes – they actually construct their own homes. Appendages on the head are usually far more numerous than in *Nereis*, and greatly modified and increased in size. Tube-living worms are filter feeders. The tentacles projecting from the head have ciliated grooves down which food particles are washed into the mouth. They do not have the eversible pharynx or jaw of *Nereis* and the parapodia are usually reduced in size.

The serpulid tube-dwellers make their shells of calcium carbonate which they secrete themselves. Some tubes are relatively straight but others are so tightly coiled that they resemble the spiral shells of snails. Another feature of serpulids is that the peristomium – the fused segments forming the head – is produced into a collar which folds back over the outside of the tube and secretes reinforcing, hoop-shaped rings. One of the tentacles from the head has a swollen branch; when the animal withdraws into its tube the structure fits exactly over the mouth of the tube.

The sabellids make tubes by cementing sand and mud particles together. The tubes are either buried in the sand or attached to rocks. *Sabella pavonina*—the peacock-worm—is a magnificent sight. Its tube is a foot long and brightly coloured tentacles project from the opening.

Terebellids make mud or sand tubes. In addition to food-collecting tentacles, they have three pairs of gills behind the head, for respiration. The serpulids and sabellids have no special structure but respire over the whole body surface.

Of all polychaetes, the worm which most closely resembles the earthworm in appearance is *Arenicola*, the lugworm. The lugworm is a burrower and like the earthworm consumes vast quantities of mud from which organic food is obtained. Evidence of its activities are the conspicuous coiled worm casts on any sandy beach. Chaetae are small in the front and middle of the body, but absent altogether at the rear; the middle region, however carries pairs of feathery gills on the dorsal surface. Sensory tentacles are absent; they would only be a hindrance to burrowing. But the pharynx can be extended. Instead of heavy jaws, the surface is coated with minute papillae which by adhesion enable the worm to pull itself forwards through the sand. (See Plates 5, 88 and 89).

Polymorphism. Occurring in several forms, usually with a fairly constant ratio between them in any one region. Human blood groups, and the occurrence of certain varieties of insects are examples. The occurrence of worker castes as well as sexual forms in many social insects is also a special case of polymorphism.

Polyp. The fixed, tube-like form of the *Coelenterata* (q.v.). (See Plates 3 and 23).

Polyphyletic. Having a mixed ancestry. A group of animals that is polyphyletic is not therefore a true grouping because they are not all related through a common ancestor.

Polyzoa (=*Bryozoa*). Old name for the animals now divided into *Ectoprocta* and *Endoprocta* (q.v.). Polyzoa is a polyphyletic grouping.

Porifera. Phylum of animals containing the sponges. They are multicellular but, because they are so very different from other multicellular organisms (*Metazoa*), they are treated as a distinct group (Sub-kingdom *Parazoa*). The sponges are simple water-living organisms lacking any sort of nervous system. The body is a hollow vessel with a layer of covering cells and an inner layer of flagellated collar cells, separated by a jelly-like material that contains numerous siliceous, calcareous, or horny crystals (spicules) These spicules are of various shapes and form a sort of skeleton.

The flagella of the collar cells beat rapidly and draw a current of water in through tiny pores called ostia. Food particles are trapped by the cells and the water passes out again through the large pore at the top (the osculum). There are three classes of sponge, separated according to the nature of the spicules. (See Plates 88, 89 and 106).

Portal Vein. One carrying blood from one capillary system to another. E.g. the *hepatic portal vein* carrying blood from the capillaries of the gut to those of the liver.

Premaxilla. Bone forming the front part of the upper jaw in vertebrates. In mammals it carries the incisor teeth, while in birds it forms most of the upper beak. (See page 221).

Premolar. One of the cheek teeth of mammals. (See *Tooth*).

Primates. Order of mammals containing monkeys, apes and men, also a few other smaller animals such as the lemurs and lorises. The more primitive primates have retained many of the early mammalian features and resemble insectivores in many ways. Most primates are specialised for life in the trees. Eye-sight and co-ordination are very well developed and the limbs are adapted for grasping. (See Plate 123–2, 3, 4).

Proboscidea. Order of mammals containing only two living forms – the African and the Indian elephant. There are, however, many fossil species – the mammoths and mastodons and strange Miocene and Oligocene forms. The phylogeny of elephants is probably better-known than that of any other group of mammals. (See Plate 123).

Proboscis. The trunk of elephants; also the coiled 'tongue' of butterflies and moths. (See *Lepidoptera*).

Proboscis Worms. (See *Nemertea*).

Progesterone. A hormone formed in the mammalian ovary after ovulation which prepares the uterus and other organs for receiving the fertilised egg and also maintains them in a suitable state throughout pregnancy.

Proglottis. One of the segments of a tapeworm. (See *Cestoda*).

Prolegs. The stumpy hind legs of caterpillars. They disappear completely in the adult insect. (See Plate 34).

Proprioreceptor. Sense organ concerned with position and balance of the body. Various nerve endings in the muscles detect the tone of the muscles and the pressure to which they are subjected, thus informing the brain of the position of these muscles. The semi-circular canals of the ear are also proprioreceptors as they inform the brain of the body's position in respect to gravity.

Prostate. Gland of the male mammalian reproductive system. Its secretions mix with the semen but its function is not fully understood.

Protective Resemblance. The resemblance of an organism to some part of its surroundings, such as a dead leaf, with the result that the organisms are protected to some extent from predators. The extraordinary resemblances seen in the insects and some other animals have been brought about by natural selection in favour of those that most resembled their surroundings. *Mimicry* (q.v.) is a special form of protective resemblance in which the animals resemble other animals in their neighbourhood.

Protein. Fat and carbohydrate molecules contain only carbon, hydrogen and oxygen atoms, but proteins always contain nitrogen atoms and sometimes sulphur and phosphorus atoms as well. Their molecules are the most highly complicated of all substances because large numbers of atoms are present in each protein molecule in various different combinations and arrangements. This also means that the number of different proteins is quite astonishing – to the extent that every single living species has some which are peculiar to it and which are not found in any other species.

The importance of proteins lies in the fact that, together with water, they form the basis of all living matter or protoplasm. They also form part of the hereditary material that is carried on the chromosomes in all cell nuclei. Enzymes, the catalysts that are so vitally necessary for life, are proteins. Proteins are also used as food stores.

Protein molecules are built up of units called amino acids. The simplest amino acid is called glycine or amino-acetic acid. It has the formula NH_2CH_2COOH. The NH_2 grouping – the amino group – is basic and the hydrogen of the carboxyl grouping (–COOH) makes this acidic. The basic amino grouping of the amino acid molecule is able to react with the acidic carboxyl grouping of another molecule to form a dipeptide. Many amino acids are able to join end to end in this way forming long chains called polypeptides and eventually protein molecules. Each protein molecule is thus built up of large numbers of amino acids.

About twenty-five amino acids are known. To a limited extent animals are able to synthesize some amino acids from simpler molecules. They are also able to convert some amino acids into others. However, a number of amino acids cannot be built up by animals or derived from others; they must be present in the diet and are called essential amino acids as distinct from the non-essential ones (which can be built up). Amino acids are able to combine in varying proportions and the same sequence of several amino acids or slightly differing sequences may be repeated many times so that a vast number of different proteins can be formed.

Proteins that occur in the nuclei of cells are called nucleoproteins. It is believed that the chromosomes are largely built up of nucleoproteins and some viruses have been shown to consist of masses of nucleoproteins. Thus certain nucleoproteins can be regarded as being the causes of several highly infectious diseases. The important molecules (nucleic acids) in the nucleus that are arranged in strings on the chromosomes contain sugar molecules. The nucleic acids (principally desoxyribose nucleic acid, DNA), together with certain proteins, the nucleoproteins, form the basis of the hereditary material whose 'instructions' regulate all the activities of an organism.

Protista. Uncommon term used sometimes for all single-celled organisms.

Protochordata. The invertebrate chordates. (See *Urochordata, Cephalochordata,* and *Hemichordata*) and (Plate 116).

Protoplasm. The substance of all living cells, usually divided into cytoplasm and nucleoplasm, the latter being confined within the membrane of the nucleus. It is not a single substance but a very complicated mixture of organic and inorganic substances in which chemical changes are continuously taking place. The composition of protoplasm therefore varies not only between species and between cells performing different functions, but also in individual cells at different times. The main component is water in which are dissolved or suspended numerous inorganic salts, proteins, and lipids. Electron microscopy indicates that there is a delicate system of fibres and channels within the protoplasm.

Protozoa. Sub-kingdom of animals all of which are composed of a single cell only. There is a well-defined nucleus which controls all of the animal's activity. There are four classes, distinguished mainly by the ways in which they move. Members of the class *Flagellata* (q.v.) have one or more whip-like hairs (flagella) and they move about by lashing these hairs. Some are plant-like and many others are parasitic (e.g. *Trypanosoma,* the organism causing sleeping sickness). The *Sarcodina* (q.v.) includes the amoeboid forms that move normally by putting out pseudopodia and 'flowing' along. (See *Amoeba*). Many forms have calcareous or siliceous shells. Members of the class *Sporozoa* (q.v.) are all parasites. They normally have no organs of movement and reproduce by forming large numbers of *spores*. The class *Ciliophora* (q.v.) contains some of the most highly organised Protozoa. They all have cilia at some stage but some adults lose the cilia. They are never amoeboid and rarely parasitic. Examples include *Paramoecium* and *Stentor*. (See Plate 106).

Proventriculus. Part of the bird stomach just in front of gizzard, where digestive enzymes are secreted. Also a part of the arthropod alimentary canal.

Proximal. (See *Distal*).

Pseudo- (=*False*).

Pseudopodium. Temporary protrusion of part of a cell (See *Amoeba*) and (Plate 4).

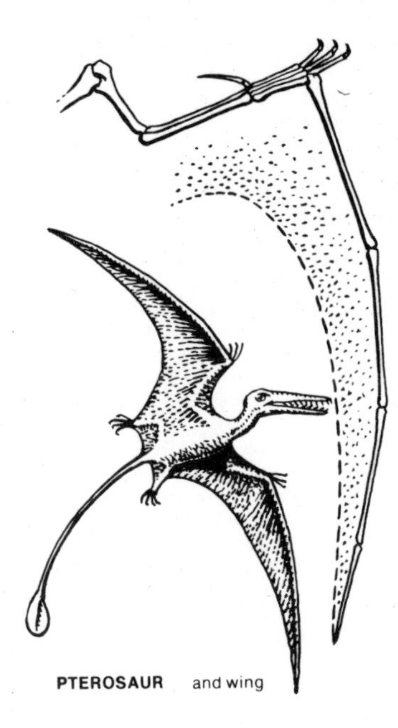

PTEROSAUR and wing

Pterosauria. Order of extinct reptiles including the pterodactyls and other flying forms. Contrary to many popular beliefs, the pterosaurs did not give rise to the birds. The similarities are due to *convergent evolution* (q.v.). The wings of the pterosaurs were formed by folds of skin stretched along the front limbs – especially the greatly elongated fourth finger. Compare this arrangement with that of the birds and the bats – the other vertebrate groups that have taken to the air. (See Plate 119).

Pteropoda. Group of pelagic *gasteropods* (q.v.) often without shells.

Pterygota. The main group of *Insecta* (q.v.). They are normally winged but may be secondarily wingless, e.g. fleas and lice, as a result of parasitic life.

Ptyalin. Starch-splitting enzyme in *saliva*. (See *Digestion*).

Pubic Symphysis. The close union on the ventral side of the two halves of the *pelvic girdle* (q.v.).

Pubis. Bone of the *pelvic girdle* (q.v.).

Pulmonary. Concerning the lungs.

Pulmonata. Group of *Gasteropoda* (q.v.) in which the mantle cavity has become modified into a lung for air-breathing. The slugs and snails.

Pulp Cavity. Central cavity of *tooth* (q.v.).

Pupa. The resting stage, often called the chrysalis, through which holometabolous insects pass while they change from larvae into adults. The pupa is normally immobile but mosquito pupae can move actively. (See Plate 63).

Pupil. The opening in the iris of *eye* (q.v.) which allows light to fall on the retina. (See Plates 45 and 46).

Pure Line. Any group of organisms that all have the same homozygous genetic constitution for a particular feature and, with the exception of mutations, will always give similar offspring when they reproduce among themselves. (See *Heredity; Gene*).

Pylorus. The junction between the vertebrate stomach and small intestine. It is provided with a muscular valve – the pyloric sphincter muscle – that prevents food from passing into the intestine until it has been sufficiently broken down.

Quadrate. Bone of the upper jaw which in most vertebrates is concerned with the articulation of the lower jaw. In mammals, however, it becomes the incus in the middle *ear* (q.v.).

Radial Symmetry. The arrangement of

organs around a central point so that there are two or more planes in which the organism can be cut to give similar halves. Characteristic of sedentary animals such as coelenterates and echinoderms. (See *Bilateral Symmetry*).

Radiolaria. Group of *Sarcodina* (q.v.) with siliceous skeletons.

Radius. Bone of fore arm on the thumb side. (See Page 217).

Radula. Scraping tongue of gasteropod molluscs. (See *Gasteropoda*) and (Plate 52).

Ratites. Term still used to some extent in classification of birds to refer to the large flightless ones – ostrich, kiwi, emu, etc. (See Page 281).

Recapitulation Theory. Theory put forward by Haeckel in 1866 suggesting that 'the life history of an individual recapitulates the whole of its ancestry. For example, the embryo of man passes from a single-celled state through stages resembling fishes, amphibians and reptiles. Haeckel's theory has been proved completely untrue. The embryo of man never resembles the adult of any other creature that ever lived. But the embryo does bear a semblance to the embryos of other vertebrates; this denotes a related ancestry.

Receptor. A sense organ: one that detects stimuli and passes a message to the brain. Receptors may be single cells on the surface, or they may be complicated structures like the eyes. Not all receptors are on the surface of the body. Many pain and pressure receptors lie embedded in the skin. (See Plate 90).

Recessive Gene. One of a pair of allelomorphic *genes* (q.v.) which makes its presence known only if it is present on both chromosomes in a cell. If it is present on only one chromosome, its effect will be masked by the dominant gene on the other.

Recombination. The occurrence in offspring of new combinations of genes and therefore characteristics. It is due to chance pairing of chromosomes when sex cells are formed and to random fusion of gametes at fertilisation. Offspring thus do not normally resemble either parent in great detail. (See *Heredity*).

Rectum. Last part of *alimentary canal* (q.v.).

Rectus Muscles. (See *Eye Muscles*).

Reflex Action. A simple form of behaviour which is independent of experience and does not involve interpretation of a nervous signal by the brain. Examples are the shutting of the eye when something comes rapidly towards it and the rapid removal of a hand from a hot object. The response

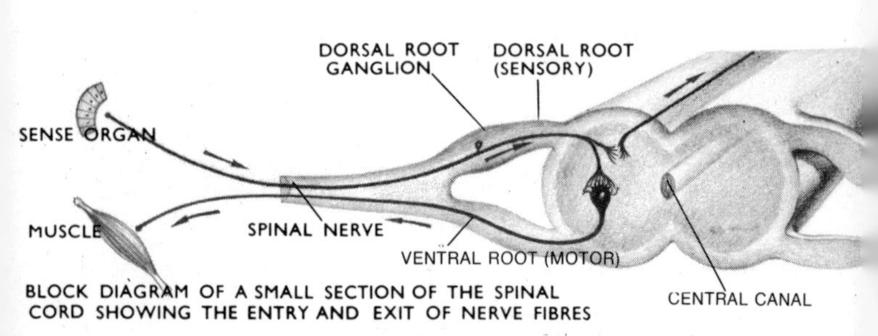

BLOCK DIAGRAM OF A SMALL SECTION OF THE SPINAL CORD SHOWING THE ENTRY AND EXIT OF NERVE FIBRES

is immediate. When the sense organ is stimulated signals pass from it along a sensory nerve to the spinal cord. The message travels out of the spinal cord along a motor nerve to the effector organ (e.g. a muscle or gland) which acts accordingly. Such a pathway is termed a reflex arc. Sensory fibres enter the dorsal part of the spinal cord while motor fibres leave the ventral part. (See *Spinal Nerves*).

Regeneration. The ability to replace parts of the body that have been lost through accident. All animals and plants are capable of it to some extent but, as a general rule, the more highly evolved an animal is, the less are its powers of regeneration. Man, for example, is able to regenerate skin and bone tissue to mend wounds and fractures, but is unable to regrow even a finger if one should be lost. Some internal organs, such as the liver, can be regenerated if a large enough part remains as a starting point. The replacement of worn-out tissues is a form of regeneration and goes on throughout life. The most obvious is the replacement of skin from below as the outer layers rub off.

Some animals are able to regenerate new limbs – in fact lizards may actually shed their tails themselves to confuse enemies and later they grow new ones. Crabs, too, can throw off a limb to escape from a enemy. This process is called *autotomy*. The most striking cases of regeneration, however, are found among the lower animals.

When a planarian is cut in half, both halves can form new animals. The cells of the damaged region lose their individuality and all become alike. They grow and divide and the growing mass takes on the correct shape – be it of a head or a tail. Gradually the cells become specialised again and begin their normal functions. The head region is the co-ordinating region and, if missing, is always the first formed structure in a regenerating body. Not until there is a head, can the other organs be reformed.

Flatworms are built up of three basic layers: an external ectoderm, an endoderm lining the gut, and a mesoderm occupying the space between the two. Planarians are flatworms with great powers of regeneration. As long as all three types of tissue are present and as long as there is sufficient food reserve in the tissues, a complete new planarian can grow from a tiny portion. The fragment has no mouth and feeding organs and so cannot get any food from outside. The cells become alike and multiply. Because food is used up during this process, the fragment gets smaller, but if sufficient cells can be formed, a tiny planarian will develop. Any original organs remaining in the fragment will be partly absorbed so that they conform in size to the rest of the new animal. A new head is formed before the rest of the body develops.

Any fragment of a planarian that regenerates naturally will produce a head at the original front end. Although the cells are completely reorganised they never lose this polarity. Regeneration in jelly-fish is very similar, but in higher animals the head cannot be regenerated. New limbs and bodies can form under the influence of the head but not vice-versa.

Renal. Concerning the kidneys.

Rennin. Enzyme of the mammalian stomach responsible for clotting milk. (See *Digestion*).

Reproduction. Reproduction is the most important function of any living species; failure to reproduce means that the species will become extinct. In response to this biological necessity a number of methods of reproduction have developed.

Amongst higher plants and animals sexual reproduction is the most widespread and successful method. At some stage, specialised reproductive cells (or gametes) develop. One gamete must combine with another to form what is called a zygote. The process of combination is called fertilisation.

Gametes must not only be capable of coming together. Between them, they must provide enough food for the new individual to develop. Usually there is a division of labour; one type of gamete – the female cell or egg – remains stationary but contains a large food supply. The other type – the male or spermatozoan – carries a minimum supply of food but is mobile and moves towards the egg.

Most commonly, male and female gametes are borne on different animals, but in some species, both are carried by one animal (See *Hermaphrodite*). Gametes differ from body (somatic) cells in the number of chromosomes in the cells. Body cells have paired sets of chromosomes (diploid condition) but when sex cells are formed the pairs split up (See *Meiosis*) and the sex cells carry only single sets of chromosomes. For example, the body cells of man have 23 pairs of chromosomes, but the gametes have only 23 single ones. At fertilisation the gametes fuse and form a zygote, which again has 23 pairs. The zygote divides by *mitosis* (q.v.) to form all the body cells which thus have 23 pairs of chromosomes.

A few animals reproduce by *parthenogenesis* (q.v.) or by asexual methods. In the latter there are no special cells – pieces of the parent break away and grow into new individuals.

The great advantage of sexual reproduction is that recombinations of genes are continually occurring. At each fertilisation different genetical material comes together. The variety of animals likely to be produced is thereby increased for it is the genes that largely control development. It follows that the chance of an animal appearing with advantageous adaptions is also increased.

With parthenogenesis, and asexual reproduction, however, the off-spring will resemble the parent, for exactly the same genes will be inherited. No variations occur. But these methods do have their advantages. Unlike sexual reproduction, large numbers of off-spring can be produced in a very short space of time. Also a single individual may colonize a whole new area, a feat which is usually impossible by the sexual method.

Though it is common to find animals and plants reproducing solely by the sexual method, it is very rare to find them breeding solely by parthenogenesis or asexual methods. In these instances the sexual and non-sexual methods alternate at more or less regular intervals (heterogamy). The advantages of both mechanisms are thus obtained.

Reptilia. A class of vertebrate animals that evolved many millions of years ago from one branch of the *Amphibia* (q.v.). Apart from a few that give birth to active young, the reptiles lay shelled eggs and are thus not dependent on the water for breeding. There is no free larval stage corresponding to the amphibian tadpole. In many ways reptiles are intermediate between amphibians on the one hand and the mammals and birds on the other. Mammals and birds arose from two different lines of reptiles. Only four relatively small groups of reptiles are alive now but the reptiles once ruled the earth with the huge dinosaurs on land, the flying pterodactyls and the aquatic ichthyosaurs.

Reptiles are covered with scales (from which it is thought birds' feathers are evolved) and when limbs are present, they have the basic pentadactyl pattern of five toes. Lungs are the sole respiratory organs. All reptiles are poikilothermic, that is they cannot maintain a constant body temperature and it varies with that of the surroundings. Reptiles are active only in warm weather.

There are four sub-classes of reptiles, divided according to the structure of the skull. Sub-class *Anapsida* contains the earliest reptiles such as *Seymouria* and surprisingly enough also has living members – the tortoises (order *Chelonia*) (q.v.). These have probably survived by virtue of their protective shells. The sub-class *Parapsida* contains only extinct reptiles – the ichthyosaurs, plesiosaurs, and certain other forms. It is probably a *polyphyletic* group (q.v.) whose members are not closely related.

The sub-class *Diapsida* is the largest of all. Living members include the snakes and lizards – order *Squamata* (q.v.), the tuatara, and the crocodiles. The dinosaurs and the pterodactyls also belong to this sub-class. (See *Dinosaur; Pterosauria*). Sub-class *Synapsida* contains only extinct forms but this line is believed to have given rise to the mammals. (See Plate 119).

Respiration. All living processes require energy. This is obtained by oxidation of food materials within the body tissues. In all animals and in the majority of plants the process depends on free oxygen absorbed from the surroundings. The absorption of oxygen, its transport to the tissues, and the oxidation reactions are all classed as respiratory activities, but the term 'respiration' is normally confined to the chemical reactions within the cells.

Protozoans and other simple animals get sufficient oxygen by simple diffusion from the surroundings. Earthworms absorb their oxygen requirements through the skin which is very well supplied with blood vessels. This arrangement is possible only in damp surroundings. In dry air, water would very rapidly be lost through the skin. All larger or more active animals have special respiratory organs to absorb oxygen. Animals living in water usually have *gills* (q.v.) to absorb oxygen from the water. Land vertebrates usually breathe (i.e. take in air) by means of lungs (q.v.). Insects and some other arthropods have a network of *tracheae* – tiny tubes that conduct air from the surroundings to every part of the body.

The essential features of respiratory organs are: a large moist surface area, very thin walls, and a good blood supply. The gills of fishes and of crustaceans consist of very thin plates of tissue over which water is caused to pass by various movements of the animal. (See *Respiratory Movement*). Oxygen, dissolved in the water, passes into the blood stream and is transported to the tissues. Because a stream of water flows over the gills there is always a fresh source of oxygen next to the gill. Lungs are internal chambers with no continuous air-flow. They have to be filled and emptied by breathing movements. Absorption of oxygen into the blood follows the same pattern in lungs and in gills. In both cases the oxygen is in solution when it reaches the respiratory surface. The blood arriving here is low in oxygen content and thus the oxygen outside passes in solution through the thin walls and into the blood which transports it to the tissues. Only a very small amount of the oxygen is carried as a simple solution in the blood. Most of it combines with a respiratory pigment (q.v.) in the blood. The compound formed is unstable and later releases oxygen in the capillaries of the body. In the body the tissues are low in oxygen content so that the oxygen released passes through the fine capillary walls and into the cells where the chemical reactions take place. These reactions are very complicated and involve numerous enzymes and intermediate stages. The net result, however, can be shown as:

food + oxygen = carbon dioxide + water + energy.

This equation holds good for both plants and animals. Glucose is a commonly used food material. Its oxidation can be shown chemically as follows:

$$\underset{\text{(glucose)}}{C_6H_{12}O_6} + \underset{\textbf{(oxygen)}}{6O_2} = \underset{\text{(carbon dioxide)}}{6CO_2} + \underset{\text{(water)}}{6H_2O} + \text{energy}$$

Most of the carbon dioxide released is removed by the blood stream. Some is carried in solution and some in combination with blood proteins, but by far the largest amount is carried in the form of bicarbonate ions. In the blood capillaries of the tissues carbon dioxide and water combine to form carbonic acid:

$$CO_2 + H_2O = H_2CO_3$$

This then breaks down into ions:

$$H_2CO_3 = H^+ + HCO_3^-.$$

At the respiratory surface the blood becomes more acid and the bicarbonates are broken down, releasing carbon dioxide which passes through the respiratory surface and out to the surroundings.

Respiratory Movement. The movement of part or parts of the body that ensures a fresh supply of air or water for the respiratory organs. Many insect bodies, especially of the larger species, pulsate at intervals forcing stale air out of the tracheae and drawing in a fresh supply. Lobsters and many other aquatic arthropods wave certain appendages about and create a current of water over the gills. Fishes take water in through their mouths and the muscles of the pharynx pump it out over the gills. Tetrapods expand their chests to draw air into the lungs. The movement of the diaphragm in mammals aids respiration by altering the size of the thoracic cavity containing the lungs. (See Plate 90).

Respiratory Pigments. Substances which occur in blood and increase its oxygen-carrying capacity. The best-known and the most efficient is haemoglobin – the reddish-purple pigment of vertebrate blood and of certain invertebrates such as earthworms. This is a complex iron-containing compound which occurs in the corpuscles of vertebrate blood or in the plasma in other animals. At high oxygen concentrations (e.g. at the respiratory surface) the pigment combines with oxygen and forms oxyhaemoglobin which is bright red. In the body tissues the oxygen concentration is low. The oxyhaemoglobin in the blood breaks down and releases oxygen which passes to the tissues. If the haemoglobin content is reduced, oxygen shortage will occur. For example, carbon monoxide forms a stable compound – carboxyhaemoglobin – with the pigment which cannot then carry oxygen. Haemocyanin, in which the metallic element is copper, is found in many crustaceans and in molluscs such as octopuses and squids. It turns blue when oxygenated. All respiratory pigments have in common the fact that they form unstable compounds with oxygen which break down at the low oxygen concentration found in the tissues. Insects, in which the tracheae carry oxygen straight to the tissues, have no respiratory pigments.

Respiratory Quotient. (R.Q.) The ratio of carbon dioxide produced to the volume of oxygen consumed during the same period. The value differs according to the type of food material being oxidised.

Resting Cell. A term used to describe a cell not at the time undergoing division, although it may be very active in other ways.

Retina. The light-sensitive layer of the *eye* (q.v.).

Rhesus (Rh) Factor. A substance (*antigen,* q.v.) that is found in the blood of a fairly constant proportion of the human population of an area – about 83% of the British population. Its occurrence is controlled by a set of linked genes. People with the factor are known as Rh-positive, those without are Rh-negative. If an Rh-negative person is given a transfusion of Rh-positive blood, *antibodies* (q.v.) may be formed and they may attack a further transfusion of Rh-positive blood. It is thus essential that Rh-negative people receive only Rh-negative blood in transfusions. During pregnancy an Rh-negative mother may receive the rhesus antigen from an Rh-positive embryo. The mother will develop antibodies which can remain in her blood and may damage a further Rh-positive baby.

This is why it is necessary for expectant mothers to have blood tests. If it is known in advance that there is a likelihood of the baby's blood being damaged, transfusion apparatus can be made ready and the baby can be saved.

Rhizopoda (See *Sarcodina*).

Rod. Light-sensitive cell of retina. Not sensitive to colour. (See *Eye*).

Rodentia. Order of mammals including rats, mice, squirrels, beavers, etc.—the gnawing mammals. In terms of species and numbers, it is the largest mammalian order. Members are characterised by the possession of a pair of continuously-growing incisor teeth in each jaw. Rodents are never very large—the capybara is the largest at the size of a small pig. Their rapid breeding rate has probably contributed to their success as also has their ability to colonise a wide variety of habitats. The incisor teeth have enamel only on the front surface so that they have sharp cutting edges. There are no canines and only a few cheek teeth. (See Plate 123).

Rotifera. Phylum of minute acoelomate animals occurring in vast numbers in fresh water and often mistaken for protozoans, although they are definitely many-celled. Rotifers are characterised by a crown of cilia which act as locomotory organs and also collect food. Although they are so tiny, rotifers have a complete food canal together with excretory and nervous systems. There is no blood system, however. The sexes are normally separate but in many species the male is extremely rare and the females reproduce by *parthenogenesis* (q.v.). (See Plate 109).

Roundworms (See *Nematoda*).

Rumen. (See *Ruminant*).

Ruminant. Cud-chewing animal—deer, antelopes, sheep, cattle, and giraffes. All belong to the order *Artiodactyla* (q.v.) and are herbivorous. Food is swallowed without chewing and is passed into the rumen—the first chamber of a complicated stomach. From there it is later regurgitated into the mouth for chewing—chewing the cud. A certain amount of bacterial breakdown of cellulose takes place in the rumen. (See Plate 2).

Saccule. Part of the inner ear. (See *Ear*).

Sacral Vertebra. Vertebra of the hip region. There is only one in amphibians but in other tetrapods there are two or more and they are normally fused together to form the sacrum. The hip girdle connects to one or more of the sacral vertebrae.

Saggital Plane. Plane running through an animal and dividing it into two similar halves. (See *Bilateral Symmetry*).

SECTION THROUGH ROTIFER SHOWING INTERNAL STRUCTURE

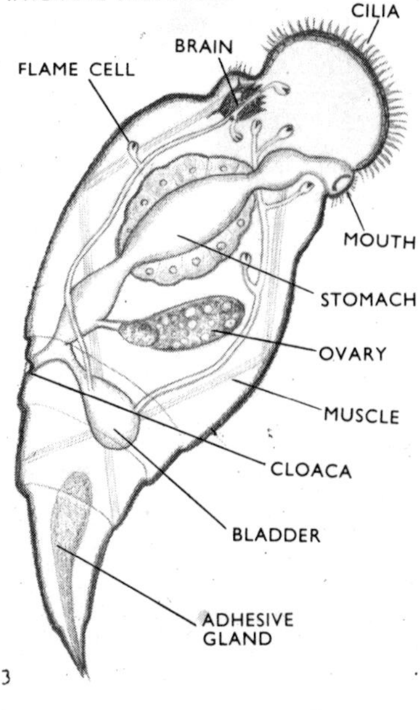

Saliva. Fluid, secreted into mouth by salivary glands, which moistens food and aids swallowing. In vertebrates it contains ptyalin, an enzyme that breaks down starch. Insects too have salivary glands and the saliva of blood-feeders normally contains substances to prevent the blood clotting.

Sarcodina. Class of *Protozoa* (q.v.) which are characterised by the possession of *pseudopodia* (q.v.). *Amoeba* (q.v.) is the typical example but foraminiferans and radiolarians are also included. These forms have skeletons around their bodies and very fine pseudopodia. (See Page 253).

Saurischia. (See *Dinosaur*).

Scaphopoda. Small class of marine *Mollusca* (q.v.). Burrowing forms with tubular shells. (See Page 272).

Scapula. Dorsal part of the *pectoral girdle* (q.v.). Shoulder blade.

Schwann Cell. Type of cell of which one or more surround every nerve fibre of the vertebrate peripheral nervous system.

Sclerotic. The tough coat of the vertebrate eye-ball. (See *Eye*).

Scolex. The 'head' of a tapeworm which becomes attached to the gut of the host by means of hooks and/or suckers. (See *Cestoda*).

Scorpionidea. Order of *Arachnida* (q.v.) containing the scorpions. (See Page 265).

The most obvious feature is the pair of large pincers (pedipalps). Behind these come four pairs of legs attached to the front region of the body (the cephalothorax). The latter is covered by a horny shield on which there are a number of small simple eyes. The hind part of the body (abdomen) is in two parts and is clearly segmented. Its rear portion is the narrow tail bearing the sting and poison glands.

Scorpions feed mainly on other arthropods and occasionally on small vertebrates. The bristles on the pincers seem to be concerned with the detection of food, the eyes being almost useless in this respect. When the prey is detected, the scorpion lashes out and catches its prey with its pincers. The food is then torn to pieces by the smaller chelicerae at the front. Scorpions have no true jaws but the bases of the pedipalps and of the first two pairs of walking legs form tooth-like projections that help to break up the food. Only the juices of the prey are consumed – they are sucked up through the small mouth into the alimentary canal.

The sting is rarely used for capturing food unless the latter is large, but some species use it more readily than others. It appears to be mainly a defensive weapon. The strength and effect of the scorpion's poison varies from one species to another. Some have only a weak poison that does not seriously harm Man. Its effects are confined to the tissues in the neighbourhood of the wound. Others, however, produce a poison that affects the nerves, producing convulsions and sometimes death. (See Plate 112).

Scrotum. Pocket of skin containing the testes of most adult mammals. Normal body temperature inhibits sperm production but the temperature in the scrotum is slightly lower.

Scyphozoa. Class of *Coelenterata* (q.v.) in which the main stage of the life history is the medusa or jellyfish. In some species there is also a polyp stage which gives rise to the medusae by budding. Some of the jellyfishes are very large. (See Page 256).

Sea Cucumber. (See *Echinodermata*).

Sea Squirt. (See *Urochordata*).

Sebaceous Gland. Oil-producing gland in the skin, associated with hair follicles. (See *Hair*) and (Plate 92).

Secondary Sexual Character. Feature that differs between the sexes yet not directly connected with the gonads. E.g. facial hair in man.

Secretin. A hormone which is produced by the wall of the first part of the small intestine in response to the acid chyme passing from the stomach. Secretin passes into the blood and promotes the flow of bile and pancreatic juice into the intestine. (See *Digestion*).

Segmentation. The repetition of a number of basically similar sections or segments along an animal's body. Not all animals are segmented – molluscs, for example, show no trace of segmentation. Some animals such as the annelids and arthropods show marked segmentation; in others, such as the vertebrates, it is less obvious – being seen mainly in the structure of the vertebral column and in the repetitive arrangement of the spinal nerves. (See Plates 84, 85 and 90).

Semen. Material produced by male reproductive organs, consisting of sperm and various other secretions from the accessory glands.

Semicircular Canals. Organs of balance in vertebrate *ear* (q.v.).

Seminal Vesicle. (=*Vesicula seminalis* q.v.).

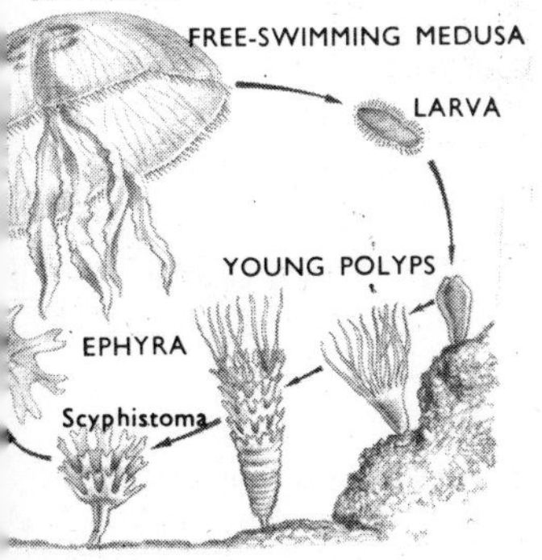

YCLE OF *Aurelia*

Seminiferous Tubules. Coiled tubules in vertebrate testis in which sperms are actually produced. (See Plate 91).

Sense Organ. (=*Receptor* q.v.).

Sensory. Concerned with receiving stimuli and transmitting them to central nervous system. (See *Motor*).

Septum. Partition, especially between segments in worms.

Sessile. Fixed to the substrate, e.g. sea anemone. Also means unstalked.

Sex Chromosomes. The *chromosomes* (q.v.) that determine sex. Although the body cells normally contain pairs of similar chromosomes, one sex (the male in mammals, female in birds and certain insects) contains a pair of dissimilar chromosomes called X and Y. These are the sex chromosomes. The opposite sex contains two X chromosomes and is called the homogametic sex. The homogametic sex produces only gametes with X chromosomes but the heterogametic sex produces equal numbers of X and Y gametes. When gametes join, they thus produce more or less equal numbers of each sex in the offspring. (See Plate 60).

Sex Linkage. The Y chromosome (See *Sex Chromosomes*) rarely carries genes other than those concerned with sex, but the X chromosome often does. These other genes are said to be sex-linked. Recessive genes on the X-chromosome will always show up on the male or heterogametic sex because there is no gene on the Y chromosome to dominate it. Consequently men show far more recessive characteristics than women for, in females, the recessive genes are more than usually over-ruled.

Sexual Selection. A possible evolutionary mechanism suggested by Darwin. It assumes that females select those males which have the most attractive (to the female) features. This could explain the evolution of the bright colours and mating behaviour of many animals but, because animals normally exist with a balance between the sexes, and most individuals will therefore be able to reproduce, it is unlikely that sexual selection has been of much importance in evolution.

Sharks. (See *Elasmobranchii*).

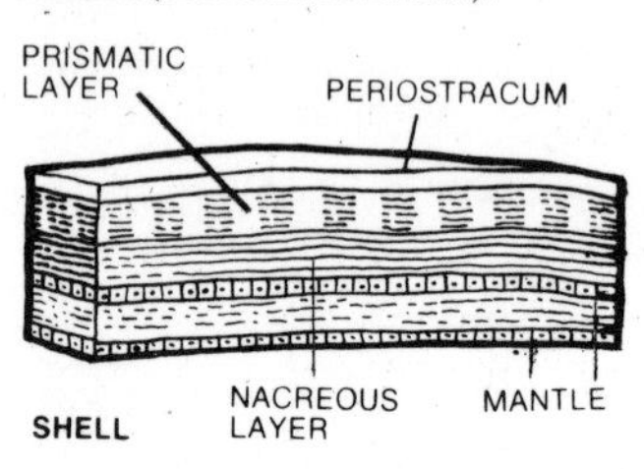

Shell. Loosely applied to any hard external skeleton but properly restricted to the hard covering of *molluscs* (q.v.) – whether a single valve as in snails or two valves as in mussels. Basically the shell is made up of three layers, an outer horn-like layer called the periostracum, a middle prismatic layer, and an inner nacreous layer. The periostracum is made of a substance called conchiolin which has a very similar chemical structure to chitin, an important part of the arthropod shell. The prismatic layer consists of prisms of calcium carbonate arranged at right angles to the periostracum and to the nacreous layer. Each prism has a many-layered column of conchiolin separating it from its neighbour. The nacreous layer is made of alternate layers of nacre or 'mother-of-pearl' (a form of calcium carbonate) and conchiolin. Whereas the prismatic layer and the periostracum are formed at the edge of the mantle, the nacreous layer is formed from the whole of the mantle and is released from its outer surface.

Silurian Period. Division of *Geological Time Scale* (q.v.).

Sinus. A space within certain bones of the face, connecting with the nasal cavity. Also an expanded vein of a type found especially in shark-like fishes. The sinus venosus is the expanded, thin-walled chamber in lower vertebrates (not birds and mammals) where blood collects before entering the heart. (See Plates 57, 82 and 83).

Sinus Venosus. (See *Heart*) and (Plate 57).

Siphon. Feeding and breathing tube of certain molluscs, formed from folds of the mantle. (See *Lamellibranchiata*).

Siphonaptera. Order of *Insecta* (q.v.) containing the fleas. These insects are secondarily wingless – an adaptation to their parasitic mode of life among the hairs of the host – and are slightly flattened from side to side. The mouthparts are adapted for blood-sucking.

Sirenia. Order of mammals which are completely aquatic – the dugongs and manatees, also known as sea-cows. (See Plates 91, 123).

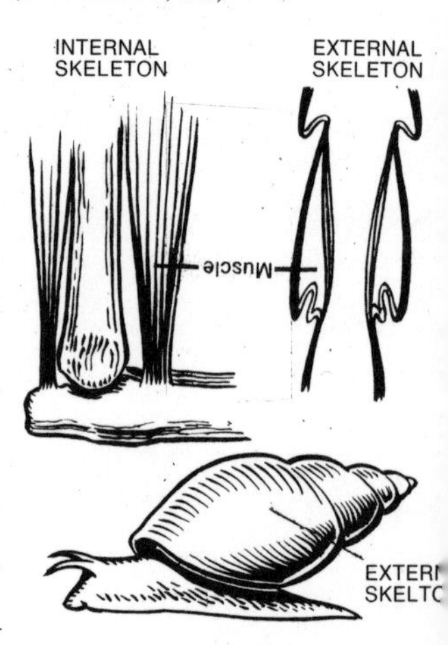

Skeleton. A feature of most animals that gives shape and rigidity to the body, protects soft parts, and provides anchorage for the muscles. The

SKELETON

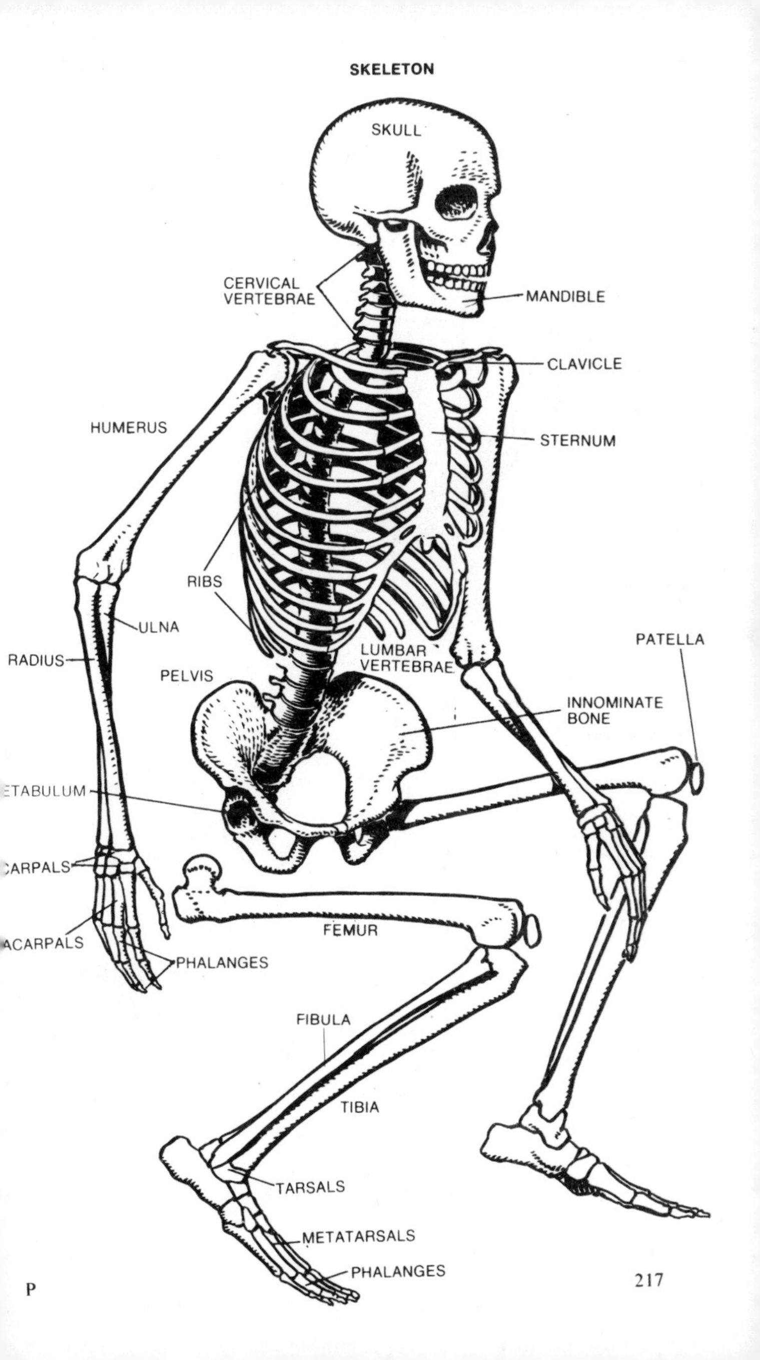
SKULL
CERVICAL VERTEBRAE
MANDIBLE
CLAVICLE
HUMERUS
STERNUM
RIBS
ULNA
RADIUS
PATELLA
LUMBAR VERTEBRAE
PELVIS
INNOMINATE BONE
ETABULUM
ARPALS
ACARPALS
PHALANGES
FEMUR
FIBULA
TIBIA
TARSALS
METATARSALS
PHALANGES

PLATE 92

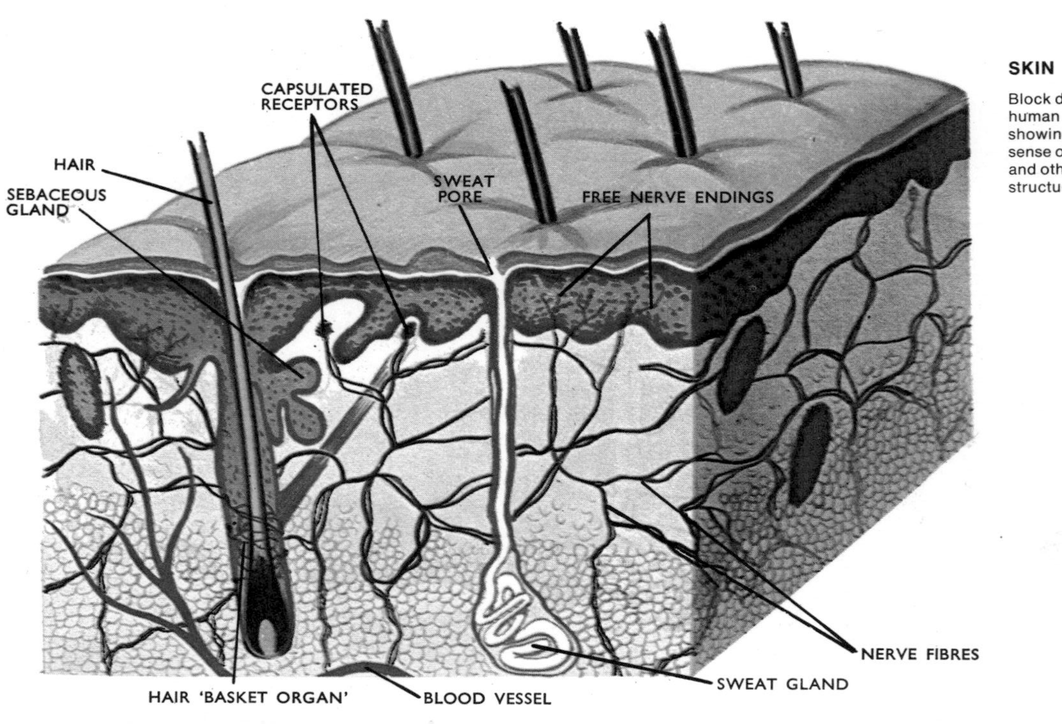

SKIN

Block diagram of human skin showing the sense organs and other structures.

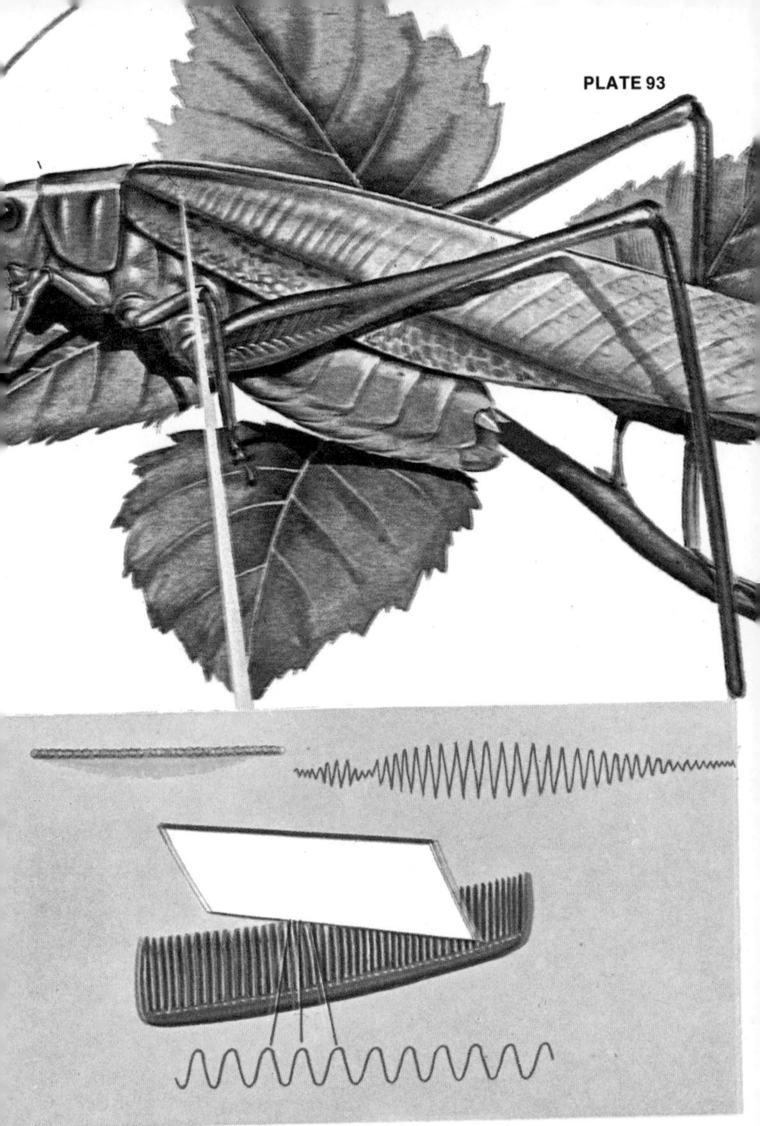

STRIDULATION

One of the long-horned grasshoppers that stridulate by rubbing the bases of the front wings together. A row of pegs on the right front wing is drawn over a ridge on the left wing. Each peg sets up a vibration as it strikes the ridge, just as the teeth of the comb set up vibrations as they hit the card. The sound gets louder in the middle of each chirp, as shown by the record of the vibrations. Short-horned grasshoppers stridulate by rubbing their hind legs against veins on the wings.

skeleton is normally quite hard and may be inside (endoskeleton) or outside the body (exoskeleton). Exoskeletons include the shells of most molluscs and the hard coverings of crabs and other arthropods. Endoskeletons are found mainly in vertebrate animals and are normally composed of a series of bones, each articulating with its neighbours to allow movement of the body.

Skin. The covering of the body, but it is more than just a covering, it is an important organ in its own right and performs a number of vital functions. This brief account deals mainly with the mammalian skin.

There are two distinct regions in the skin – the outer epidermis and the dermis underneath it. The innermost layer of the epidermis is the Malpighian layer. Its cells are living and divide quite frequently in a plane parallel to the skin surface. This layer contains pigment and is responsible for the colour of the skin. As the cells of the Malpighian layer divide, the outer ones are pushed towards the surface and become flattened. They gradually lose all their protoplasm and end up as horny scales which flake off as scurf. On some parts of the body, however, these cells build up thick horny layers (e.g. the sole of the foot). Hair, nails and feathers are all outgrowths of the epidermis.

Underneath the Malpighian layer is the dermis. It is composed largely of connective tissue and, unlike the epidermis, contains many nerves and blood vessels. Elastic fibres in the dermis give skin its elasticity but in old age, the skin loses this property and wrinkles develop.

One of the most obvious functions of the skin is that of protection. Its elasticity is some protection against mechanical damage and its waterproof quality prevents excessive water-loss. The skin also prevents the entry of germs which could harm the body tissues.

Mammals are warm-blooded creatures and can keep their body temperature more or less constant. The skin plays a large part in this temperature control. If, for any reason such as vigorous exercise or fever, the body temperature rises, the temperature of the blood reaching the brain will be higher. Nerve impulses are then sent out to the blood vessels and muscles of the skin. The vessels widen and carry more blood close to the skin surface and the blood loses heat to the air.

When the body temperature falls, several changes occur. The chemical reactions within the body are usually speeded up to produce more heat energy. Shivering may occur – this is a subconscious act that, through muscular action, produces warmth. Mammals are able to fluff up their hairs by contraction of the muscles attached to the bases of the hairs. This traps a thicker layer of air around the body and reduces heat-loss. Goosepimples in Man are produced by contraction of the same muscles.

The blood-vessels of the skin contract when the body temperature falls and less heat is lost to the air. The skin is then pale for less blood is flowing near the surface.

Sweating is another very important temperature control mechanism, especially in Man. Sweat glands are tiny coiled tubes lying in the dermis and opening onto the skin surface. The human body has perhaps three million of them scattered over the surface. Water and various salts accumulate in the tube and pass out onto the skin surface where the water evaporates. As a rule, it evaporates immediately and is unnoticed but the total cooling effect of the evaporation is quite considerable. In a humid climate, or during exercise, sweat may be unable to evaporate fast enough and beads of perspiration form on the skin. Sweating is controlled by the nerves and in cold weather the rate is reduced. The water and other waste materials still have to be removed however, and this explains the greater number of visits to the lavatory in cold weather. The salts passed out with sweat are not all waste and include some sodium chloride. The salt content of the diet should be increased in hot climates. Sweating is not effective in those mammals that are clothed with dense hair. In hot weather many hang their tongues out and lose water and heat from their mouths. (See Plates 91 and 92).

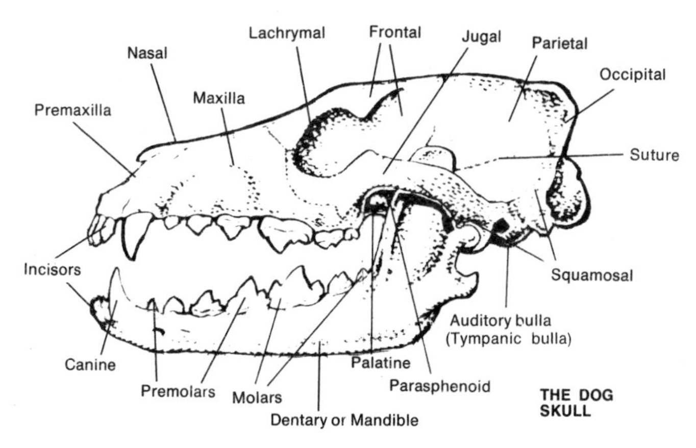

THE DOG SKULL

Skull. The bony case enclosing the vertebrate brain, and the associated bones of the face and jaws. Made up of a large number of bones which are more or less tightly joined to their neighbours by intricate joints called sutures.

Slug. (See *Gasteropoda*).

Smooth Muscle. (See *Muscle*).

Snail. (See *Gasteropoda*).

Snake. (See *Squamata*).

Solenocyte. (See *Flame Cell*).

Species. The smallest normally-used category of *classification* (q.v.). The members of a species are generally very much alike and can all interbreed. They cannot, however, interbreed with other species to produce fertile off-spring. This breeding among them-selves ensures that the species remains distinct, although of course genetic variations can occur within the species. The variations will be 'smoothed out' by interbreeding in one area but, where a species lives over a wide range, the variations in one region may not be the same as those elsewhere. The ani-mals at each end of the range will differ therefore to some extent and the two forms are called sub-species. At first, these sub-species can breed with each other but, if they remain separ-ated – by mountains or sea for example – the differences will increase until the animals can no longer interbreed. One species has then evolved along two different lines and produced two species.

Sperm. Male sex-cell.

Spermatheca. Organ possessed by cer-tain female and hermaphrodite animals for receiving sperm from the male during mating. The sperm is then shed from the spermatheca onto the eggs as they are laid. Queen ants and honeybees mate only once and store sperm for several years, using it up very gradually as they lay their thousands of eggs. (See *Oligochaeta*) and (Plates 84 and 85).

Spermatogenesis. The formation of sperms.

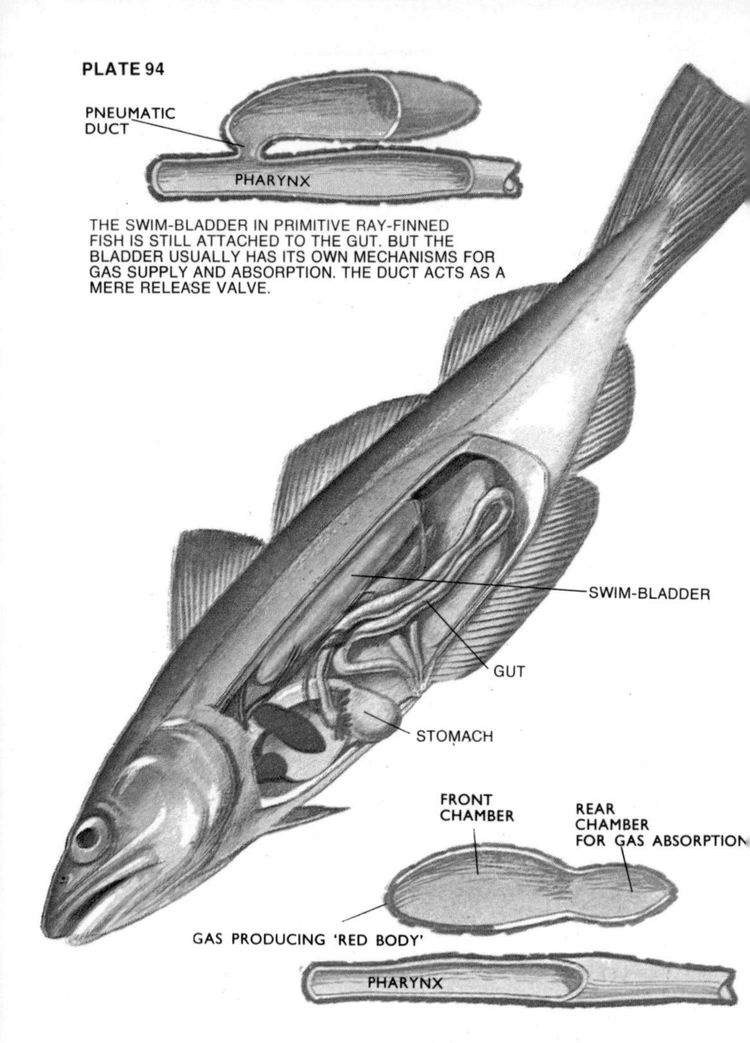

IN MORE ADVANCED RAY-FINNED FISH THE BLADDER HAS LOST ITS CONNECTION WITH THE GUT. GAS IS SUPPLIED BY THE RED BODY AND ABSORBED TOWARDS THE REAR OF THE STRUCTURE

SWIM BLADDER

The swim bladder is a buoyancy aid in many bony fishes. The swim bladder and the lungs of tetrapods have a common origin as an outgrowth of the gut.

SYMBIOSIS

The association between hermit crab and anemone benefits both – the anemone protects the crab and, in return, is carried to fresh feeding grounds. The barnacles on the shell are commensals – living together with the others but having little effect on each other.

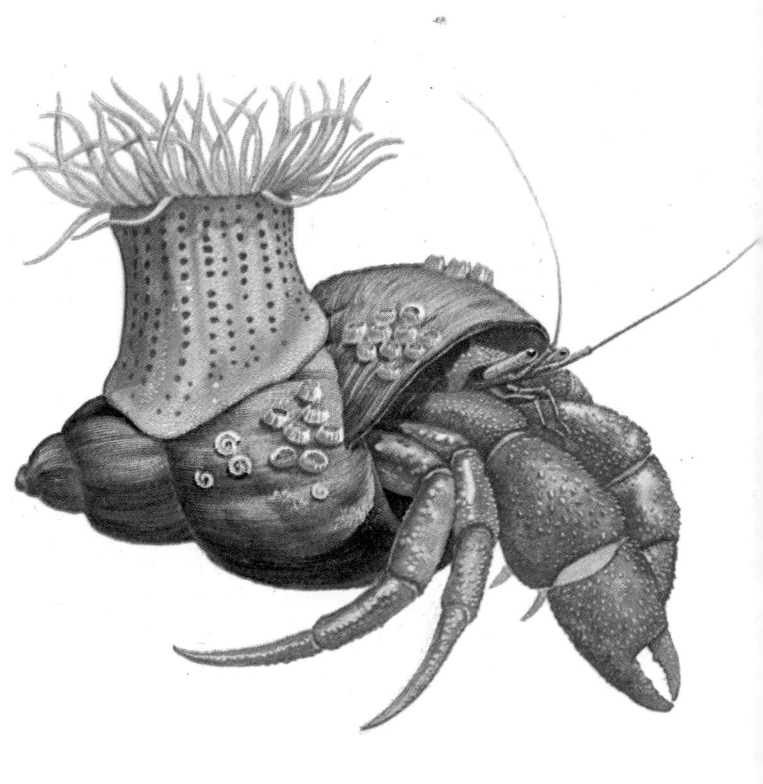

Spermatophore. A 'packet' of sperm that is introduced into the female other than by the penis. The male spider deposits a spermatophore and carries it to the female in a specially modified pedipalp. Male newts deposit spermatophores that the females pick up with the lips of their cloacae.

Sphincter. A ring of muscle in the wall of a tube which is able to close that tube. E.g. Pyloric sphincter controlling passage of food from stomach to intestine.

Spider. (See *Araneida*).

Spinal Column. The back bone. (See *Vertebral Column*).

Spinal Cord. The main nerve tract in vertebrates. It is normally enclosed within the spinal column.

Spinal Nerve. One of the paired nerves which arise from the spinal cord in each segment of the vertebrate body. Each nerve has two roots – a dorsal root containing sensory fibres (fibres running from sense organs), and a ventral root containing motor fibres running to muscles and glands. The dorsal root has a swelling (ganglion) containing the cell bodies of the nerve cells but the bodies of the motor nerve cells are within the spinal cord. The dorsal and ventral roots join up on leaving the spinal column. (See Page 208).

Spiracle. The opening of an insect breathing tube (trachea). Also the small opening present in many fish – especially sharks – just in front of the gill slits. The spiracle is actually the remnant of the first gill slit. (See *Visceral Arches*) and (Plates 34, 35 and 90).

Spleen. A mass of spongy tissue in the intestinal region of most vertebrates. The spleen and the *lymphocytes* (q.v.) that it produces play an important part in defending the body against bacteria. The spleen also acts as a store for red blood cells, releasing them when necessary. Dead blood cells are removed from the blood and broken down in the spleen. (See Plate 36).

Spontaneous Generation. The idea, squashed by Pasteur, that living things, especially micro-organisms such as fungi and bacteria, arose spontaneously from dead organic material. Pasteur showed conclusively that the micro-organisms associated with dead and decaying matter originated from spores in the air and that spontaneous generation does not occur.

Spore. Tiny reproductive body – often only a single cell. There is often a thick wall which enables the spore to survive drought and cold. By forming spores, animal species can become very widely distributed for the tiny spores are easily transported by wind, water, or other animals. It is only the lower animals that form spores although many plants do so. When favourable conditions return the spores develop into new individuals.

Sporozoa. A class of *Protozoa* (q.v.) all of which are parasitic. Some are amoeboid but many have no organs of locomotion in the adult stage. The majority live inside the cells of the host at some stage. Examples include *Monocystis* which parasitises earthworms and *Plasmodium,* the organism causing malaria. (See Page 253).

Squamata. Order of *Reptilia* (q.v.) containing lizards (sub-order Lacertilia) and snakes (sub-order Ophidia). Lizards are fairly typical reptiles, normally with limbs. It is thought that the snakes have evolved from a group of lizards that took to living underground, losing their limbs and sense of hearing in the process. Snakes have no normal eyelids but there is a transparent third eyelid which covers the eye permanently. The bones of the skull are modified and some are only loosely attached to each other so that the jaw can open widely to swallow prey. The fangs are large teeth connected to poison glands. Associated with the long, narrow body, only the right lung develops in snakes: the left remains merely as a tiny sac. (See Plate 119–5, 6).

Stapes. Bone of the middle *ear* (q.v.) of mammals.

Statocyst. Organ of balance consisting of granules (statoliths) in a chamber. As the animal moves, the granules fall against sensitive hairs and nervous impulses inform the animal of its position with regard to gravity. (See *Otolith*).

Stegocephalia. Extinct sub-class of *Amphibia* (q.v.). (See Page 277).

Sterile. (1) Unable to reproduce by sexual methods. (2) Free from living organisms.

Sternum. Vertebrate breast-bone. (See Page 217).

Steroids. Important organic compounds that play a vital part in many bodily activities. Vitamins and hormones often contain steroid molecules. Chemically steroids are saturated hydrocarbons and they resemble fats in many of their properties.

Stomach. Expanded region of the *alimentary canal* (q.v.) where food is mixed and some digestion takes place.

Striated (Striped) Muscle. (See *Muscle*).

Stridulation. The production of sound by rubbing one part of the body (the scraper) against another (the file). It is particularly well developed among insects of the order Orthoptera – grasshoppers and crickets. As a rule, only the male stridulates and it is presumably concerned with attracting a mate. Short-horned grasshoppers have a row of pegs on their hind legs and they rub these against a vein on the wing. Other forms rub parts of the wings together. (See Plate 93).

Strobilus. The body of a tapeworm. (See *Cestoda*).

Sub-species. (See *Species*).

Succus Entericus. Digestive juice containing several enzymes, produced by the small intestine. (See *Digestion*).

Suture. A join – especially the interlocking joins of the bones of the skull, or of the chambers of an ammonite shell. Also used to describe the junction between the segmental plates of an arthropod skeleton. (See Plate 3).

Sweat Gland. An organ of the *skin* (q.v.) of mammals which is important in temperature control and water-loss. (See Plate 92).

Swim-Bladder (=*Air Bladder*). A gas-filled sac lying above the gut of bony fishes. The walls secrete or absorb gas to maintain the buoyancy of the fish as it dives or rises through depths. It is derived from the lungs of the ancestral fishes and in some modern forms it still retains its connection with the pharynx. (See Plate 94).

Symbiosis. A close association between two organisms of different species which benefits both individuals.

Perhaps the best known example of symbiosis is that between a hermit crab and a sea anemone. The anemone is often found attached to the shell in which the hermit crab lives. In their long history hermit crabs have developed the habit of sheltering within the empty shells of molluscs such as periwinkles and whelks. The hind portion of the body has lost its hard covering and would otherwise be unprotected. As the crab gets bigger it outgrows its shelter and so has to find a new one. Often, a sea anemone attaches itself to the crab's shelter and it may envelop part of the crab's own shell as well. The growth of the crab and anemone keep pace with each other and the crab has no need to change its shell – more and more of

PLATE 96

TASTE

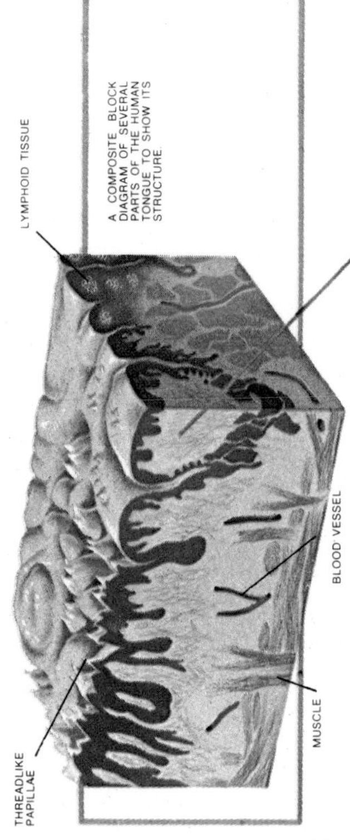

A COMPOSITE BLOCK DIAGRAM OF SEVERAL PARTS OF THE HUMAN TONGUE TO SHOW ITS STRUCTURE.

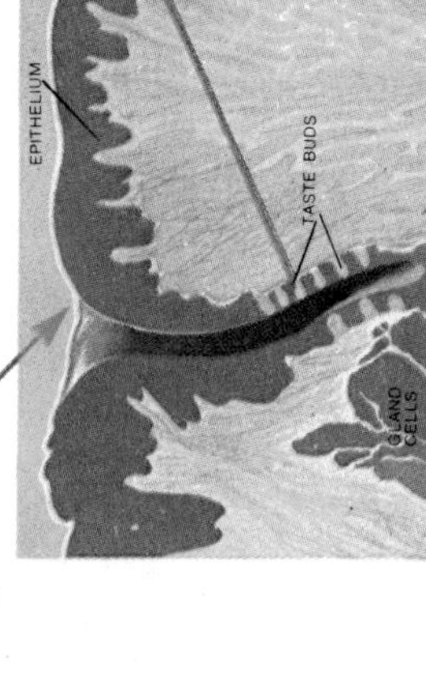

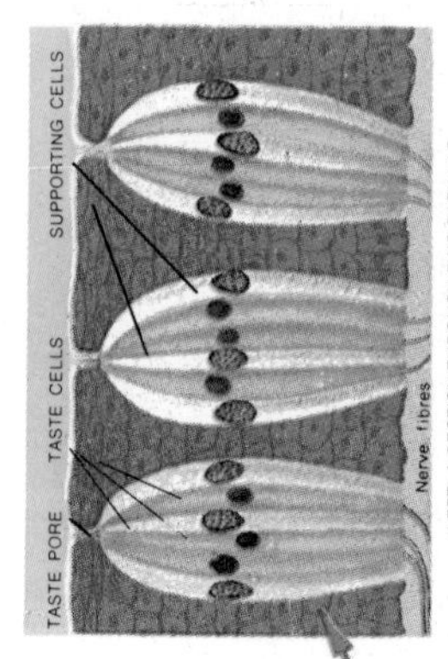

(LEFT) A SECTION THROUGH TWO PAPILLAE ENLARGED TO SHOW THE POSITION OF THE TASTE BUDS IN THE EPITHELIUM. (ABOVE) A HIGHLY MAGNIFIED VIEW OF THREE NEIGHBOURING TASTE BUDS SHOWING THE TASTE CELLS AND SUPPORTING CELLS.

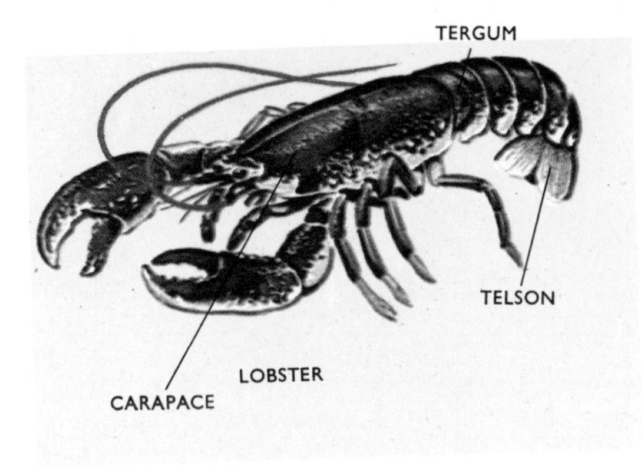

PLATE 97

TELSON
The hind segment of arthropods.

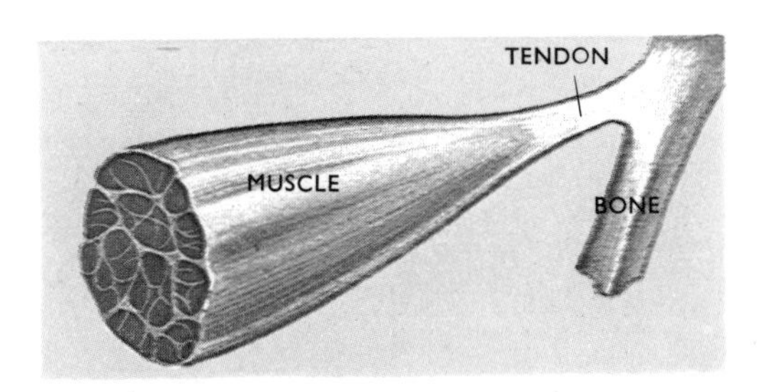

TENDON

Tendons are composed of tough collagen fibres which withstand the strains involved.

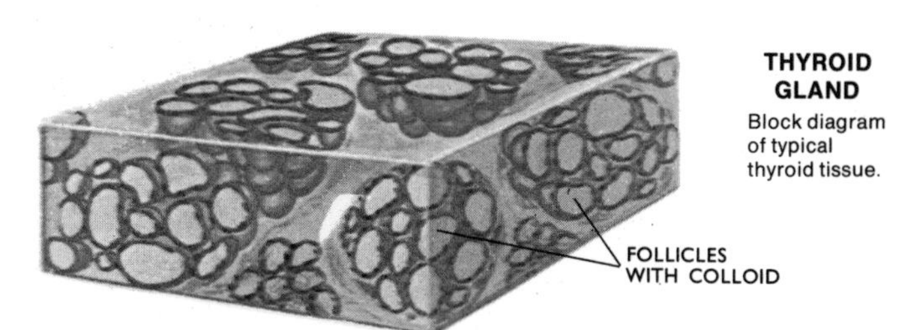

THYROID GLAND

Block diagram of typical thyroid tissue.

it is sheltered by the anemone. As the crab moves about in search of food the anemone is brought into contact with a greater supply of food and the crab no doubt gains a certain amount of defence from the anemone's stinging cells.

Many coelenterates and some flatworms have geen algae living in their tissues. *Hydra viridis* owes its green colour to the many algal cells in its tissues. Corals (particularly reef corals) and sea anemones also have symbionts in their tissues. Recently it has been shown that in reef corals the algae are of no food value and the amount of oxygen that they release bears no relation to the needs of the coral. They are certainly of value in using up the waste substances produced by the coral, however, and it is probable that the same applies for sea anemones and for *Hydra viridis* too. The algae obtain shelter and the waste substances for food.

A most interesting association is that between *Carteria* and the flatworm *Convoluta*. When very young the latter lives the life of a normal flatworm, feeding in the same way as other free-living forms. However, at an early age it obtains a 'stock' of symbionts, loses its gut and becomes completely dependent on them for its food supply. The symbionts obtain a supply of carbon dioxide and nitrogen-containing waste materials. They are also brought out into the light by the animal at appropriate times. The flatworm is supplied with oxygen and food and has its waste materials removed.

Very few animals are able to produce enzymes capable of breaking down cellulose and most plant-feeders and wood-feeders rely on bacteria and/or protozoans in their food canals to break down the cellulose. This is a good example of symbiosis. There are also several well-known associations between birds and large game animals. These birds rid their partners of injurious and annoying insects and in doing so obtain a ready supply of food. Partners in symbiosis are called *symbionts*. (See Plate 95).

Sympathetic Nervous System. Part of *Autonomic Nervous System* (q.v.).

Symphysis. A tight joint allowing only slight movement between neighbouring bones, e.g. pubic symphysis between the two halves of the pelvic girdle.

Synapse. Junction between neighbouring *nerve cells* (q.v.).

Synapsida. Extinct sub-class of *Reptilia* (q.v.) one line of which gave rise to the mammals. (See Page 280).

Syndactyly. Condition in which the digits are joined. It may be normal – e.g. webbed feet of aquatic animals – or caused by genetic abnormality.

Synovial Membrane. Connective tissue surrounding joints and forming a bag containing synovial fluid.

Syrinx. Expanded lower end of the trachea in birds where sound is produced. As in the mammalian larynx (See *Voice*) there are two membranes which vibrate. In the song birds they are moved by a complicated series of muscles.

Systematics. The study of the classification and phylogeny of living organisms. (See Pages 236, and 238).

Systemic Arch. The fourth *aortic arch* (q.v.) of the vertebrate embryo. It develops in tetrapods to become the main vessel supplying blood to the body.

Tactile. Concerning the sense of touch.

Tapetum. Reflecting layer behind the retina of many nocturnal and crepuscular animals. It reflects back onto the rods light that would otherwise be lost. The tapetum is responsible for the coloured reflection from the eyes of cats and other animals when a torch is flashed at them at night.

Tapeworms. (See *Cestoda*).

Tarsus. The ankle region of the hind leg. Contains a number of *tarsal bones*. (See Page 217).

Taste. One of the chemical senses. In vertebrates taste receptors occur mainly on the tongue, a few elsewhere in the mouth and pharynx, and on the epiglottis. Some projections (papillae) on the tongue have flask-shaped taste buds scattered over them. These consist of groups of specialised cells that have nerve fibre endings between them and wrapped round them. When the taste buds are stimulated, signals pass along the nerve fibres to the brain. The taste buds are moistened by the saliva and by the fluids released by special gland cells in the tongue. An essential feature of both taste and smell receptors is that the chemical must pass into solution before it can stimulate the receptor. During dry cold weather the senses of taste and smell may be very much reduced.

By testing the reaction of different parts of the tongue to different substances it has been established that the greatest response for each of the four 'types' of taste – salt, sweet, acid (sour) and bitter – is in a different region of the tongue. The tip is most sensitive to sweet and salty substances; the sides to acid substances; while the back of the tongue is most sensitive to bitter substances. It is probable that there are different receptors for each distinct taste but very detailed study has revealed no differences in the anatomy of the receptors. Some chemicals have different tastes when applied to different parts of the tongue. The texture of food and its temperature will also affect the apparent 'taste' of the food, for touch and temperature receptors in the mouth will also be stimulated by its presence. The taste of a substance is thus dependent on a number of factors. (See Plate 96).

Taxis. Movement of a whole organism in response to some stimulus, such as the smell of food which causes the animal to move towards the source of the smell.

Taxonomy. The study of the naming and classification of animals.

Teeth. (See *Dental Formula* and *Tooth*).

Teleostei. Order of bony fishes (*Actinopterygii*) including about 20,000 known species – the vast majority of living fishes. Teleosts seem to have arisen during Triassic times and have since almost replaced all earlier bony fishes. There has been a tendency to a reduction of scales and a shortening of the body. The more primitive teleosts – herrings, salmon and others – have soft fin rays and retain the duct between the gut and the *swim-bladder* (q.v.). The more advanced members of the order – perch, cod, and the various flat fishes – have lost the connection between gut and swim-bladder and the fin rays are stiff. There is a wide range of form among teleosts with the sea horses, angler fish, flatfish, and eels all included with the more typically shaped fishes. (See Plate 117–8, 9 and 10).

Telson. The last segment of the abdomen of arthropods. It does not always develop – insects do not have one for example – but the scorpion sting and the fan-shaped tail of lobsters are examples of a well-developed telson. (See Plate 97).

Temperature Control. (See *Skin*).

Tendon. Bundle of collagen fibres connecting muscles to bones. (See Plate 97).

Tergum. The thickened dorsal region of the arthropod cuticle. (See Plate 97).

Territory. An area inhabited or dominated by an animal or a family of animals, especially for the purpose of reproduction. Territory is marked out by scent, or by singing in the case of

PLATE 98

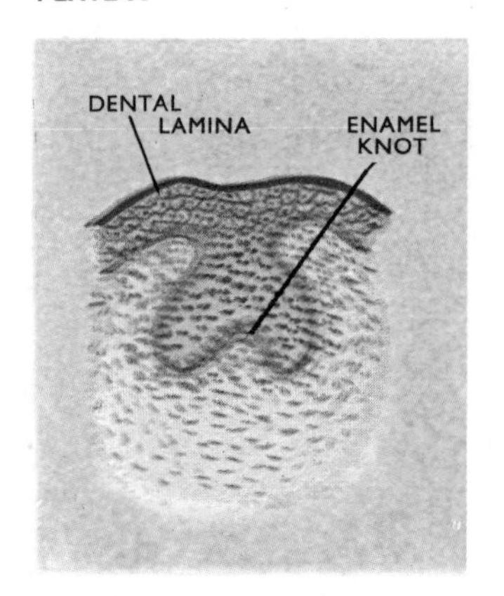

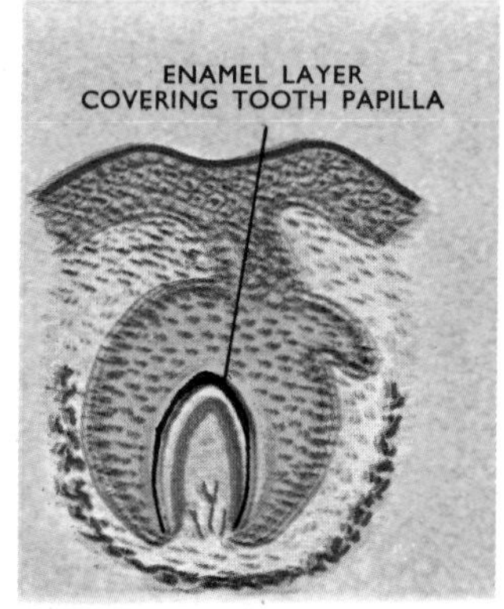

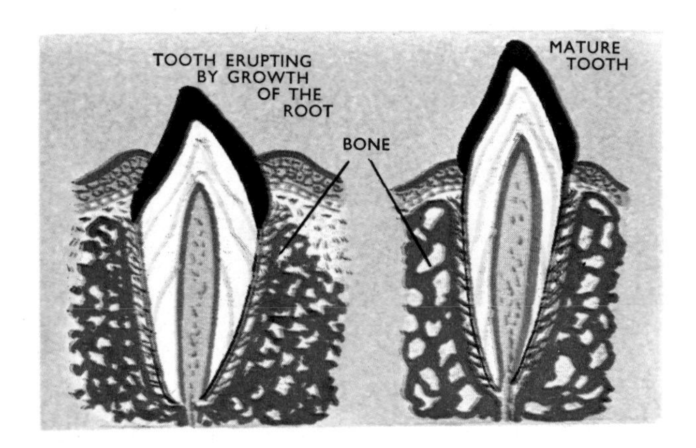

TOOTH

Six stages in the development of a mammalian tooth.

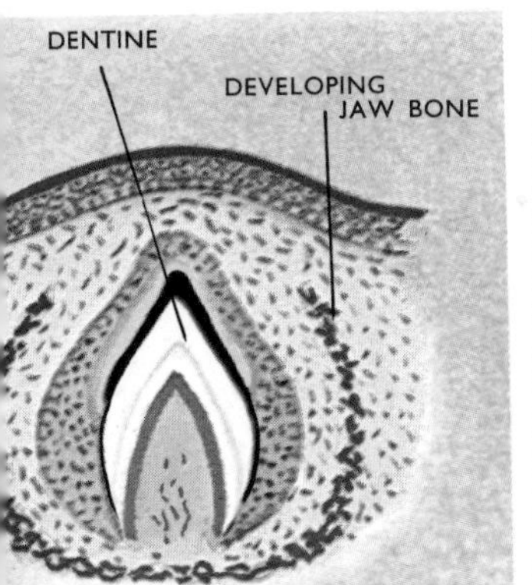

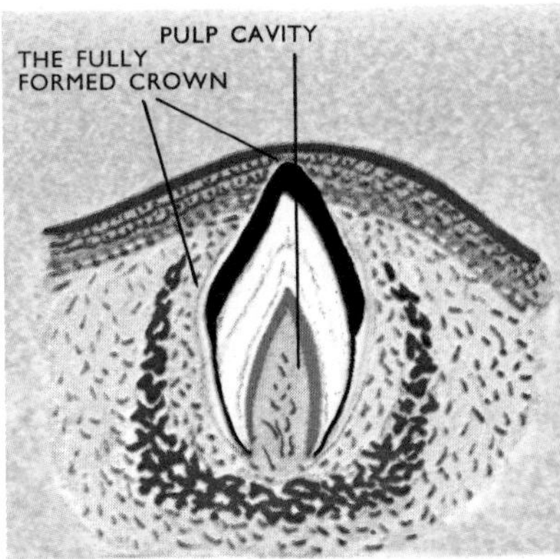

The detailed structure of a human premolar tooth.

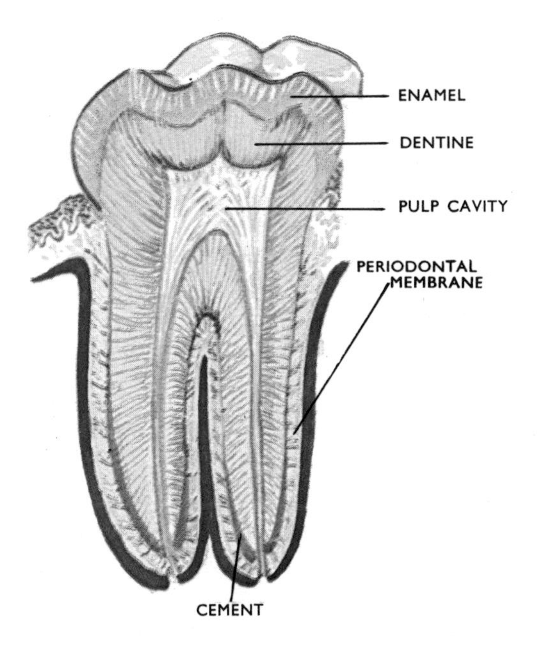

birds, and intruders of the same species are attacked. Territory is possibly a mechanism of population control for it prevents too many animals from breeding in one area.

Tertiary Period. Division of *Geological Time Scale* (q.v.).

Testis. Male gonad producing sperms and various sex hormones. (See Plates 84, 85 and 91).

Testosterone. Vertebrate male hormone. It is responsible for the development of many male characteristics.

Tetrapoda. Term embracing all the basically four-footed animals – i.e. all the land-living vertebrates.

Therapsida. Extinct order of mammal-like reptiles (sub-class *Synapsida*).

Thorax. (1) Region of the vertebrate body surrounded by ribs (when present) and enclosing the heart and lungs. (2) Central region of the insect body consisting of three segments and normally carrying three pairs of legs and two pairs of wings. (See Plate 62).

Threshold. The level of intensity of a stimulus below which it does not evoke a response from a sense organ. (See *All-or-Nothing Law*).

Thymus. Glandular organ in neck or chest region of vertebrates. Its function is not fully understood but it appears to be concerned with sexual development. If the thymus is removed the development of the reproductive system is delayed. After maturity is reached the thymus degenerates.

Thyroid Gland. An important endocrine gland found in the neck region of vertebrates. Its function is to incorporate iodine from the diet into large organic molecules – thyroid hormones – which act on all other parts of the body. It has an extremely rich blood supply and it is mainly made up of hollow, spherical sacs or follicles whose walls are one cell thick. The cavity of each follicle is filled with a protein-like jelly known as colloid.

The colloid contains proteins, enzymes, the thyroid hormones produced by the cells of the follicle wall, and the compounds from which they are built up. The amounts of each that are present vary from time to time and from one follicle to another. The colloid is more than a reservoir, therefore. It is somewhat like a wholesale warehouse, always keeping a basic stock of numerous articles, some finished and others ready to be put together, the numbers of each varying as fresh supplies come in and as orders are despatched. A feature better shown in the thyroid than in any other endocrine gland is the storage of hormone outside the cells that produce it.

Present knowledge indicates that the major hormone secreted by the thyroid is thyroxine. Its molecule is formed by the combination of two molecules of tyrosine (an amino acid) each of which has had two hydrogen atoms replaced by two atoms of iodine with the elimination of another amino acid – alanine. A substance similar to thyroxine but containing only three iodine atoms is also produced by the thyroid. It is called tri-iodothyronine and, although produced in smaller amounts than thyroxine, it has a greater effect on the body cells. Both hormones cause an increase in the metabolic rate. The failure of the thyroid produces both mental and physical retardation. Lack of iodine on which the thyroid can act produces similar effects. Goitre – enlargement of the thyroid – is also produced by lack of iodine in the diet and it is interesting to note that goitre occurs more commonly in inland and mountainous areas where the iodine content of the soil is low. Administration of iodine or thyroid extract can cure these deformities.

The activities of the thyroid are closely related to those of the tissues as a whole but the relationship is not a simple one. The pituitary gland is particularly important in controlling the thyroid. It produces the thyrotropic hormone which causes the thyroid to elaborate more thyroid hormone. The amount of thyroid hormone in the blood itself affects the production of thyrotropic hormone; a high level reducing its production, a low level increasing it. (See Plate 97).

Tibia. The shin bone – larger of the two bones in the lower hind leg. (See Page 217).

Tissue. A patch or group of similar cells all performing the same function, e.g. muscle cells, liver cells, etc.

Toads. (See *Anura*).

Tonsil. Lymphoid tissue in throat region of tetrapods, concerned with the defence of the throat and mouth region against bacteria.

Tooth. Bony process in the jaws of most vertebrates concerned mainly with the capture and breaking up of food. The teeth of reptiles and other lower vertebrates are all of a simple conical shape, but mammalian teeth are of several different types, modified according to the diet. At the front of the jaws there are a number of chisel-shaped incisor teeth. These are followed by a stabbing or eye tooth – the canine – and then the grinding cheek teeth – premolars and molars. The majority of mammals have two sets of teeth – a first milk set, and a permanent set replacing them later in life. Molar teeth, however, are not preceeded by milk teeth. The precise number, structure and arrangement of teeth differ between animals that have different diets. (See *Dental Formula*).

In spite of the differences in external form, all teeth are constructed on the same basic plan. Projecting from the gum is the crown of the tooth. The part embedded in the gum and reaching into a socket in the jaw bone is known as the root. The body of the tooth is made up of hard bone-like substance known as dentine. Inside this is the pulp cavity which contains blood vessels and nerves. Branches from these, together with fine protoplasmic threads, penetrate the maze of fine canals which spread throughout the dentine. Covering the crown of the tooth is a layer of enamel of varying thickness. It is made up almost entirely of apatite crystals with calcium phosphate filling. Apatite crystals are made up of calcium phosphate plus calcium fluoride or calcium chloride. Calcium phosphate is also mainly responsible for the hardness of dentine. The enamel crystals are elongated and are all arranged with their ends towards the surface of the enamel. Around the root of the tooth, enamel is replaced by cementum, another bone-like material which fixes the tooth firmly in the socket of the jaw. However, between the jaw bone and the cementum there is a layer of tissue – the periodontal membrane – which is in contact with the tissues of the gums and with the pulp cavity. Incisor and canine teeth have a single root, premolars have a double root and molars have three branches to the root.

Although teeth are composed of hard bone-like tissue and are embedded within the jaw bones, they are in fact, derived from the skin in much the same way as the placoid scales of shark-like fishes. The similarities of structure and development of these scales and the teeth of vertebrates make it certain that both have evolved from the bony plates that covered the primitive fishes. Tooth formation begins in the early embryo. Buds of both milk and permanent teeth are formed and they develop slowly, the various layers growing until the complete crown is formed within the gum. The teeth become embedded in the jaw bones because the jaw bones grow around the developing teeth in the embryo. When the crown is complete, the tooth erupts through the gum by growth of the root. The permanent teeth develop even more slowly at the base of the milk teeth. Pressure of the developing permanent teeth forces out the milk teeth later in life. (See Plates 98, 99 and 100).

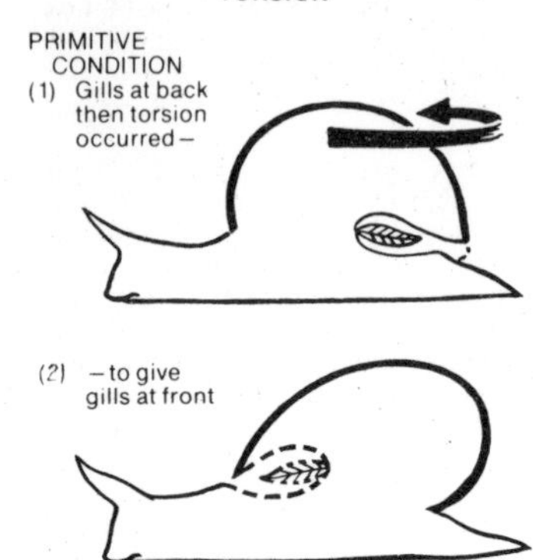

Torsion. Gasteropods with coiled shells have a mantle cavity at the front with the gut positioned behind. The mantle cavity appears behind the gut but during development the position is reversed. This is called torsion. (See *Gasteropoda*).

Trachea (1). Wind-pipe of tetrapods, leading from throat to bronchi. (See *Lung*). (2) Breathing tube of *Insecta* (q.v.). (See Plates 62, 73 and 105).

Tracheole. The fine ending of tracheae in *Insecta* (q.v.).

Trematoda. Class of *Platyhelminthes* (q.v.). All are endoparasitic and covered with a thick, structureless cuticle, sometimes equipped with spines. They have suckers with which they attach themselves to their hosts. The mouth leads to a two-branched gut. Some species have only one host but more usually there are two or more hosts involved in the trematode life history and the trematode passes through several larval stages. Examples include *Fasciola,* the liver fluke and *Schistosoma,* the cause of Bilharzia in man. (See Plate 108).

Triassic Period. Division of *Geological Time Scale* (q.v.).

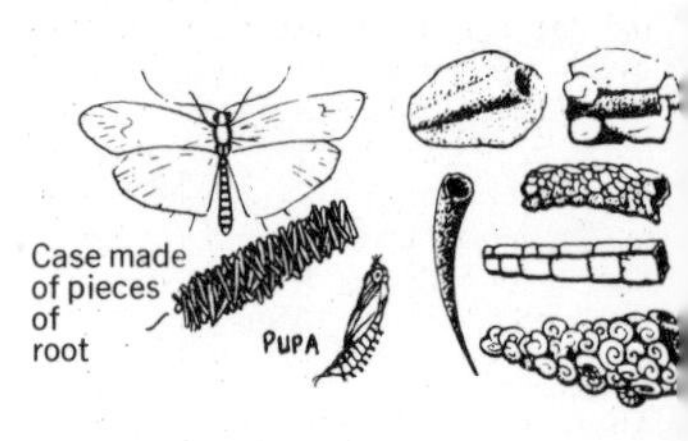

Trichoptera. Order of *Insecta* (q.v.) containing caddis-flies. The wings and body of the adult are covered with fine hairs. Metamorphosis is complete and the larvae live in water. The majority of the larvae build cases of small stones, leaves, or other fragments, in which they conceal their soft bodies. (See Plate 113).

Trigeminal Nerve. 5th *cranial nerve* (q.v.) of vertebrates.

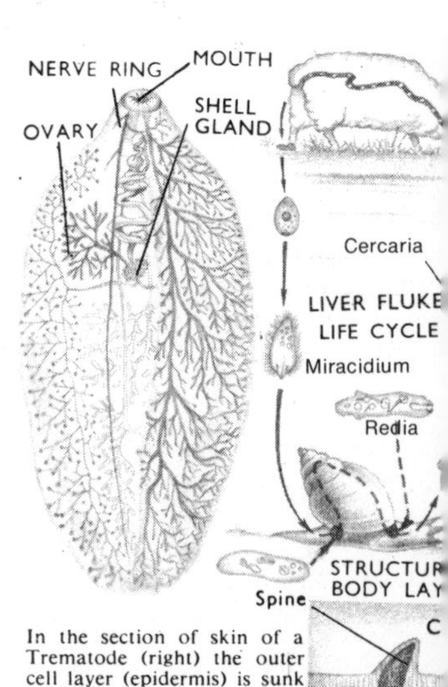

In the section of skin of a Trematode (right) the outer cell layer (epidermis) is sunk into the underlying tissue (parenchyma). There is a thick cuticular covering which often contains spines. The cuticle is associated with the parasitic habit of flukes.

Trilobita. Extinct class of arthropods that abounded in the Cambrian Seas and reached a peak in the Ordovician Period. They were still important in Silurian times but only a few species survived after then. The latest trilobites lived during the Permian Period, about 220 million years ago, after which they disappeared for ever.

The trilobites form a distinct class of the phylum *Arthropoda*. The name *Trilobita*, refers to the way in which the body appears divided into three lobes by two grooves running along its length. Like the other arthropods, trilobites had an external skeleton. It was probably horny, and, at least on the upper surface, heavily impregnated with calcium carbonate. (See *Geological Time Scale*) and (Plates 100 and 111).

Triploblastic. Having three body layers – ectoderm, endoderm, and mesoderm. All metazoa apart from coelenterates are triploblastic. (See *Diploblastic*) and (Plate 24).

Trochlear Nerve. 4th *cranial nerve* (q.v.) of vertebrates.

Trypanosome. A flagellate protozoan of the genus *Trypanosoma*. Trypanosomes are parasites and cause some serious diseases such as sleeping sickness in man and nagana in cattle. The organisms are transmitted by tsetse flies in whose bodies they undergo certain important changes.

Trypsin. Important digestive enzyme. (See *Digestion*).

Trypsinogen. Precursor of trypsin. (See *Digestion*).

Tube Feet (=*Podia*). Characteristic feature of *Echinodermata* (q.v.).

Tubulidentata. Order of mammals with a single member, the Aardvark (*Orycteropus*). This strange creature is found over much of Africa and feeds entirely on termites which it gets by digging open their nests with its strong claws. In common with the ant-eaters, there is a long snout and tongue, but the peg-like teeth are quite unlike those of any other mammal. (See Plate 123–9).

Tunicata. (See *Urochordata*).

Turbellaria. Planarian worms. Class of free-living *Platyhelminthes* (q.v.) which rarely exceed an inch in length. Most of them live in water – all of them in damp places – and they can be seen crawling over the mud of most ponds. Their gliding movement is caused by the beating of the cilia which cover the body wall and propel the animal along. Planarians are carnivorous, feeding on a variety of small worms and arthropods.

Small prey are taken into the gut and surrounded with digestive enzymes. The fats are directly broken down into soluble food but proteins and carbohydrates are absorbed by the cells lining the gut and digested there.

For organisms too large to be ingested whole, turbellarians have a special device. Just inside the mouth, the first part of the gut (the pharynx) is very muscular, and can actually be protruded. It becomes attached to the victim and a backward and forward pumping motion, together with the action of digestive enzymes, breaks the food into more manageable lumps which are then taken into the gut.

Deprived of food for long periods, turbellarians will actually begin to digest themselves. They shrink in size as eggs, reproductive organs, muscles and parts of the gut are consumed. On normal feeding they return to their full size, regenerating all the lost organs.

Planarians are classified according to the structure of the gut which varies from a simple sac to a highly branched system. There is a simple nervous system showing the development of a brain at the front. Most planarians have a number of simple eyes – there is no lens but pigmented cells no doubt aid the animal to distinguish light and dark. There is also

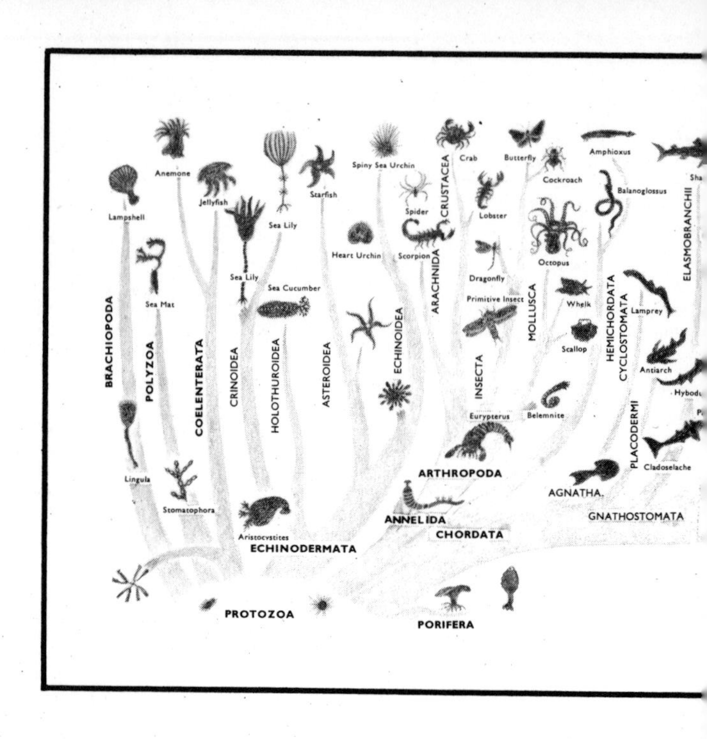

THE RELATIONSHIPS OF THE MAIN GROUPS IN THE ANIMAL KINGDOM

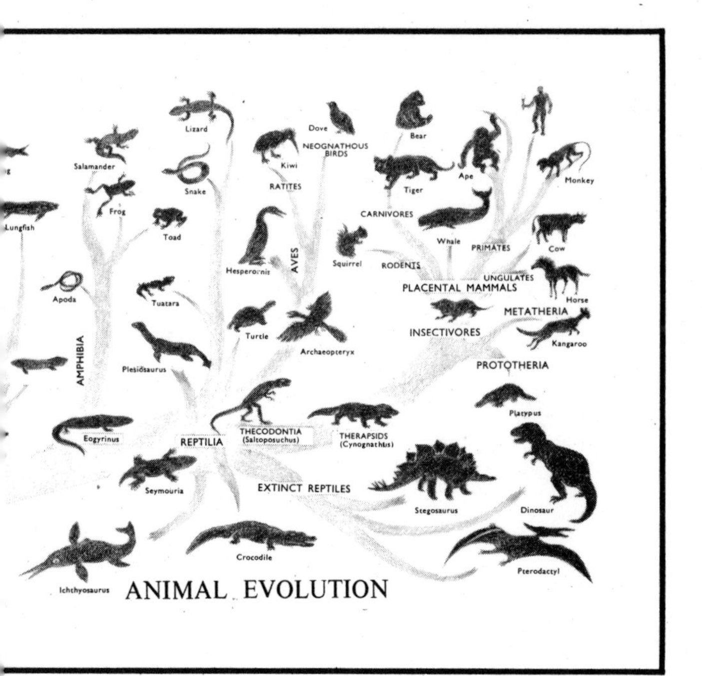

ANIMAL EVOLUTION

FOR READERS' CONVENIENCE THE CHART ON THE PREVIOUS PAGES IS ENLARGED HERE TO FACILITATE MORE DETAILED STUDY

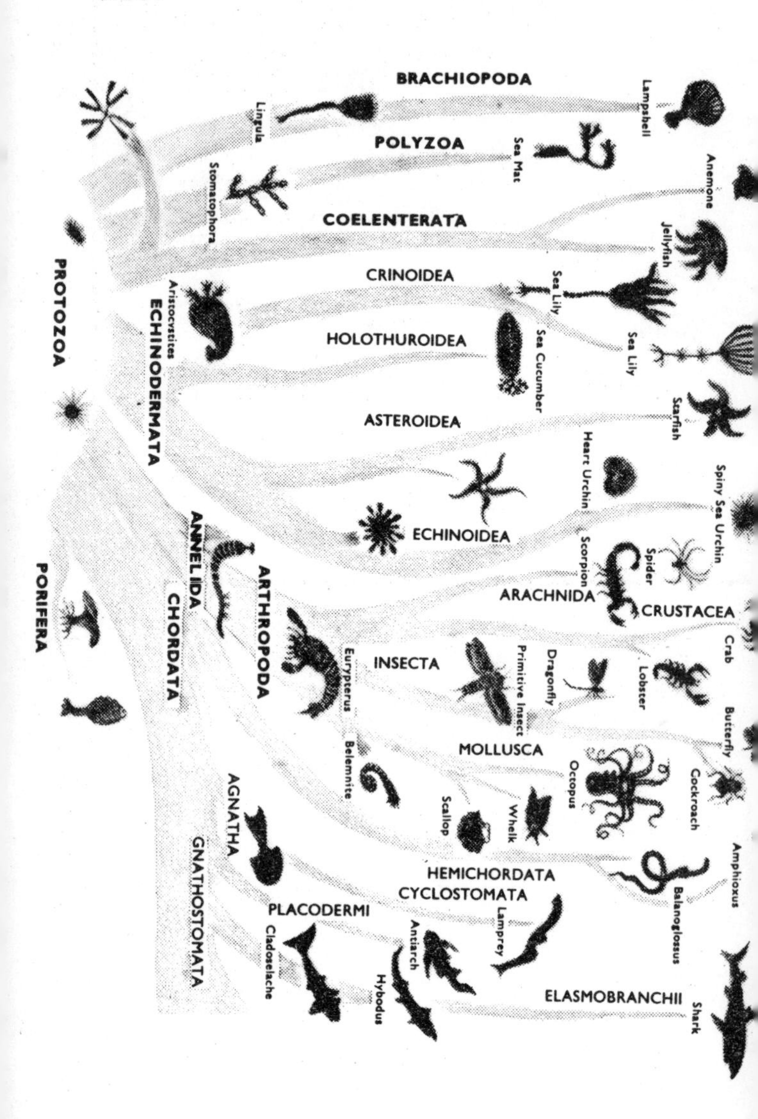

Perch
Herring
Polypterus
TELEOSTEI
Lungfish
Leptolepis
DIPNOI
Palaeoniscus
Ceratodus
Dipterus
Salamander
Frog
Toad
Apoda
AMPHIBIA
Eogyrinus
Lizard
Snake
Tuatara
Plesiosaurus
Seymouria
REPTILIA
Crocodile
Kiwi
Dove
NEOGNATHOUS
BIRDS
RATITES
AVES
Hesperornis
Turtle
Archaeopteryx
THECODONTIA
(Saltoposuchus)
THERAPSIDS
(Cynognathus)
EXTINCT REPTILES
Bear
Tiger
Ape
Monkey
CARNIVORES
Squirrel
RODENTS
Whale
PRIMATES
Cow
UNGULATES
PLACENTAL MAMMALS
Horse
METATHERIA
INSECTIVORES
Kangaroo
PROTOTHERIA
Platypus
Stegosaurus
Dinosaur
Pterodactyl

a well-developed chemical sense that helps the animals to find food. (See Plates 101, 102 and 108).

Tympanic Bulla. Thick bony case enclosing the inner ear apparatus at the back of the skull. (See Page 221).

Typanum. Ear-drum. (See *Ear*).

Typhlosole. Infolding of the dorsal wall of the gut of earthworms that increases the surface for absorption. (See *Oligochaeta*) and (Plate 5).

Ulna. One of the bones of fore-arm – on the side of the 5th digit. (See Page 217).

Umbilicus. Navel – the region where the umbilical cord connecting the embryo mammal to the placenta joins the embryo. At birth, the umbilical cord breaks and the end comes away from the navel a little later when the blood vessels and other tissues have been sealed up. (See Plates 38, 39 and 88).

Ungulate. A hoofed mammal. There were many hoofed mammals in the Tertiary Period some 50 million years ago and various groups of these have given rise to the modern ungulates – horses, deer, pigs, and cattle, etc. – and to the so-called 'near ungulates' – the elephants, conies, and sea-cows which represent early offshoots of the main line of hoofed animals. Ungulates are normally herbivorous and tend to live in herds. The hard hooves are well-suited to life on open grassland. (See *Artiodactyla; Perissodactyla*).

Unguligrade. Walking on the tips of one or more toes. Most hoofed mammals walk in this way. (See *Artiodactyla; Perissodactyla; Digitigrade; Plantigrade*) and (Plate 30).

Urea. $CO(NH_2)_2$ – the main waste product of protein metabolism in mammals and aquatic vertebrates. It is very soluble in water and therefore easily excreted. Birds and reptiles and other animals, such as insects, that develop within shelled eggs cannot get rid of their embryonic waste products and they excrete uric acid which is almost insoluble and so does not interfere with metabolism. Uric acid excretion goes on throughout life. As water is not lost with the excretory products, the animals can live in dry places.

Ureter. Duct taking urine from kidney to bladder. (See Plates 42 and 103).

Urethra. Duct from urinary bladder to the outside of the body in mammals.

Urinogenital System. Because of the close association of the excretory and reproductive systems in vertebrates it is convenient, or almost necessary, to study them together. The combined systems can be conveniently referred to as the urinogenital system. (See Plate 103).

Urochordata. Sub-phylum of *Chordata* (q.v.) containing the sea-squirts. The adult sea-squirt appears to show no resemblance whatever to a typical chordate – it is a soft, jelly-like sack, normally attached to the sea bed. Many can be likened to a coffee-pot in shape and further in that water goes in at the top (mouth) and out through the 'spout' – the atriopore. The mouth leads into a large sac – the pharynx – and here is the clue to the chordate nature of the animal: the pharynx wall is pierced by numerous gill slits whose lining is covered with cilia. These cilia beat continuously and draw water in through the mouth. The gill slits strain out any food particles and the water passes through the slits to a space surrounding the whole body. This space is the atrium and it opens to the outside through the atriopore. The anus also opens into the atriopore.

It was not until the life-history of the sea-squirts was unfolded that the chordate affinities of these creatures were confirmed. The egg develops into a tadpole-like creature which is clearly a chordate with a notochord, hollow dorsal nerve cord, and a pharynx with one or more pairs of gill slits. The young sea-squirt or ascidian tadpole as it is often called, does not feed and settles on the sea bed in a few days to develop into an adult. The free-swimming form would appear to be a means of spreading the species. Adults also reproduce by budding in some species and develop into large often brightly coloured colonies. (See Plate 103).

Urodela. Newts and salamanders – sub-class of *Amphibia* (q.v.). (See Plate 118–4, 5, 6 and 7).

Urostyle. Slender, unsegmented region of vertebral column of frogs and toads, associated with pelvic girdle.

Uterus. The mammalian womb where the embryo is nourished by the placenta. The lining of the uterus undergoes cyclic changes during the reproductive life of the animal. (See *Oestrus Cycle; Menstrual Cycle*). The uterus wall is highly muscular and when the embryo is fully-developed, the muscles contract strongly and force the embryo out through the vagina or birth canal. (See Plate 88).

Utricle. Part of the inner *ear* (q.v.).

Uvula. Soft extension hanging from the mammalian mouth. (See Plate 82–83).

Vacuole. Fluid-filled space within a cell.

Vagina. Birth canal connecting *uterus* (q.v.) with the outside of a female mammal. (See Plate 103).

Vagus Nerve. 10th *cranial nerve* (q.v.) of vertebrates.

Variety. Animal or group of animals that differ from the typical form in one or more features and that will continue to show these differences in succeeding generations. (See *Sub-species; Polymorphism*).

Vascular. Fluid-conducting. In animals the vascular system is normally the blood system but in *echinoderms* (q.v.) there is a water vascular system.

Vasoconstriction. A narrowing of blood vessels to restrict blood flow. It is a muscular action under the control of the vasomotor nerves – part of the sympathetic nervous system. (See Plate 91). *Vasodilation* is the expanding of the blood vessels. Both processes occur in blood vessels of the skin in response to environmental temperature changes. (See *Skin*).

Vector. An animal that carries disease-causing organisms and transmits them to another species. E.g. Tsetse flies are vectors of the sleeping sickness parasite.

Vein. Blood vessel carrying blood back to the heart from the tissues. (See also *Artery*). Also the stiffened supporting framework of an insect wing. The veins in this case carry not only blood but nerves and tracheae (breathing tubes). (See Plates 15, 16 and 17).

Vena Cavae. Large veins, one in front and one behind the heart, which collect blood from all the other veins (apart from the pulmonary vein) and pass it into the heart for recirculation through the lungs.

Venation. The arrangement of the veins in an insect wing. It is important in classification.

Ventral. Concerning the underside of the body. (See *Dorsal*).

Ventral Aorta. The main artery leaving the heart of fishes and larval amphibians. It send branches to the gills. (See Plate 36).

Ventricle. Major pumping chamber of the *heart* (q.v.).

Vermes. An old term used for centuries to include anything that was worm-like. This large heterogeneous group has now been broken down into many different phyla, including Annelida, Nematoda, and Platyhelminthes.

Vertebra. One of the bones making up the spinal or vertebral column. Vertebrae are present in almost all

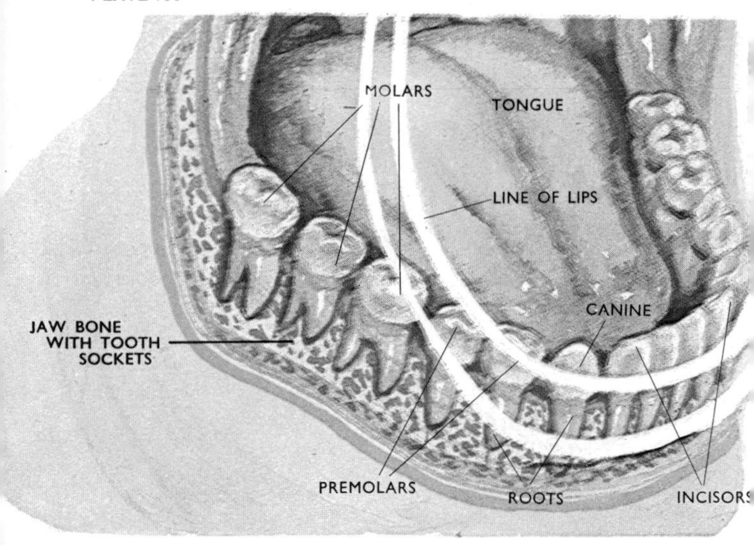

TOOTH

The arrangement of the teeth in the human lower jaw.

TRILOBITA

Calymene, a common Silurian trilobite fossilised in limestone.

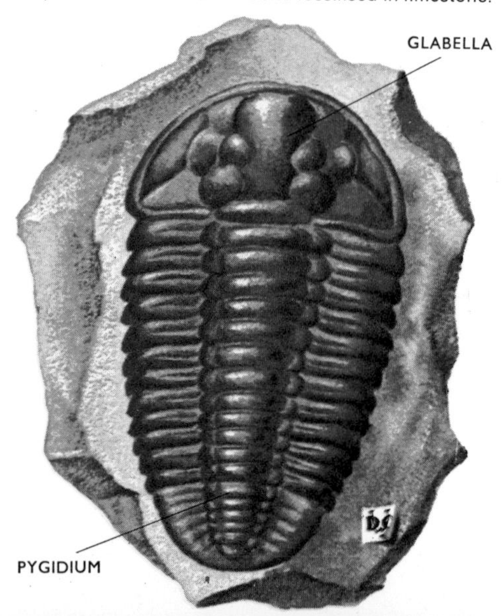

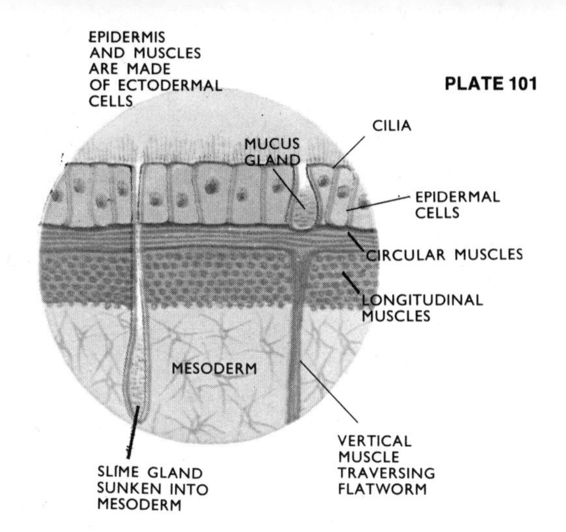

TURBELLARIA

Section of a flatworm showing structure.

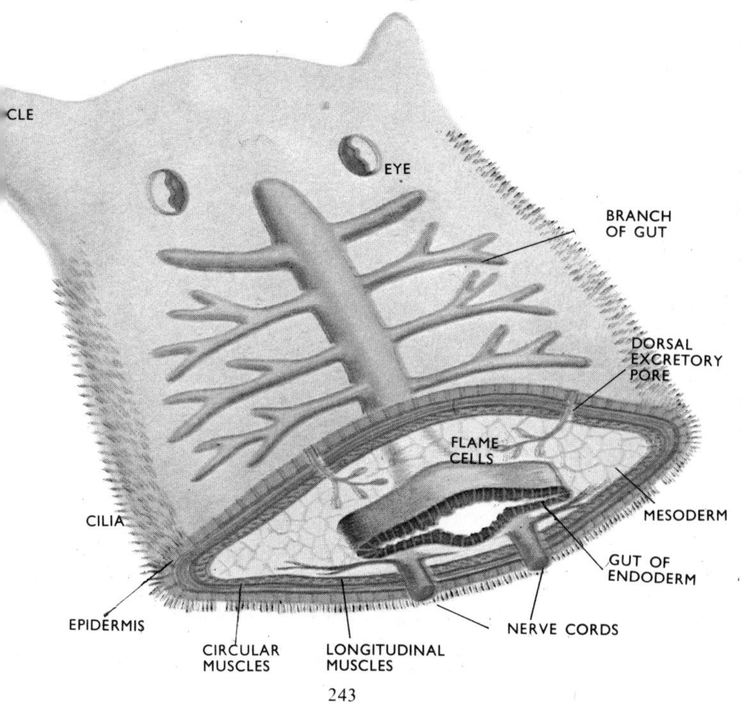

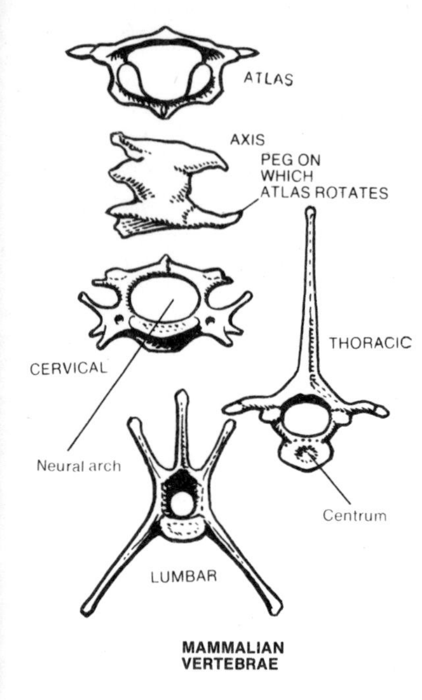

MAMMALIAN VERTEBRAE

vertebrates replacing the embryonic notochord (the living lung-fishes and the cyclostomes have no vertebrae but retain the primitive notochord). The vertebra consists of a solid bony centrum and a hollow neural arch on the dorsal side. The spinal cord runs through the neural arch. Each vertebra is linked to its neighbours by a cushion of cartilage which allows a little movement and thus enables the animal to bend. All the vertebrae of fishes are similar but the land-living vertebrates (tetrapods) show a number of variations. The first two vertebrae (those nearest the skull) are specially modified for the carriage of the head. The first vertebra is the *atlas* which articulates with the back of the skull. The centrum is hollow. Nodding the head involves movement between the skull and the atlas. The second vertebra is the *axis*. On the front there is a peg which fits into the hollow centrum of the atlas. (The peg is, in fact, formed from the missing part of the atlas.) The rotation of the head involves a swivelling of the skull and atlas on this peg of the axis.

Behind the axis there are a number of cervical or neck vertebrae (in mammals there are normally seven – a giraffe has no more vertebrae in its neck than a mouse has). Behind the neck region there are a number of thoracic vertebrae which have projections for the articulation of the ribs. Vertebrae of the lumbar region behind the ribs are normally larger than the rest. They are followed by the sacral vertebrae which often fuse into one structure called the sacrum. The hip girdle is attached to one or more sacral vertebrae. Behind the sacral region there are a number of small tail or caudal vertebrae. (See Page 217).

Vertebrata. Sub-phylum of *Chordata* (q.v.) which includes all the back-boned animals – fishes, amphibians, reptiles, birds, and mammals. They differ from the other chordates in the possession of bony or cartilaginous skull surrounding the brain. In most of them the notochord is replaced by vertebrae of bone or cartilage. The skin is several layers thick. (See Plate 104) and (Page 276).

Vesicula Seminalis. Organ where sperm is stored after leaving the testis.

Vestigial. Of very reduced form when compared with the ancestral structure. For example, the hind limbs of whales have been reduced during the course of evolution until they are now represented only by tiny bones inside the body. These bones are the vestigial limbs. (See Plate 21).

Viable. Able to live or develop. Used especially for embryos.

Vibrissae. The stiff whiskers of the face of most mammals, but especially noticeable in cats, which act as touch receptors. Cats are thought to use their vibrissae for, among other things, judging the width of gaps in relation to the size of their bodies.

Villus (plural villi). Projection in wall of intestine. (See *Alimentary Canal; Digestion*) and (Plates 1 and 2).

VISCERAL ARCHES of theoretical fish before jaws became attached to hyoid arch

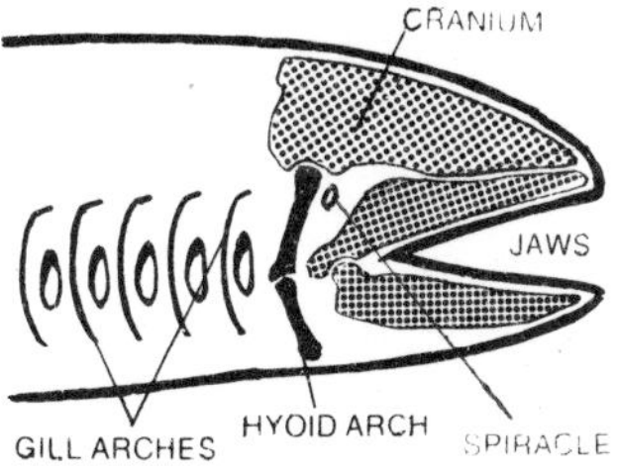

Visceral Arches. The partitions and skeletal rods separating the gill slits of fishes. The rods and the associated muscles are important in the *respiratory movements* (q.v.) of the pharynx. Modern fishes have five pairs of visceral (or branchial) arches, one behind each gill slit. It is thought that the earlier, jawless fishes had more than five pairs of visceral arches and that jaws evolved from one of the more anterior pairs. In the earliest jawed fishes, the jaws were not connected to the arch behind them – the hyoid arch – and there was a complete gill slit behind the jaws. In later fishes, however, the jaws extended further back and became supported by the hyoid arch. This involved compression of the first gill slit behind the jaws and it is now represented in many fish by the small spiracle. In land-living vertebrates the visceral arches are not required for respiratory movements and the upper jaw becomes fixed to the base of the skull. This frees the upper part of the hyoid arch which becomes part of the middle *ear* (q.v.), transmitting sound from the eardrum to the inner ear. The other arches are reduced and incorporated as small cartilages into the hyoid apparatus and larynx in the throat.

Vitamins. Complicated organic compounds that must be provided in an animal's diet if it is to remain healthy. Only tiny amounts are needed but if they are not supplied, certain abnormalities occur. Such abnormalities caused by vitamin deficiency are called deficiency diseases and it was through investigation of these diseases that the vitamins were first discovered. Many diseases once thought to be caused by germs are now known to be caused by lack of vitamins and it is possible to cure them by giving the required vitamin. The importance of a mixed diet in providing vitamins is now realised.

One of the chief effects of vitamin deficiency is a slowing down of growth so it is important that children particularly should be well supplied with vitamins. It is during this early period that the human body is growing most actively and consequently the effects of vitamin deficiency will be most pronounced. McOllum and Davies in 1915, working in the United States, introduced a system of naming vitamins, dividing them into two groups. Those in the one group that dissolved in fat they called the 'fat-soluble A' group and the others, that dissolved in water, they called the 'water-soluble B' group. Within these groups many vitamins were recognised. Each became known by a letter (e.g. vitamin A, vitamin C) or by a letter with a subscript for vitamins each with similar properties (e.g. vitamins B_1–B_{12}). Many vitamins have now been made synthetically and, though the naming of them by letters has not been dropped completely, there is an increasing tendency to use the chemical names. Thus vitamin C is known as ascorbic acid, vitamin B_1 as aneurin (Britain) or thiamin (U.S.A.), and vitamin B_2 as riboflavin. (See Page 248).

Vitelline Membrane. Membrane immediately surrounding the egg cell or ovum.

Vitreous Humour. Fluid in chamber behind lens of eye (q.v.).

PLATE 102

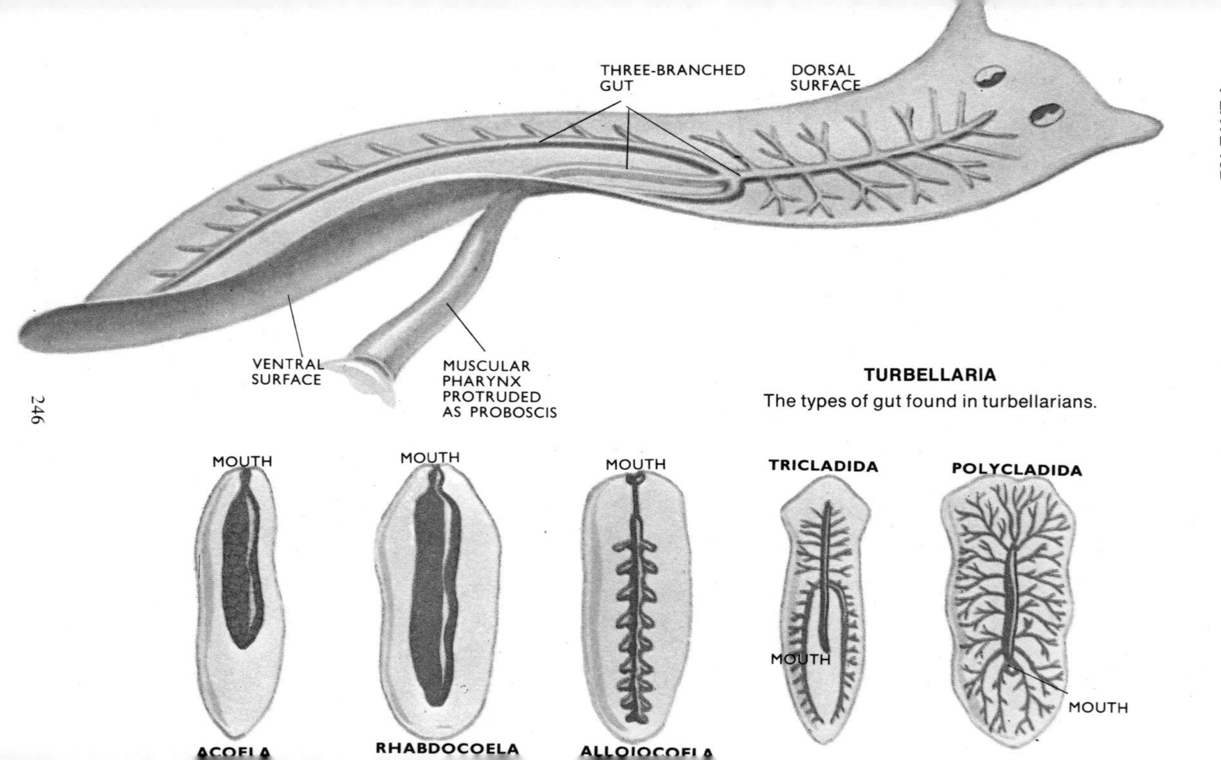

TURBELLARIA
The types of gut found in turbellarians.

PLATE 103

URINOGENITAL SYSTEM

The excretory and reproductive systems of male and female rabbits.

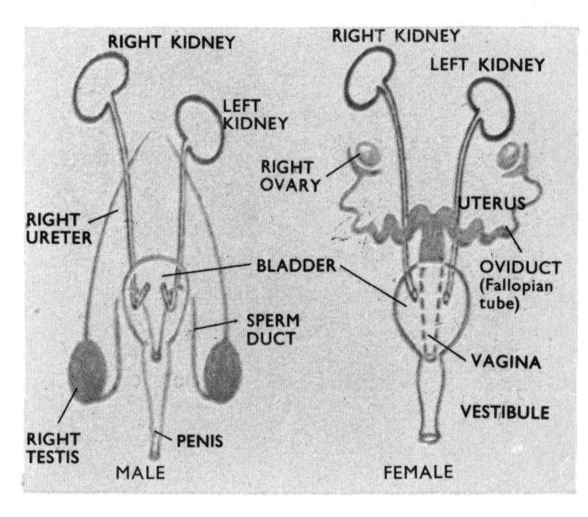

UROCHORDATA

The structure of larval and adult sea-squirts.

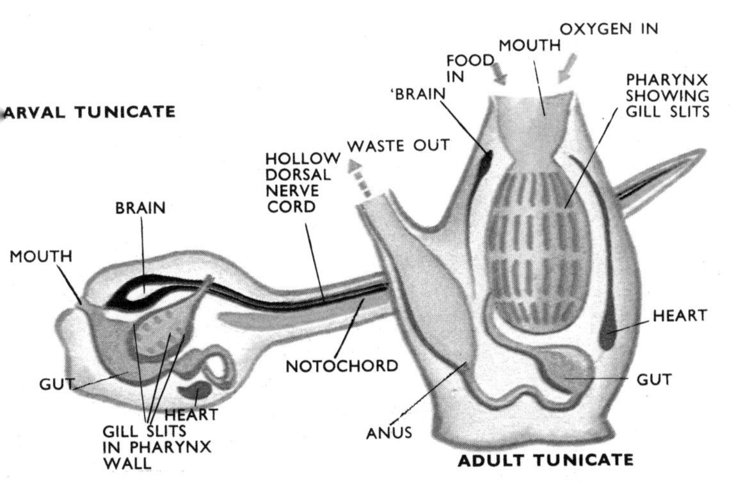

MAIN VITAMINS NEEDED BY MAN

	VITAMIN		FOOD SOURCES	FUNCTION IN THE BODY	MAIN EFFECTS OF DEFICIENCY
FAT SOLUBLE	A	(Axerophthol)	Fish liver oils, butter, eggs, margarine, cream, green vegetables, carrots.	Growth and building of new cells. Associated with resistance of epithelia to infection, (particularly of eyes, gut and lung passages). Formation of eye pigments.	Xerophthalmia (hardening of cornea); Night blindness (poor vision in the dark); Dryness of skin; Poor bone growth.
FAT SOLUBLE	D_2	(Ergocalciferol)	Fish liver oils, margarine.	Necessary for normal absorption of calcium and phosphorus.	Rickets; Osteomalacia (softening of the bones); Unhealthy teeth.
FAT SOLUBLE	D_3	(Cholecalciferol)	Fish liver oils, butter, eggs, cream, liver, margarine	Necessary for normal absorption of calcium and phosphorus.	Rickets; Osteomalacia (softening of the bones); Unhealthy teeth.
FAT SOLUBLE	E	(Tocopherols)	Wheat germ oil, green vegetables, eggs.	Necessary for proper development of foetuses and male sex cells. Prevents fats from being oxidized.	Inadequate nourishment of the muscles (muscular dystrophy). Loss of fertility.
FAT SOLUBLE	K_1	(Phylloquinone)	Lettuce, kale, spinach, pig liver, tomatoes.	Blood clotting process.	Loss of blood clotting power. Excessive bleeding (particularly in new born).
...UBLE	B_1	(Thiamin)	Yeast, whole cereals, liver, eggs.	Important in carbohydrate Metabolism	Beri-beri
...UBLE	B_2	(Riboflavin)	Milk, yeast, liver, wheat germ, meat, cheese, eggs, green vegetables.	Vital part in cell chemistry particularly oxidations.	Inflammation of the tongue.
...UBLE	B_5	(Nicotinic acid)	Liver, kidney, meat, wheat germ, yeast, green vegetables.	Part of some enzyme systems; Important in carbohydrate and protein metabolism	Dermatitis (inflammation of the skin). Pellagra (disease affecting alimentary system, skin and

H (Biotin)	... vegetables, nuts.	enzymes (e.g. those causing breakdown of unwanted proteins).	of appetite.
B_{12} (Cyanocobalamin)	Liver.	Necessary for formation of red blood cells, synthesis of methyl (CH_3) groups.	Pernicious anaemia (blood disease). Spinal cord wastes away.
C (Ascorbic acid)	Oranges, lemons, grapefruit, tomatoes, uncooked vegetables	Formation of collagen. Healing of injuries.	Scurvy (bleeding of gums and other parts of body, painful joints).
Choline	Liver, pancreas, soya beans.	Fat metabolism. Synthesis of acetylcholine (substance released at nerve endings). Exchange of methyl groups between substances.	Cirrhosis (disease of the liver). Bleeding of kidney.

Many other vitamins have been discovered and are known to be necessary to other animals but have yet to be proved essential to man.

Viviparous. Giving birth to active young which have been nourished inside the mother – usually by means of a placenta.

Vocal Cords. (See *Voice*) and (Plate 105).

Voice. The mammalian voice is produced in the larynx, or voice-box, which is a special part of the windpipe in the throat. Around the larynx there are various cartilages – the large one at the front (thyroid cartilage) forms the Adam's Apple in Man. Inside the voice-box are two sheets of tissue called the vocal cords. These are responsible for the actual sound production.

During normal breathing the vocal cords are relaxed and there is a triangular opening between them. During sound production the cords are tightened by their muscles and as air is forced up from the lungs the cords vibrate. The opening between the cords opens and closes rapidly and sets the air vibrating with a fundamental frequency corresponding to the rate of vibration of the cords. This fundamental frequency determines the pitch of the note. There are also many overtones or harmonics produced. These are of less intensity than the fundamental note but of higher pitch. They give the note quality. A pure note, without overtones, sounds tinny.

Notes of different fundamental pitch are produced by changing the position and tension of the vocal cords. The volume of sound is controlled by the pressure of the air pushed through the voice box by the lungs.

A man's voice is deeper than that of a woman or child. This is because during adolescence the larynx enlarges – the Adam's Apple gets bigger – and the vocal cords grow. Just as a double-bass produces a lower note than a violin, so the vocal cords of a man produce a lower note than the shorter cords of a woman or child.

All mammals have this basic

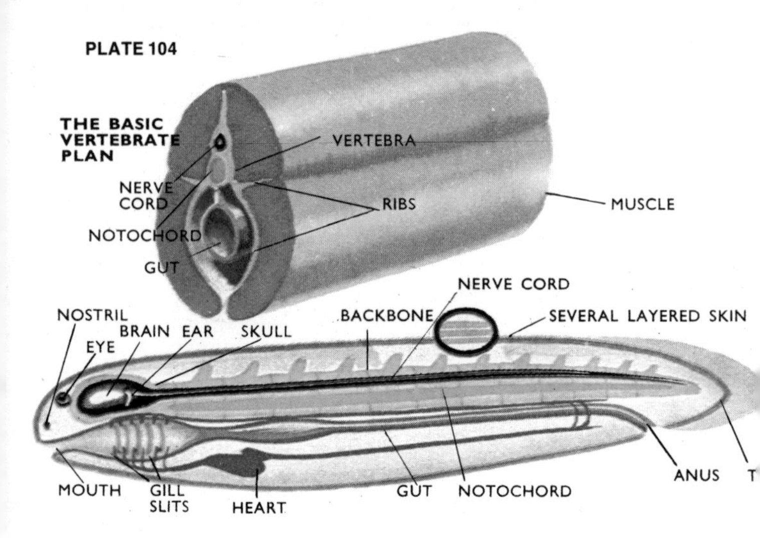

VERTEBRATA

The structure of a generalised vertebrate.

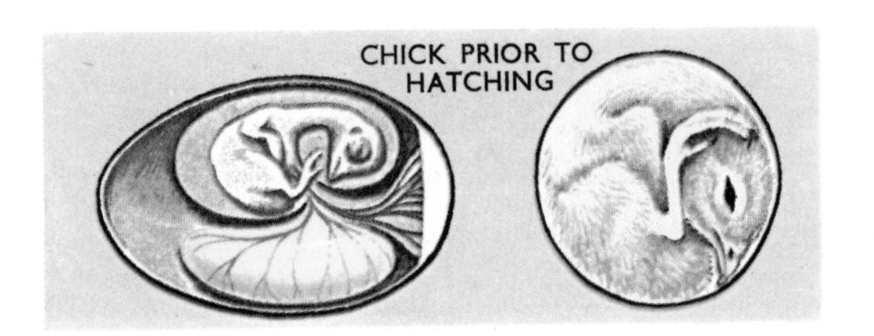

YOLK (SAC)

The yolk sac is an outgrowth of the gut and is gradually resorbed into the body, together with its rich food reserve.

PLATE 105

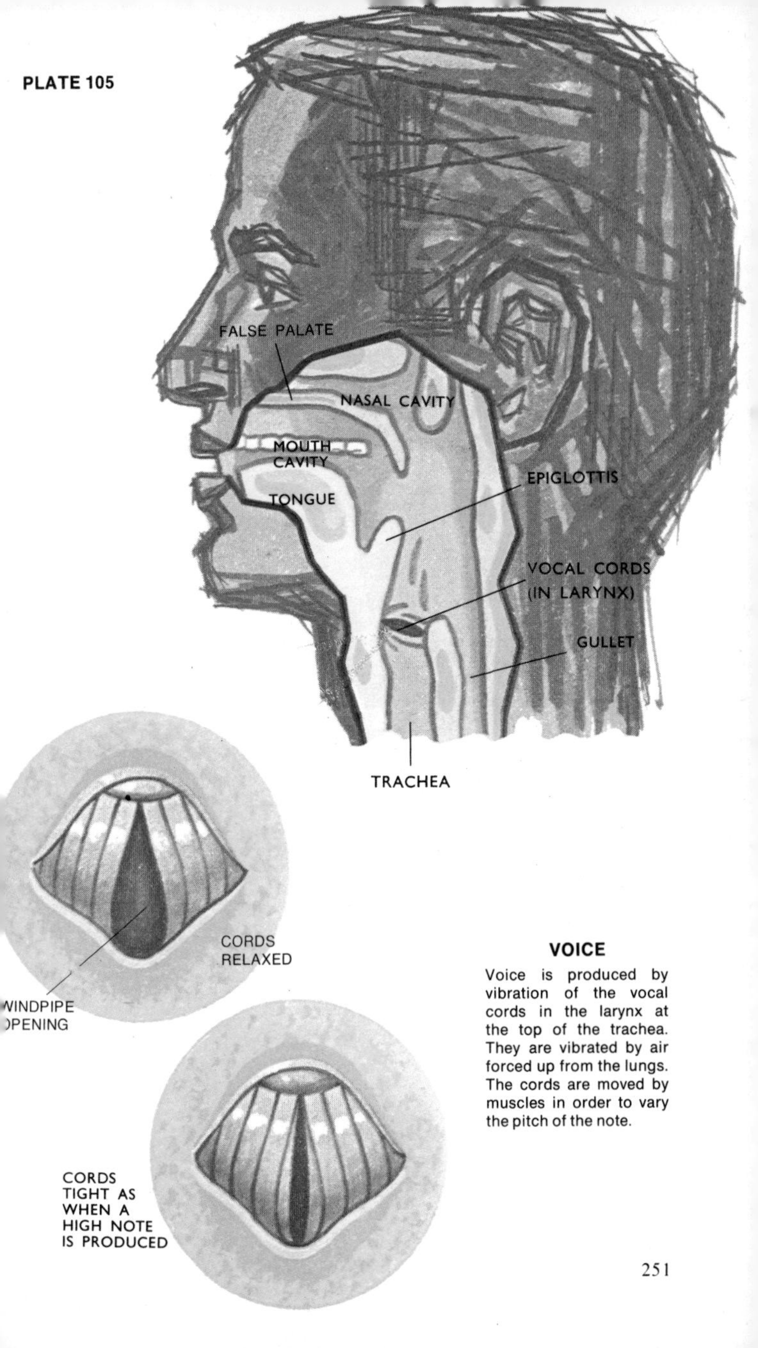

VOICE

Voice is produced by vibration of the vocal cords in the larynx at the top of the trachea. They are vibrated by air forced up from the lungs. The cords are moved by muscles in order to vary the pitch of the note.

arrangement for making sounds although the size of the cords varies a great deal. The sound is produced in the voice box but its quality is determined by the mouth and nasal region of the breathing tract. These regions are cavities in which some of the overtones are lost, while others are emphasised. Man has fine control over his facial muscles and, just by changing the shape of the mouth, he can produce a very different sound. This is called articulation. The sound 'oo' is altered to 'ee' simply by altering the shape of the mouth. The vocal cords are still vibrating at the same frequency but a different set of overtones is being emphasised and the quality is therefore changed. Other animals have not this fine control and their voices lack the variety of sounds. (See Plate 105).

Wallace's Line. An imaginary line separating the Malay Archipelago into two regions, each with its characteristic plants and animals. For example to the east of the line, the marsupials and monotremes are the only native mammals: to the west only placentals occur. This suggested to Wallace that the islands to the west were once joined to Asia and those to the east to Australia. The line that bears his name passes between Borneo and the Celebes in the north and between the islands of Bali and Lombok in the south.

Warning Coloration. (See *Aposematic Coloration*).

Wasp. (See *Hymenoptera*).

Whale. (See *Cetacea*).

White Matter. Tissue of vertebrate central nervous system which is composed mainly of nerve fibres connecting the different parts of the CNS. The myelin covering of the fibres gives them their white appearance. (See *Grey Matter*).

Xiphosura. Order of *Arachnida* (q.v.) containing the king crab (see P. 265).

Yolk. Food store found in the eggs of most animals. It is very rich in protein. In the eggs of vertebrates (other than mammals) the yolk is found in the *yolk sac* which is a pouch of the embryo gut. Yolk is absorbed from the sac which gradually shrinks and is itself absorbed into the embryo before hatching. (See Plates 38, 39 and 104).

Zooplankton. The animals of the plankton (q.v.) as opposed to the plants (*phytoplankton*).

Zygomatic Arch. The cheekbone of a mammal. Formed by the union of the jugal bone at the front and part of the squamosal at the back. (See Page 221).

Zygote. The diploid cell formed as the union of two haploid sex-cells or gametes. The zygote is the first cell of a new generation and gives rise by division to all the cells of the new individual. (See *Heredity; Fertilisation*).

THE ANIMAL KINGDOM

Most living things can be placed fairly easily in one of two groups: the Animal and Plant Kingdoms. The basic difference is in the manner of feeding. Plants usually contain *chlorophyll*—the green colouring matter which enables them to make food from non-living material in the soil and air. Animals cannot do this and must rely on plants or other animals as a source of food. The Animal Kingdom contains two major groups: the Protozoa and the Metazoa. The former are tiny animals of only one cell (or they may be regarded as acellular). All other animals (the Metazoa) are made up of hundreds or even millions of cells. Metazoans are arranged in a number of groups called *Phyla* (singular Phylum) which contain various smaller groups (*Classes*). Within the classes there are a number of *Orders* which are even smaller groups. The animals in each group have a number of features in common. The smaller the group, the more characters there will be in common.

Animals which are alike in every respect are grouped together as a single *species* (spee-sees) and closely related species into a *genus* (*jen*-us). Throughout this classification a genus is given as an example. A *family* is a group of related *genera* (plural of genus) and an order is a group of families. (See *Classification and page 236*)

Phylum **PROTOZOA.** These are tiny single-celled animals. All the processes of living are performed within this one cell. The four classes are separated mainly according to the way in which they move. Young forms often differ from adults and so for simplicity we discuss the adults only. Members of the class **Flagellata** have one or more whip-like hairs by which they move. They are often parasitic, living inside other animals. Example: *Trypanosoma* (2) – the organism causing sleeping sickness. The **Sarcodina** (sar-co-die-na) are *amoeboid* and rarely parasitic. Chalky and sandy skeletons are often present. Examples include *Amoeba* (1), *Elphidium* (7) and *Acanthometra* (6). Members of the class **Sporozoa** are all parasites. They normally have no organs of movement and reproduce by forming large numbers of spores. Example: *Plasmodium* (5)—the Malaria parasite. The class **Ciliophora** (silly-off-ora) contains some of the most highly organised Protozoa. They all have cilia (sill-ia) at some stage but some adults, e.g. *Acineta* (9), lose the cilia. They are never amoeboid and rarely parasitic. Examples include *Paramoecium* (3) (para-meesium) and *Stentor* (4).

METAZOA (Many-celled Animals). In these animals not all the cells act in the same way. They are specialised to do different jobs.

Phylum **PORIFERA** (The Sponges). This phylum differs so much from other metazoa that it is sometimes put in a separate group—the Parazoa.

These are simple water-inhabiting animals. The body is a hollow vessel. Its wall consists of a layer of covering cells and an internal layer of flagellated cells, separated by jelly-like material containing numerous crystals [*spicules* (12)] of a sandy or chalky nature. The spicules form a skeleton. The flagella beat rapidly and draw water into the central hollow. Tiny food particles are collected by the cells and the water then passes out of the main opening. There are three classes: **Calcarea** [e.g. *Leucosolenia* (8)] with chalky spicules; **Hexactinellida** [e.g. *Euplectella* (11)] with sandy spicules; and **Demospongia** [e.g. *Halichondria* (10)] which contains the soft sponges such as the bath sponge.

See plate 106

PLATE 106

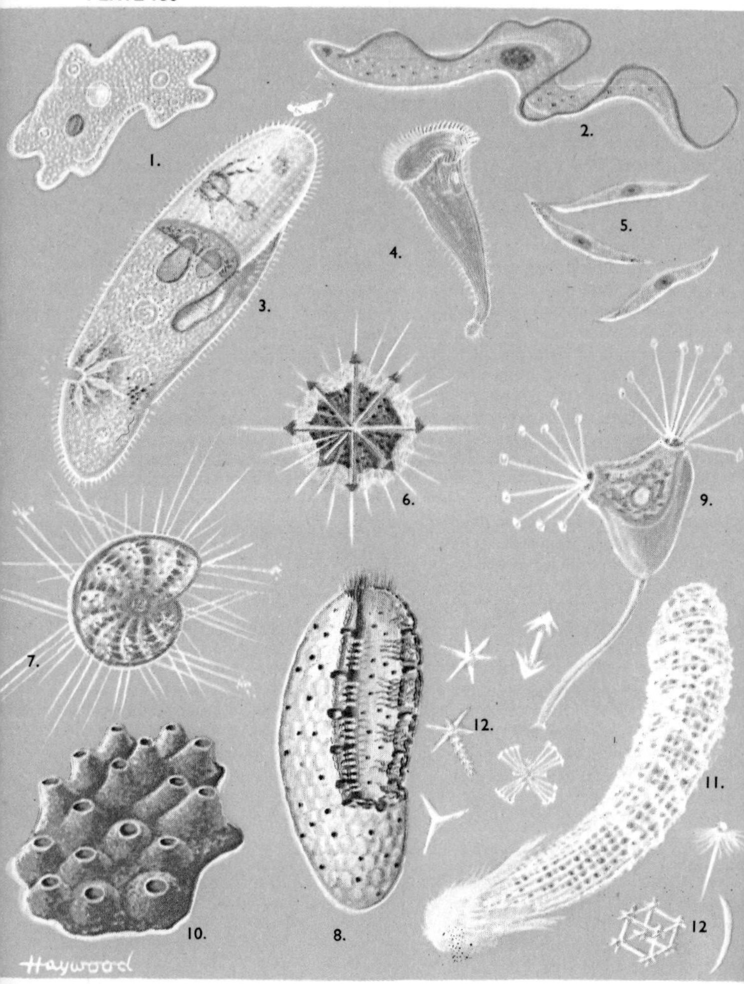

PROTOZOA AND PORIFERA (See page 253 for key)

COELENTERATA (See page 256 for key)

COELENTERATA

Phylum **COELENTERATA** (see-lent-er-ata). These are *diploblastic* animals whose body wall consists of two cell layers (*ectoderm* and *endoderm*) separated by a jelly-like mass (the mesogloea) (mee-zo-glee-a). The mouth (the only opening) leads into a single cavity (the *enteron*) where some digestion occurs. Some of the endodermal cells are amoeboid and absorb food particles and digest them. There is a simple nervous system (a *nerve net*) whose cells spread all over the body through the mesogloea. Arms or *tentacles* are usually present and are covered with stinging cells (*nematocysts*). New individuals often develop as 'buds' on the parent and eventually become detached. There are two basic forms of coelenterate: the *polyp* and the *medusa*. Both types occur in the life cycle of some species. The animals show *radial symmetry*. The Class **Hydrozoa** contains a number of orders, the members of which usually have both polyp and medusa in the life cycle. *Hydra* (2) itself is an exception. having no medusa. The animals often grow in colonies which may have a horny covering (the *perisarc*). Examples: *Obelia* (1) and *Bougainvillea* (3). The order Hydrocorallina contains colonial forms with a chalky external covering. There are two types of polyp—one with mouth and tentacles, the other with tentacles only The latter type catch food and pass it to a mouthed polyp. Example: *Millepora* (5). These animals are often found in association with the true corals (see below). The Portuguese 'Man-of-War' [*Physalia* (6)] belongs to the order Siphonophora. Each 'Man-of-War' is in fact a free-swimming colony of many types of polyp all attached to one large 'float'. The Class **Scyphozoa** (sky-foe-zoa) contains the true jellyfishes. The free-swimming jellyfish is the medusoid form but there is often a polyp stage in the life cycle. The tentacles hang down in the water and catch small fish and other animals as food. Examples: *Lucernaria* (7), *Geryonia* (4), *Carybdea* (8), *Nausithoe* (9), *Aurelia* (10) and *Rhizostoma* (11). The Class **Actinozoa** contains solitary and colonial forms. They exist as polyps only. The enteron (gut cavity) is divided by sheets of tissue (*mesenteries*) arranged vertically. The mesenteries contain muscular tissues and also increase the area of the digestive cells in the body. There are eight mesenteries in the order Alcyonaria [e.g. *Alcyonium* (12)] whose members also have eight tentacles. Members of the order Zoantharia [e.g. *Actinia* (13), *Caryophyllia* (14 and 15)] have six mesenteries or multiples of six. These Zoantharia are the sea anemones and the true corals. Anemones are distinguished from corals because the latter produce a hard chalky skeleton round themselves and the anemones remain soft. The anemones and some corals exist singly, but many corals live in large colonies whose skeletons build up the coral reefs of tropical islands.

(See Plate 107)

CTENOPHORA
PLATYHELMINTHES

Phylum **CTENOPHORA.** Free-living, solitary, diploblastic animals probably related to the Coelenterata, although there is neither polyp nor medusa, and were at one time included in that group. The Ctenophora or *Sea Gooseberries* live in the surface layers of the sea, swimming by means of cilia. There are no nematocysts. There are two classes: **Tentaculata** with tentacles [e.g. *Hormiphora* (1)], and **Nuda** [e.g. *Beroe* (2)] whose members are without tentacles.

The Coelenterata and Ctenophora are two-layered animals. All higher groups are three-layered with *mesoderm* tissue between the ecto- and endoderm. There is usually a cavity apart from the gut in these *triploblastic* animals. It may be derived from the cavity of the embryo (e.g. blood system cavity or *haemocoel*) or it may be *coelomic* (i.e. derived from the mesoderm itself). In most animals both types of cavity are present, but there are a number of phyla whose members have no coelom. These are the Acoelomate animals of which the best known are the flatworms.

Phylum **PLATYHELMINTHES.** The flatworms are bilaterally symmetrical, slightly flattened triploblastic animals with no body cavity – the space between body wall and the gut is full of cells. This is the acoelomate (without coelom) condition. If the gut is present it has only one opening – the mouth. The reproductive system is usually *hermaphrodite* (male *and* female organs in one animal).

Class **Turbellaria** are free living forms – Planarians. They have cilia and are classified according to the arrangement of the digestive system. Example: *Planaria* (3, 4).

Class **Trematoda** are all parasitic and have a two-branched gut. The adults have a thick non-cellular covering (*cuticle*) with suckers but no cilia. Examples: *Polystomum* (5) and *Fasciola* (6, 7) – the liver-flukes.

The tape-worms (Class **Cestoda**) have no gut and are completely parasitic in the food canal of other animals. The head has hooks or suckers and the body usually consists of numerous segments (proglottides) each containing sex-organs. These segments break off and pass out of the body. They have to be picked up by another host to continue the life cycle. Most Cestodes infest more than one type of animal in the life cycle. Example: *Taenia* (9). Some, however, live in the gut of fishes and do not produce proglottides [e.g. *Gyrocotyle* (8)].

(See Plate 108)

PLATE 108

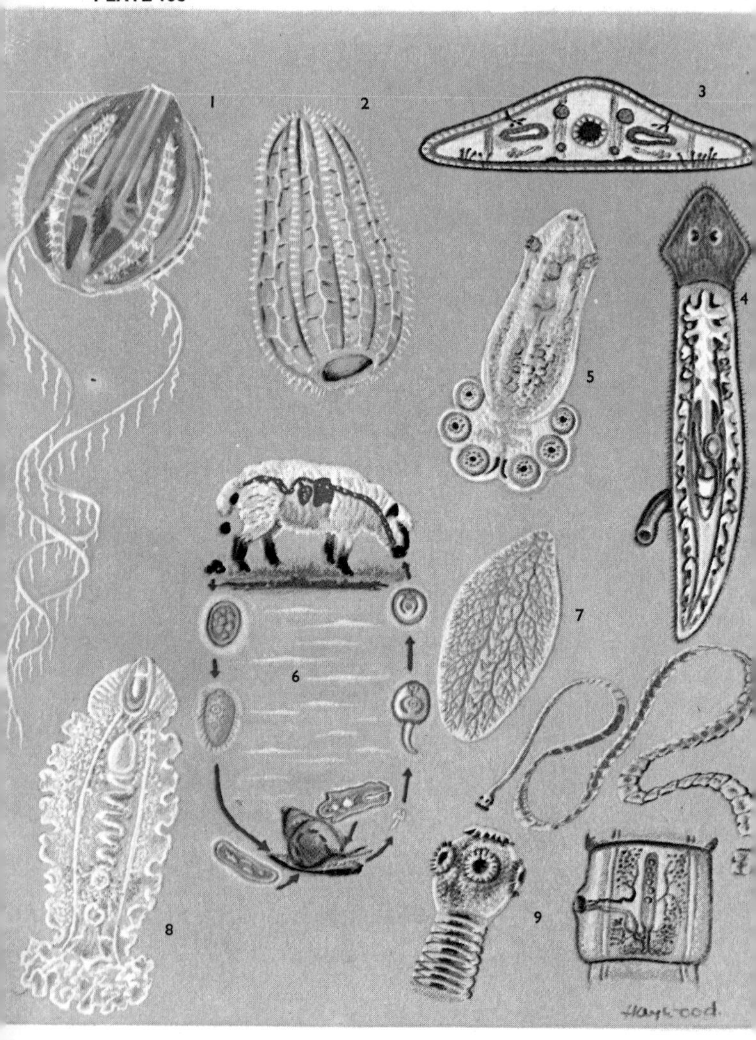

CTENOPHORA AND PLATYHELMINTHES (See page 257 for key)

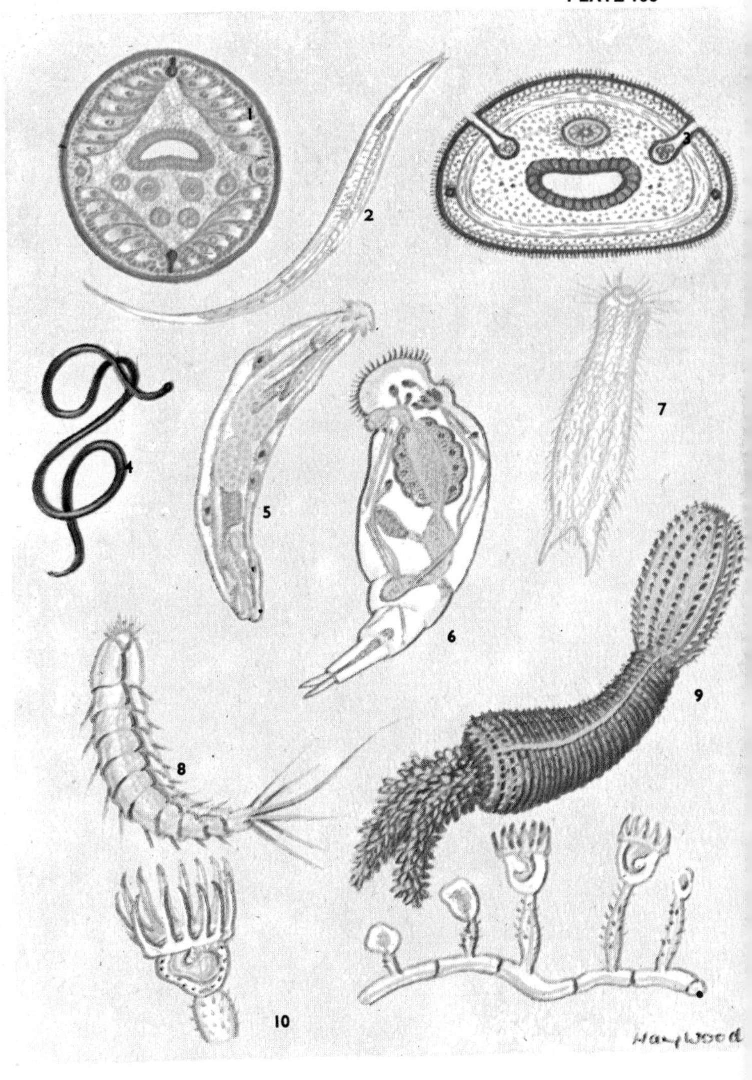

NEMATODA AND OTHER MINOR GROUPS (See page 260 for key)

NEMATODA NEMERTEA NEMATOMORPHA ACANTHOCEPHALA ROTIFERA GASTROTRICHA KINORHYNCHIA PRIAPULIDA ENDOPROCTA

The **Minor Acoelomate** Animals. Apart from the Platyhelminthes there are several other acoelomate groups best considered as separate phyla.

Phylum **NEMATODA** (Roundworms). These are non-ciliated animals, frequently parasitic [e.g. *Ascaris* (1 & 2)]. Others live in the soil and often do much damage to plant roots. There is a flexible cuticle. The spaces between the organs are filled with large vacuolated cells which give the appearance of a body cavity. The sexes are usually separate.

Phylum **NEMERTEA.** Worm-like but slightly flattened and ciliated. The body spaces are filled with *parenchyma* cells. They are free living and mainly marine. A characteristic feature is the tube-like *proboscis* which lies in a cavity above the gut and can be shot out to capture prey in the manner of the coelenterate nematocysts. Example: *Lineus* (3).

Phylum **NEMATOMORPHA** (Hair worms). These small animals differ little from Nematodes. The hair worms have one or more hosts during the life cycle. Example: *Gordius* (4).

Phylum **ACANTHOCEPHALA.** Similar to nematodes but these animals have a hooked proboscis with which they cling to the gut wall of their host. There are two hosts in the life cycle – an arthropod and a vertebrate (usually a fish). Example: *Neoechinorhynchus* (5).

Phylum **ROTIFERA.** Tiny animals with a ciliated disc for moving and feeding. They live in fresh water where they are often mistaken for protozoans. Example: *Hydatina* (6).

Phylum **GASTROTRICHA.** Minute worm-like animals which have cilia and various bristles or spines. They live in water, feeding on protozoans. Example: *Chaetonotus* (7).

Phylum **KINORHYNCHIA.** Similar to the last group but marine and without cilia. Example: *Echinoderes* (8).

Phylum **PRIAPULIDA.** Marine worms with a large *haemocoelic* cavity. Example: *Priapulus* (9).

Phylum **ENDOPROCTA.** Usually colonial animals in fresh or salt water. The body spaces are filled with parenchyma. Example: *Pedicellina* (10), often found encrusting sea weeds.

See plate 109

ECTOPROCTA BRACHIOPODA CHAETOGNATHA ANNELIDA

The **COELOMATE** animals. The body organs rest in a cavity (the *coelom*) in the mesoderm layer.

Phylum **ECTOPROCTA.** These animals are small *sedentary* (fixed) forms usually living in colonies. They are often called *Polyzoa* and are frequently found crusting rocks and sea-weeds along the shore where their hard body-cases long outlast the living animal. The mouth is surrounded by a ring of ciliated tentacles which trap food particles in the water. Example: *Plumatella* (1).

Phylum **BRACHIOPODA.** Lamp shells. These are all marine animals. The shell is *bivalve* (i.e. with two parts). Coiled ciliated arms within the shell produce a current of water which brings food to the mouth. Example: *Terebratula* (2).

Phylum **CHAETOGNATHA** (Keet-o-gnaytha). Arrow worms. These small, elongated planktonic animals live at the sea surface using their horny teeth and jaws to feed on other small animals. The outer covering is extended to form 'fins'. Example: *Sagitta* (3).

Phylum **ANNELIDA.** These are *segmented* animals (i.e. the body has a number of segments all basically alike). They have a coelom, a blood system and a fairly complex nervous system. There are six classes. Class **Polychaeta** (Polly-keeta). (Bristle-worms). Almost all marine animals with many bristles (*chaetae*) arising in groups in each segment. They feed with jaws [e.g. *Nereis* (4)] or ciliated arms [e.g. *Sabella* (5)] or merely a tubular mouth [e.g. *Arenicola* (6)]. Many polychaetes construct chalky or sandy tubes in which they spend all their lives. Class **Oligochaeta** (Earth-worms). Annelids with few bristles. They live on land [*Lumbricus* (7)] or in water (*Tubifex*). Class **Hirudinea** (Leeches). Annelids usually without chaetae but with suckers at both ends. The mouth is modified for blood sucking. Example: *Hirudo* (8). Class **Archiannelida** contains a number of small marine animals often without chaetae. Example: *Nerilla* (9). Class **Echiuroidea** contains other small animals with cilia and without much segmentation. Example: *Bonellia* (10). Animals of the Class **Sipunculoidea** have large coelomic spaces and no chaetae. Example: *Sipunculus* (11).

(See Plate 110)

PLATE 110

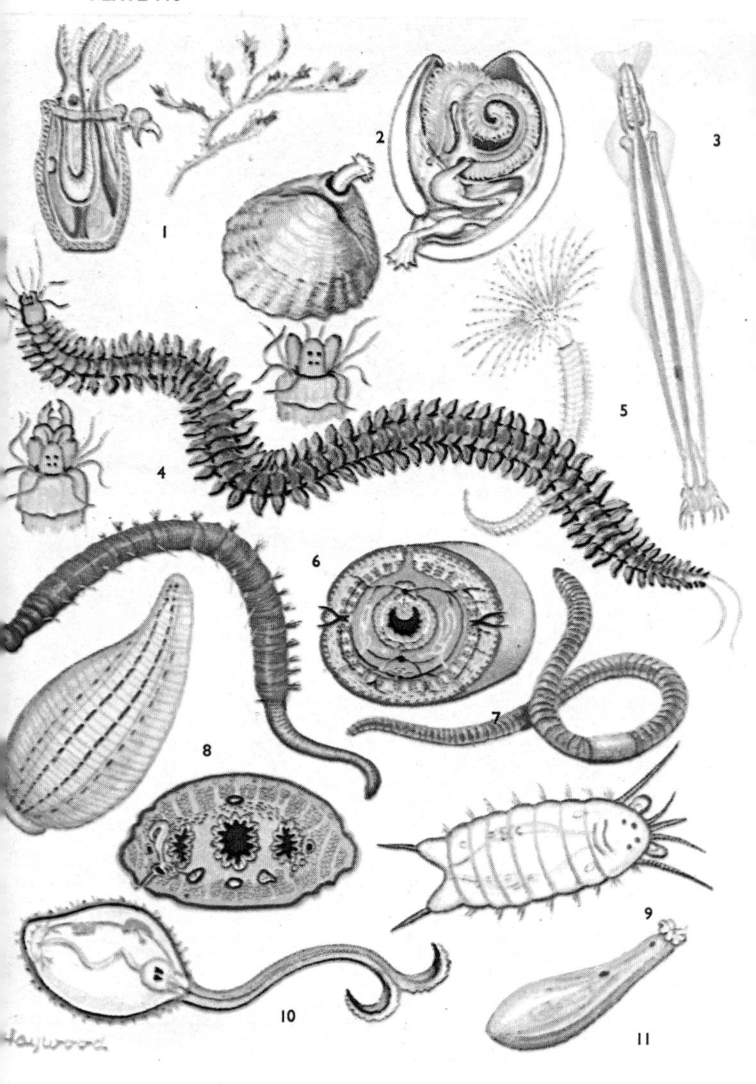

ANNELIDA, BRACHIOPODA AND OTHER GROUPS (See page 261 for key)

PLATE 111

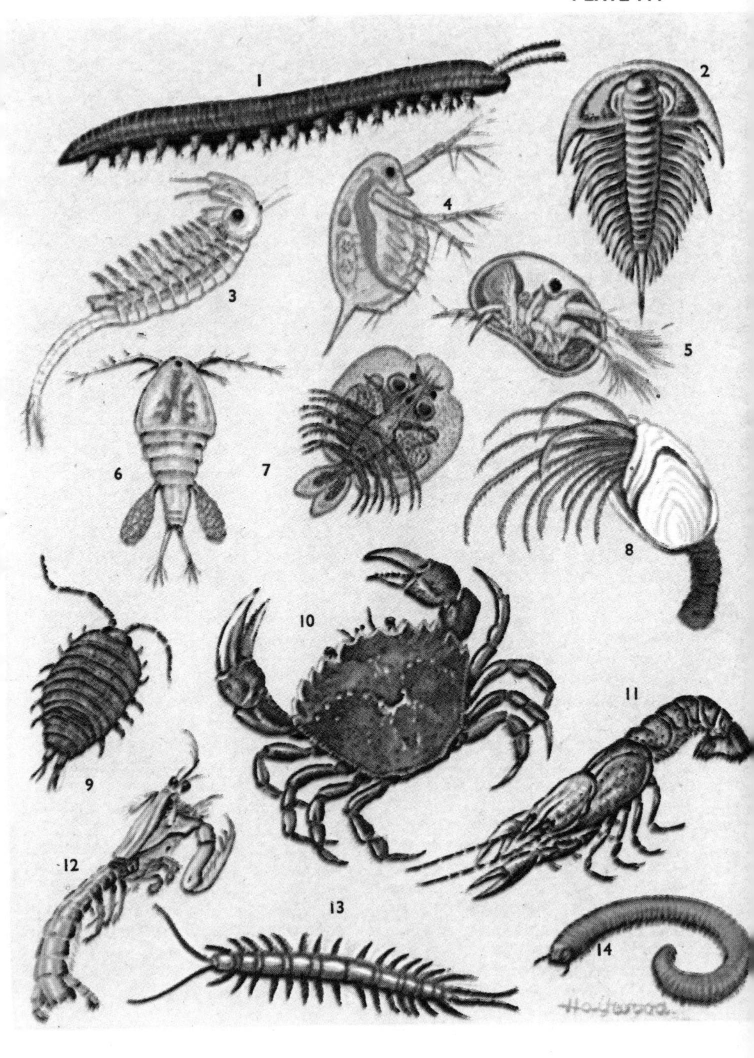

ONYCHOPHORA, TRILOBITA,

CRUSTACEA AND MYRIAPODA (See page 264 for key)

ARTHROPODA

The Phylum **ARTHROPODA** (Ar-throp-od-a) is a large one containing the 'jointed-limbed' animals. These are bilaterally symmetrical segmented animals normally covered by a stout cuticle. The coelom is reduced and largely replaced by the *haemocoel* (blood space). With one exception (*Peripatus*), cilia are absent. The limbs of the head segments are modified as sense organs (*antennae*) or as feeding organs (i.e. *mouthparts*).

Class **Onychophora** contains a number of tropical and Australasian animals. They have many pairs of limbs but retain various worm-like characters. They live only in damp places. Example: *Peripatus* (1).

Class **Trilobita** has no living members but many fossil species are known. All appear to have been marine. Example: *Olenellus* (2).

Class **Crustacea.** These are mainly aquatic (i.e. they live in water). The cuticle often has a deposit of calcium carbonate (lime) in it, making it hard. It may also be very thick. The plate-like covering of the trunk region present in animals such as crabs is called the *carapace*. The limbs on the body (*trunk limbs*) may be used for feeding and breathing as well as movement. There are six sub-classes containing a number of orders.

Sub-class **Branchiopoda.** These animals have at least four pairs of trunk limbs and usually many more. These limbs are broad and fringed with bristles. The latter trap food particles which are passed back to the mouth. The limbs also act as gills for breathing. The animals move by means of their head limbs (antennae) or trunk limbs. Examples include the fairy shrimp. *Chirocephalus* (3) and the water flea *Daphnia* (4).

Sub-class **Ostracoda.** These tiny animals are almost enclosed by the carapace which forms a shell round them. They swim and feed by means of the head limbs. Example: *Cypris* (5).

Sub-class **Copepoda.** These are free or parasitic animals which lack a carapace. They swim by means of head *and* trunk limbs although the parasitic forms often have no limbs. The mouth-parts filter food particles from the water. Examples: *Cyclops* (6) and *Calanus*. The latter lives in the surface layers of the sea and forms an important part of the diet of herrings.

Sub-class **Branchiura.** These animals [e.g. *Argulus* (7)] are temporary parasites of fish but otherwise swim freely.

Sub-class **Cirripedia.** This sub-class contains the sedentary barnacles [e.g. *Lepas* (8)] and some parasitic forms (e.g. *Sacculina*). The barnacles trap food with their trunk limbs.

Sub-class **Malacostraca.** This sub-class contains a wide variety of forms. Most have stalked eyes and a large carapace. The head limbs perform most of the feeding activity while the trunk limbs are for movement. Branches of the trunk limbs act as gills in some cases. Woodlice, crabs, crayfish and shrimps are all included in this sub-class. Examples: *Ligia* (9), *Squilla* (12), *Carcinus* (10), *Astacus* (11).

Class **Myriapoda.** These are terrestrial arthropods that breathe by means of *tracheae*. There are two sub-classes: Chilopoda – the centipedes [e.g. *Lithobius* (13)], and Diplopoda – the millipedes [e.g. *Iulus* (14)].

(See Plate 111)

ARACHNIDA

The Class **ARACHNIDA** (a-RACK-nid-a) is another division of the jointed-limbed animals (Arthropods). The cuticle is impregnated with a horny substance called chitin (ky-tin). The front part of the body has six pairs of *appendages* (limbs) of which the last four pairs are legs. The hind part of the body does not normally have limbs. The front pair of appendages are normally claw-like and are called *chelicerae* (key-LISS-er-ee). This contrasts with the thread-like *antennae* always present on the first segment of other arthropods. There are no true jaws: the bases of the front limbs are used to 'chew' the food. The second pair of limbs are called *palps*. Breathing is normally by *gills* or *tracheae*.

Order **Scorpionidea** contains the Scorpions. They have clawed palps and a sting in the tail. Example: *Scorpio* (1).

Order **Pseudoscorpionidea.** These are small animals often found among dead leaves. They resemble scorpions in shape except that there is no tail. Example: *Neobisium* (2).

Order **Xiphosura** (Ziff-o-sura) contains a single type – *Limulus* (3), the king crab. This animal has a thick leathery carapace and can burrow into the sand. It lives in shallow water around the coasts, especially in North America.

Order **Araneida** (A-ran-AY-ida) contains the spiders. The hind part of the body is joined to the front by a narrow waist. Attached to the chelicerae there is a poison-gland which paralyses the prey of the spider when bitten. There are silk glands and spinning organs which are used to produce the characteristic webs. Example: *Aranea* (5).

Order **Palpigrada.** These are small elongated animals normally found under stones and in similar places. Example: *Koenenia* (6). Order **Solifuga.** Animals of warm climates. They have very hairy bodies and long palps (*pedipalps*). Example: *Galeodes* (4). Order **Acarina.** Animals with little sign of segmentation. The body is short and often rounded. *Mites* and *Ticks* are included in the order. The mites may be free living or parasitic. Ticks are blood-sucking animals whose chelicerae are modified for sucking. Examples: *Acarus* (7) (mite), *Ixodes* (8) (tick).

Order **Phalangida** (Fal-AN-jidda). These are the *'harvest spiders'* with small rounded bodies and long legs. Example: *Mitopus* (10). Order **Pantopoda** contains marine animals which appear to be 'all legs'. The hind part of the body is very reduced and there is an extra pair of limbs on the front part. Example: *Nymphon* (9).

Order **Tardigrada,** e.g. *Macrobiotus* (11), are tiny animals found in rotting vegetation, etc.

Order **Pentastomida,** e.g. *Demodex* (12), are small worm-like parasites with hooked claws. The young stages resemble mites.

(See Plate 112)

 (See page 265 for key)

INSECTA – APTERYGOTA AND HOLOMETABOLA

(See page 268 for key)

PLATE 113

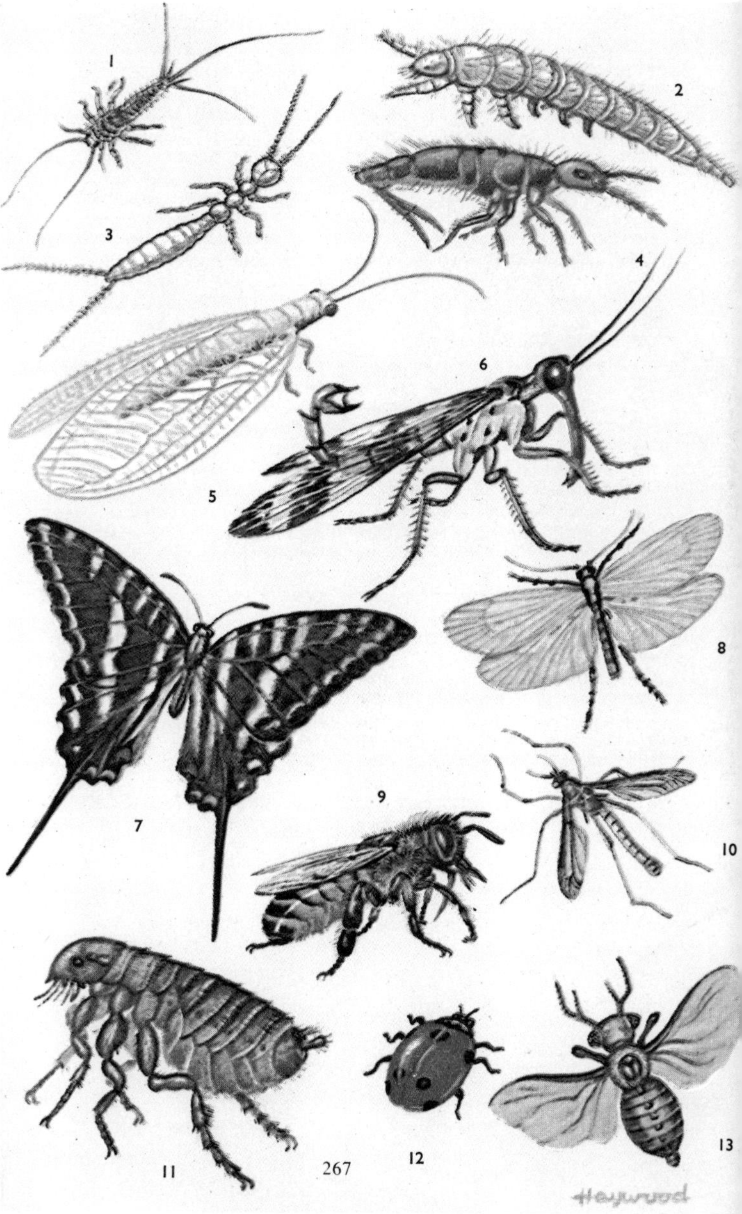

1 2 3 4 5 6 7 8 9 10 11 12 13

Heywood

INSECTA

The insects (Class **INSECTA**) are probably the best known of the arthropods. In the adult the body is divided into three distinct regions: *head, thorax* and *abdomen*. The head bears the eyes, antennae and mouth-parts; the thorax bears three pairs of legs and usually two pairs of wings. There are no limbs on the abdomen but there may be bristles or fine threads. The insects breathe by means of *tracheae* except for some young stages which live in water have gills.

Imms recognised twenty-nine orders of insects. Four are contained in the sub-class **Apterygota** (Ap-terry-go-ta). These insects are all wingless and live mainly in decaying vegetation. Order **Thysanura** contains the bristle-tails and silver-fish, e.g. *Lepisma* (1). Orders **Diplura** [e.g. *Campodea* (3)] and **Protura** [e.g. *Acerentomon* (2), contain small soil-living insects. The springtails (order **Collembola**) are frequently found in rotting vegetation, moss, etc. Example: *Axelsonia* (4). The sub-class **Pterygota** contains the remaining twenty-five orders. They are normally winged, but some groups – especially the parasitic ones – have developed a wingless condition. There are two major groups: the *Holometabola* which contains all those insects which undergo a marked change (*metamorphosis* – met-a-mor-foe-sis) from young to adult stage, and the *Hemimetabola* whose members do not undergo such marked changes.

Holometabola: Order **Neuroptera** (New-ROP-terra) contains lace-wing flies and others with delicate netted wings, e.g. *Chrysopa* (5). Scorpion-flies [e.g. *Panorpa* (6)], so called because of the up-turned tail of the male, make up the order **Mecoptera.** The order **Lepidoptera** contains the familiar butterflies and moths whose bright colours are due to pigments in minute scales on the wings. Example: *Papilio* (7). The caddis-flies of order **Trichoptera** (Trick-op-terra) have wings covered with fine hairs instead of scales. Example: *Halesus* (8). Order **Diptera** includes the true flies such as house-flies, mosquitoes and 'daddy-longlegs'. They have only one pair of wings. The hind pair are modified as balancing organs called *halteres* (hal-ter-ees). Example: *Tipula* (10). Order **Siphonaptera** (Sigh-fon-AP-terra) [e.g. *Pulex* (11)] contains the fleas. These are wingless insects adapted to blood sucking. They are external parasites of man and other animals. Order **Hymenoptera** contains the bees, wasps and ants, many of which live in large colonies. Example: *Apis* (9). Beetles belong to the order **Coleoptera.** The front wings are tough and leathery and often brightly coloured. Example: *Coccinella* (12). Order **Strepsiptera** contains some curious insects [e.g. *Stylops* (13)] which are internal parasites of bees.

(See Plate 113)

INSECTA

Hemimetabola: Order **Ephemeroptera** (Eff-em-er-op-terra) contains the mayflies. The young stages live for several years in water. There is a brief adult life in the air. Example: *Ephemera* (1). Dragonflies (order **Odonata)** are also aquatic in the young stages. They are fiercely carnivorous – catching flies and other insects as they fly along. Example: *Libellula* (2). Order **Plecoptera** are the stone-flies [e.g. *Perla* (3)], again aquatic as young. The order **Grylloblattodea** contains a few tiny soil-living insects without wings. Example: *Grylloblatta* (4). Stick and leaf-insects [e.g. *Phyllium* (6)] are grouped together as the order **Phasmida** (Faz-mid-a). The order **Orthoptera** contains the grasshoppers and crickets (e.g. *Gryllus*). The fore-wings are usually tough. The hind legs are often long and used for jumping. Earwigs belong to the order **Dermaptera.** The fore-wings are small leathery flaps. At the end of the abdomen there is a pair of projections usually modified as 'pincers'. Example: *Forficula* (5). The order **Embioptera** is represented only in tropical and sub-tropical regions. The insects are known as web-spinners. They are small and live in colonies in silken tunnels under stones, etc. Example: *Embia* (9). Cockroaches are members of the order **Dictyoptera** which also includes the Praying Mantids. The fore-wings are leathery and cover thin hind-wings. The mouth parts are hard jaws for biting. Termites are social insects of the order **Isoptera.** There are several forms in each colony such as soldiers, food gatherers and 'house-workers'. Example *Archotermopsis* (8). The order **Zoraptera** [e.g. *Zorotypus* (7)] contains a few tiny insects of soil and rotting vegetation chiefly in the tropics. The order **Psocoptera** (Sok-op-terra) contains various small insects with or without wings. They are common on trees, in birds' nests and on rubbish dumps. Example: *Peripsocus* (11). Biting lice (order **Mallophaga**) and sucking lice (order **Siphunculata**) are both wingless orders. The lice are parasitic on birds and mammals. As the names suggest, the biting lice [e.g. *Lipeurus* (12)] have biting jaws, while the sucking lice [e.g. *Pediculus* (13)] have adaptations for sucking. The order **Hemiptera** contains the bugs. They have sucking mouths and feed on blood and other body fluids or plant juices. Examples: *Notonecta* (10) – the Water Boatmen: *Aphis* (15). Thrips are small black insects (order **Thysanoptera**) often found in flowers. Example: *Taeniothrips* (14).

(See Plate 114)

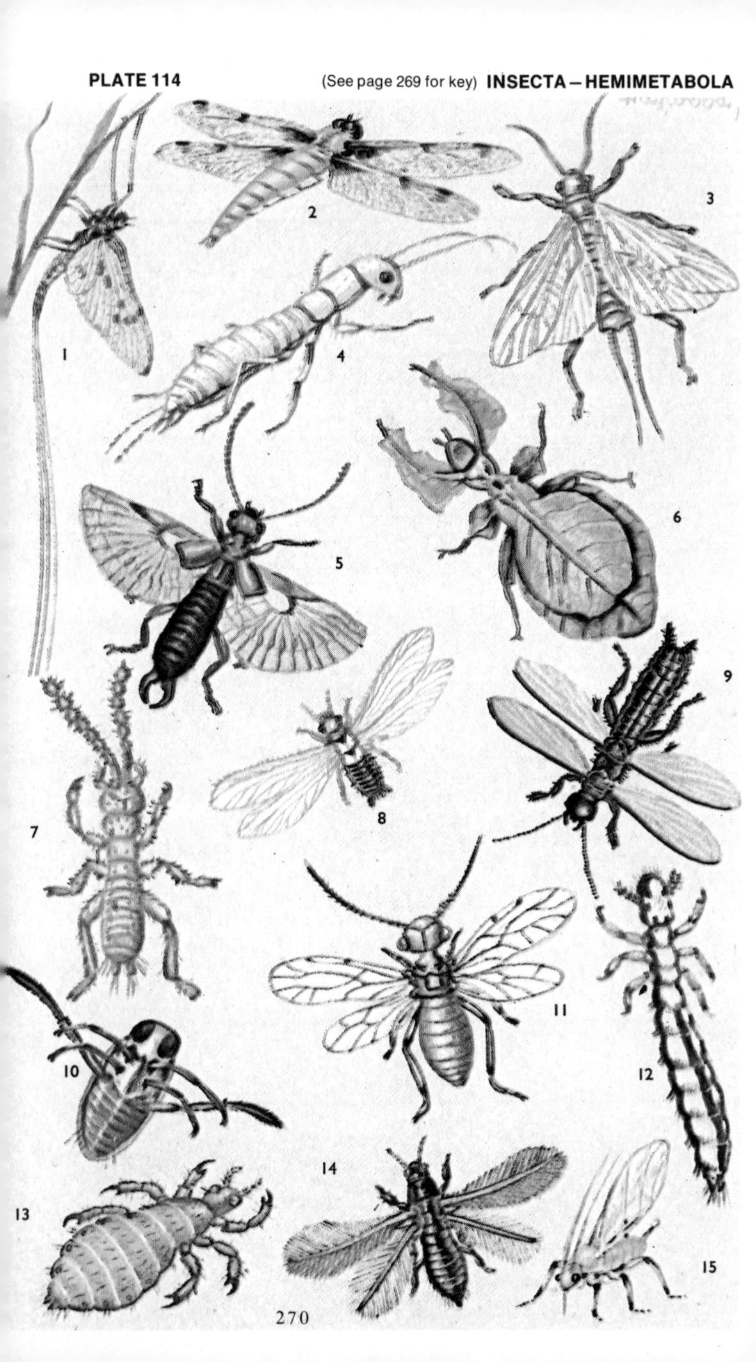
1
2
3
4
5
6
7
8
9
10
11
12
13
14
15

PLATE 115

MOLLUSCA (See page 272 for key)

MOLLUSCA

Phylum **MOLLUSCA.** These are unsegmented, coelomate animals with soft bodies usually covered with a chalky shell. The head is usually well developed together with a muscular *'foot'* which is the main organ of movement. The molluscs inhabit land, sea and freshwater.

Class **Amphineura** contains a few bilaterally symmetrical marine animals without eyes. The shell may be of many units, e.g. *Chiton* (kite-on) (1), or of one unit (*Neopilina*).

Class **Gasteropoda** contains many forms (slugs and snails) with tentacles and usually a twisted body. Most marine forms breathe by means of gills but land and freshwater snails by means of lungs. They feed by means of a rasping tongue (*radula*). Examples include *Buccinum* (2), *Littorina* (3), *Coryphella* (5), *Helix* (6) and *Limax* (4).

Class **Scaphopoda.** These animals live in open-ended tubes and burrow in the sand with their triangular foot. Example: *Dentalium* (7).

Class **Lamellibranchiata** contains the *bivalve* molluscs – bilaterally symmetrical animals whose shell is in two parts. They are mainly filter feeders (i.e. they extract tiny particles of food from the water flowing over the gills). The collected particles are trapped in a stream of mucus which flows to the mouth. Examples: *Anodonta* (8), *Mytilus* (9) and *Ensis* (10).

Class **Cephalopoda** (kef-allo-poe-da) contains the squids and octopuses and the pearly nautilus. *Sepia* (11) and *Loligo* (13) have ten 'arms' around their mouths while *Octopus* (12) has only eight. The squids have horny internal skeletons but *Octopus* has no skeleton. Food is caught in the tentacles and passed to the horny jaws. *Nautilus* (14) has an external shell and many tentacles without suckers.

(See Plate 115)

ECHINODERMATA
CHORDATA

Phylum **ECHINODERMATA** is the last large group of invertebrate animals. They are radially symmetrical and all marine. The outer-covering contains numerous chalky plates which protect the animal and give it a rough appearance. The young stages show resemblances to the back-boned animals (vertebrates) rather than to other invertebrates which we have so far mentioned.

Sub-phylum **Eleutherozoa** contains four classes of free living forms.

Class **Asteroidea** contains the star-fishes [e.g. *Asterias* (1)] which have broad arms each containing a branch of the stomach.

Class **Ophiuroidea.** These are also star-shaped, but the arms are slender and do not contain branches of the gut. Example: *Ophiura* (2).

Class **Echinoidea** contains the sea-urchins – rounded animals usually covered with spines. Example: *Echinus* (3).

Class **Holothuroidea.** These are the sea-cucumbers – sausage-shaped echinoderms with tentacles around the mouth. Example: *Holothuria* (4).

The sub-phylum **Pelmatozoa** contains one class – **Crinoidea** – whose members (sea-lilies) are fixed by a stalk for at least part of their lives. Examples: *Antedon* (5), *Rhizocrinus* (6).

Phylum **CHORDATA.** All the vertebrate animals belong to this phylum. They possess *gill-slits,* passages connecting the *pharynx* to the outside; a hollow dorsal nerve cord, and a *notochord.* The latter is a rod of supporting tissue replaced early in the life of most chordates by the backbone. There are, however, a few chordates – the *protochordates* – without backbones. *Balanoglossus* (7) (sub-phylum **Hemichordata**) is a burrowing worm-like marine animal.

Sub-phylum **Urochordata** contains the sea-squirts [e.g. *Ciona* (8)]. The young sea-squirts are like tadpoles (9), but the adults are sedentary fixed forms.

Sub-phylum **Cephalochordata** contains *Amphioxus* (10, the Lancelet). It has a well-developed notochord, many pharyngeal slits and is generally fish-like. It lives in shallow water round the coasts of all the oceans.

(See Plate 116)

PLATE 116

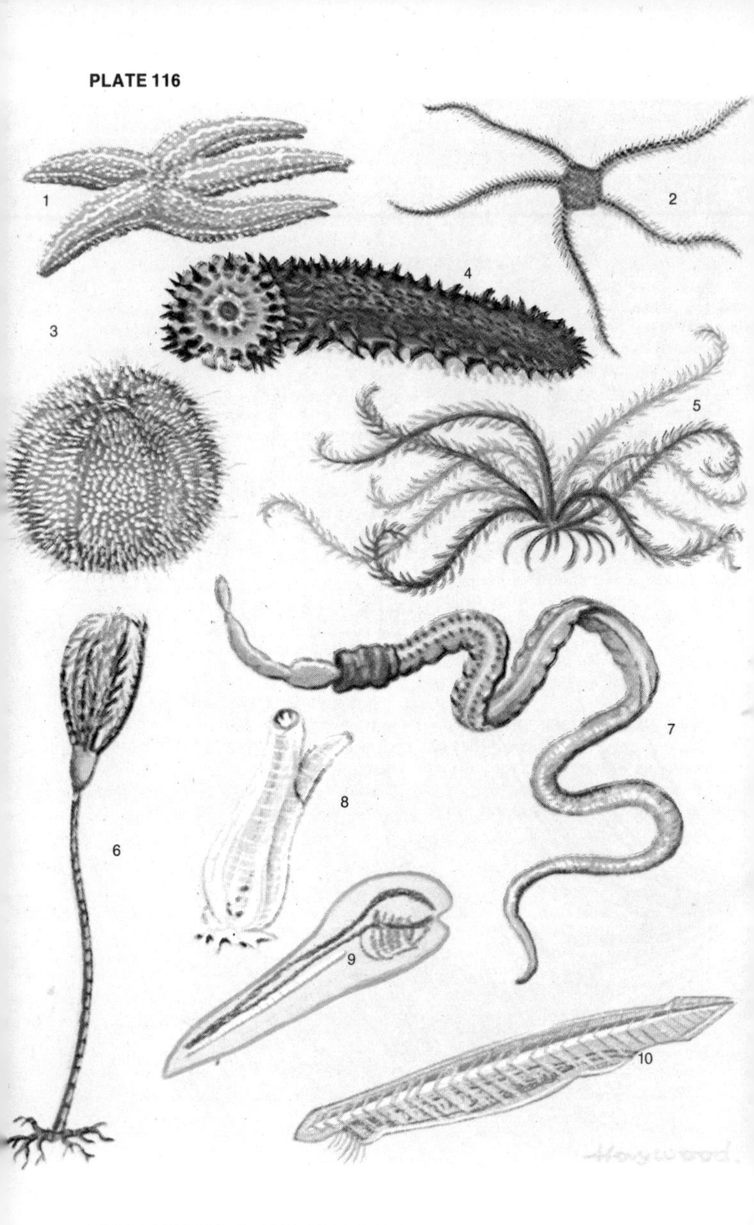

ECHINODERMATA AND PROTOCHORDATA (See page 273 for key)

FISHES (See page 276 for key)

CHORDATA

CYCLOSTOMATA CHONDRICHTHYES OSTEICHTHYES

The sub-phylum **Vertebrata** contains all the backboned animals (i.e. those with an internal skeleton).

Super-class **Agnatha** (meaning without jaws) contains many extinct species and a number of living ones in the class **Cyclostomata.** This includes lampreys and their relatives which have neither jaws nor limbs. The young forms resemble *Amphioxus* in some ways. Some adults are parasitic on fish; they have a sucking mouth and a rasping tongue. Example: *Lampetra* (1).

Super-class **Gnathostomata** (jawed-mouths) contains all the other vertebrates including fishes, reptiles and man. The Class **Chondrichthyes** (=*Elasmobranchii*) contains the cartilaginous fishes – the sharks and rays – whose skeleton consists of cartilage instead of bone. They do, however, have sharp, bony spines on the outside of the body. There is no *operculum* (the gill cover of other fishes) and the tail is asymmetrical. Examples: *Scyllium* (2) (the Dogfish), *Raja* (3).

The Class **Osteichthyes** (Ost-ee-ick-thees) contains the bony fishes whose skeleton is of true bone. There are two major groups. The Sub-class **Actinopterygii** contains most of the world's living fish. There are two pairs of fins – *pectoral* and *pelvic* – each of which has a broad base and is not fleshy. There is normally an air-bladder which acts as a 'buoyancy tank'. Order **Palaeoniscoidei** (Pal-ee-on-isk-oy-day-ee) contains many fossil forms and two present-day African fish. *Polypterus* (4) has heavy scales and in many ways resembles the ancient heavily armoured fish. Order **Chondrostei** (Cond-ros-tay-ee) contains more extinct fish and the present-day sturgeons [e.g. *Acipenser* (6)]. The skeletal bone is reduced and most of the skeleton is of cartilage, but there is no close connection with the cartilaginous fishes. The order **Holostei** when it first appeared many millions of years ago had many heavily armoured members but the heavy scales were gradually reduced and modern fishes arose from this group. Examples of Holostei still living are *Lepidosteus* (5) and *Amia* (7) – both American fish. The order **Teleostei** contains the modern fishes with symmetrical tails and thin scales. There are, however, many variations. Examples include *Clupea* (8) (Herring), *Hippocampus* (9) (Sea horse) and *Lophius* (10) (Angler).

The Sub-class **Crossopterygii** contains the lungfishes and their relatives. Only a few genera exist today but they go back a long way and it is certain that this type of fish – whose air-bladder can sometimes function as a lung – gave rise to the land animals. The fins have fleshy lobes. Examples include the lungfish *Protopterus* (11) and the coelacanth *Latimeria* (12).

The term 'Pisces' is a useful one when referring to fishes in general but it does not refer to any particular group.

(See Plate 117)

AMPHIBIA

The Class **AMPHIBIA.** The members of this class—as the name suggests—are capable of life in and out of water. The earliest land-living vertebrates must have been of this type—having developed from lung fishes in the Devonian period, about three hundred million years ago. Many of the early forms are known from fossil remains but it must not be thought that the modern forms are 'living fossils' resembling the ancestral amphibians. The modern frogs and toads are highly specialised animals, very successful in their own habitats. They are, however, dependent upon water for breeding and are, with some exceptions, confined to areas where water is available. Here they are common and form an important section of pond communities. Only very few amphibians can live in salt water.

Sub-class **Stegocephalia** (Steg-o-sef-alia) contains only extinct amphibians such as *Ichthyostega* (1), *Eryops* (2). The earliest of these animals were still very fish-like and possessed scales like those of fishes. However, very gradually these amphibians evolved into definite terrestrial types.

Modern amphibians are arranged in three distinct sub-classes. The adults have lungs but breathe to some extent through the damp skin, oxygen from the air passing into the blood stream here. The eggs are normally laid in water and hatch into larval forms—*tadpoles* (3) which breathe by means of external gills. The gills are lost in the adults, however.

The sub-class **Urodela** contains the tailed amphibians—newts and salamanders. Many of the latter retain larval characters in the adult and continue to live in water: e.g. *Necturus* (4). Others, such as *Salamandra* (6), are almost completely terrestrial. Newts [e.g. *Triturus* (5)] are normally terrestrial as adults, but some species of *Ambystoma* (7) remain aquatic and actually become sexually mature without metamorphosis. (See neoteny)

Sub-class **Anura** contains the frogs and toads—a very large group inhabiting the whole world. They are very much modified for jumping. The toads [e.g. *Bufo* (8)] are more fully adapted for life on land than frogs but still usually return to water to breed. *Pipa* (9) is an aquatic toad which carries its young in pits on its back. Frogs of the genus *Hyla* (10) live in trees, so do some of the other frogs. The common frog (11) is a member of the genus *Rana*.

Sub-class **Apoda** contains a few burrowing animals of tropical regions. They have no limbs and resemble earthworms, although there are small scales in the skin. The eggs are laid on land. Example: *Ichthyophis* (12).

(See Plate 118)

1
2
3
4
5
6
7
8
9
10
11
12
Haywood

REPTILIA (See page 280 for key)

PLATE 119

REPTILIA

Class **REPTILIA.** This group of animals developed many millions of years ago from one branch of the Amphibia. The reptiles lay shelled eggs (apart from some which give birth to active young) and are thus not dependent upon water for breeding. There is no free larval stage similar to that of the amphibian tadpole. The reptiles are intermediate between amphibians on the one hand and birds and mammals on the other. Only four groups of living reptiles are known, but there were many others in the past. They were abundant during the Jurassic period, about 150 million years ago when the huge dinosaurs were living, but from then on gradually disappeared, leaving the few modern forms.

Reptiles are covered with scales and when limbs are present they have five *digits* (i.e. fingers). They breathe by lungs only. Their activity depends upon the temperature of the surroundings. British snakes and lizards go to sleep (hibernate) during the winter and are sluggish in summer unless warmed by the sun.

The reptiles are grouped into sub-classes according to the structure of the skull.

Sub-class **Anapsida** contains the earliest reptiles such as *Seymouria* (1) and also the modern tortoises and turtles (order **Chelonia**). These latter animals have probably survived by virtue of their protective shells. They have no teeth. Examples: *Testudo* (2) and *Chelone* (3).

Sub-class **Parapsida** is extinct and contained the plesiosaurs and ichthyosaurs; e.g. *Ichthyosaurus* (4).

Sub-class **Diapsida** is the largest group of reptiles. It contains the order **Squamata** [snakes and lizards such as *Micrurus* (5), and *Lacerta* (6)]. As well as these animals this sub-class contains the New Zealand tuatara [*Sphenodon* (7)] and the crocodiles and alligators (order **Crocodilia**); e.g. *Crocodilus* (8). The large dinosaur reptiles and the pterodactyls are also included in the sub-class. Examples: *Diplodocus* (9), *Iguanodon* (10), and *Pterandon* (11). The sub-class **Synapsida** contains no living members but this group probably gave rise to the mammals. Example: *Dimetrodon* (12).

The large plant-eating dinosaurs had relatively small heads and brains and must have been clumsy creatures. The vegetation must have been very abundant in order to support them. At the end of the Cretaceous period – when the climate was cooling down – the vegetation could not support the animals and this perhaps aided the decline of the 'ruling reptiles'.

(See Plate 119)

AVES

This class contains the birds, whose chief characteristics are constant body temperature (warm-bloodedness), feathers and the egg-laying habit. The majority can fly and all living birds are toothless.

The sub-class **Archaeornithes** (Ark-ay-OR-nith-ees) contains the famous fossil bird *Archaeopteryx* (1) which had teeth and claws on its wings. All living birds are included in the sub-class **Neornithes** which contains four *super-orders*. The first – **Odontognathae** – contains a few extinct toothed forms such as *Hesperornis* (2). The super-order **Palaeognathae** contains the large flightless birds **(Ratites)** such as the ostrich [*Struthio* (4)], kiwi and cassowary, in a number of closely related orders. Penguins [e.g. *Spheniscus* (3)] belong to the super-order **Impennae.** They are confined to the Southern Hemisphere – mainly Antarctica – and are adapted for swimming. Their wings are like flippers. All flying birds belong to the **Neognathae** which contains many orders. The order names all end in *-formes*. The **Gaviiformes** contain the divers [e.g. *Gavia* (6)], of fresh and salt-water habitats. They are similar to the grebes [e.g. *Podiceps* (5)] of the **Podicipediformes** which inhabit inland waters making large floating nests. **Procellariformes** are all sea birds with long narrow wings; e.g. *Diomedea* (8), the albatross. The **Pelecaniformes** are diving birds feeding on fish. They usually nest in colonies; e.g. *Morus* (9), the gannet. Herons [e.g. *Ardea* (7)], flamingoes and storks belong to the order **Ciconiiformes.** They are mainly fish-feeding waders. The **Anseriformes** contain the ducks [e.g. *Anas* (10)] and swans. They are specialised for water life and feed with their flat bill. Hawks [e.g. *Vultur* (13), the condor] and the other day-flying birds of prey belong to the **Falconiformes.** They have sharp beaks and strong claws. The **Galliformes** are the game-birds. Mainly ground-living, they are poor fliers. Examples include the domestic fowls [e.g. *Meleagris* (11), the turkey], pheasants and peacocks. **Gruiformes** include the rails and cranes – water and marsh-living birds as a rule. Examples include *Fulica* (14), the coot, moorhens and cranes [e.g. *Grus* (12)]. They are normally good runners but do not fly well.

(See Plate 120)

1
2
3
4
5
6
7
8
9
10
11
12
13
14

1
2
3
4
5
6
7
8
9
10
11
12
13

AVES (cont.)

Wading birds such as snipe and redshanks *Tringa* (1) are typical of the order **Charadriiformes.** They have long legs and long beaks with which they pick up invertebrate animals for food. Lapwings are also included here as are the gulls [e.g. *Larus* (2)]—a specialised branch suited for life around the sea-shores. The **Columbiformes** are the pigeons [e.g. *Ducula* (3)] which are normally tree-living and good fliers. The extinct dodo was a ground-living member of this order. Cuckoos [e.g. *Cuculus* (4)] belong to the **Cuculiformes.** Some species build nests but most lay eggs in nests of other birds. The parrots (order **Psittaciformes**) are generally brightly coloured, tree-living birds. They live mainly upon fruits and seeds which they open with their curved beaks [e.g. *Melopsittacus* (5), the budgerigar]. **Strigiformes** are the owls—mainly night-flying birds of prey whose ears and eyes are large and able to detect mice and other animals from afar [e.g. *Tyto* (6), the barn owl]. The nightjar —*Caprimulgus* (7)—flies at dusk feeding on insects. It is a well camouflaged woodland bird of the order **Caprimulgiformes.** The **Micropodiformes** include the swifts, and humming-birds, which are very fast fliers with long narrow wings. The swifts [e.g. *Apus* (8)] are insect eaters, while the humming-birds feed on nectar from flowers. The **Coraciiformes** are mainly tropical and sub-tropical and brightly coloured. They include the long-beaked bee-eaters, the hornbills and the kingfishers [e.g. *Halcyon* (9)]. The latter are specialised for diving and catching fish. Woodpeckers (**Piciformes**) are adapted for climbing and wood-boring. The hard beak is used to probe holes in bark in the search for insect food [e.g. *Picus* (10)]. This order also includes the large-billed toucans.

The order **Passeriformes** contains almost as many species as the other orders combined. There are many families and the members are often called the 'perching birds' because the four toes are arranged for gripping branches. These birds are never very large—the crows [*Corvus* species (11)] are the largest. Finches, warblers and sparrows are all passeriformes. So also are the tits [*Parus* (12)] and the swallows, although the latter [e.g. *Hirundo* (13)] are very specialised for life in the air. Insect food is caught in flight as the bird rapidly turns from side to side.

The birds arose from reptiles millions of years ago. The mammals did likewise and the two groups have dominated the terrestrial scene ever since. The constant high temperature of both types of animal and the elaborate nervous system must have contributed to their success.

(See Plate 121)

MAMMALIA

The Class **MAMMALIA.** These animals are the most highly organised vertebrates. Their most obvious characteristics are hair and the mammary glands with which the female suckles her young. The mammals share with birds a constant high body temperature (enabling them to be active in cold weather). Most mammals retain their young in the womb until a fairly late stage of development. The first mammals appeared about 150 million years ago; they were about the size of small rats. They have since evolved many forms and spread all over the Earth. There are eighteen orders of mammals living today. Order **Monotremata** contains the duck-billed platypus [*Ornithorhynchus* (1)] and the spiny ant-eater [*Tachyglossus* (2)] of the Australian region. These animals lay eggs, and although they have hair and feed their young with milk they are very primitive mammals.

The order **Marsupialia** contains the 'pouched mammals' such as the Kangaroos [*Macropus* (3)], opossums [e.g. *Didelphys* (4)] and Koala bears [*Phascolarctos* (5)]. They occur only in Australasia and some parts of America. Young marsupials are born at a very early stage and nursed in the mother's pouch until two or three months old. All mammals other than the monotremes and marsupials are *placentals.* The young are kept within the mother's body and nourished through a special tissue – the *placenta* – until they are fairly well advanced. The order **Insectivora** is the most primitive of the placental groups. It includes the shrews, hedgehogs and moles [e.g. *Talpa* (6)], which feed mainly on insects and other small invertebrates. Bats are also mainly insect-feeders but some eat fruit too. They belong to the order **Chiroptera.** The bats are the only truly flying mammals; their wings are formed from thin membranes stretched between the long hand fingers and the hind limb. They are almost or quite blind and find their way by *echo-location;* high-pitched noises are emitted and the reflected sound is picked up by the large ears [e.g. *Plecotus* (7)]. There is a strange animal found in the Malayan region which shows resemblances to insectivores and to bats and also to some lemurs. It is called the 'flying lemur' or *Galeopithecus* (8), and is placed in a separate order – **Dermoptera.** It has folds of skin between front and back legs and uses them to glide down from trees where it feeds on fruit and leaves. The order **Edentata** contains three groups of animals all found in South America. Their teeth are reduced or absent – consistent with a diet of soft-bodied animals, especially ants. Examples include the armadillo [*Dasypus* (11)], the giant ant-eater [*Myrmecophaga* (9)], and *Bradypus* (10) – the three-toed sloth.

(See Plate 122)

PLATE 122

MAMMALIA (See page 285 for key)

MAMMALIA (See page 288 for key)

MAMMALIA (cont.)

The order **Pholidota** contains the scaly ant-eaters. *Manis* (1), of Africa and Asia. They have large claws and a long tongue which are used to feed upon ants and termites. The order **Primates** contains the monkeys, apes and man as well as *Tarsius* (2) and the lemurs of Madagascar. The fingers and toes are adapted for grasping branches, etc., as the primates were originally tree-living. The apes, e.g. *Pan*—the chimpanzee (3)—are tailless and differ in this respect from monkeys, e.g. *Cebus* (4). The **Rodentia** are very common animals—rats,mice, squirrels and many others. They are never very large and breed very rapidly Example *Sciurus* (5). Rabbits and hares, e.g. *Lepus* (6), belong to the order **Lagomorpha,** although they are in many ways similar to the rodents.

The order **Cetacea** (whales) are completely adapted for life in the water. The hind limbs have disappeared and the only hair is a patch of bristles around the mouth. There are two groups—the toothed whales such as *Physeter* (7) and the toothless, *whalebone* whales. The **Carnivora** is a large order with many species. The sub-order Fissipeda contains the dogs, cats, bears, and other groups such as weasels and badgers (*Meles,* 8). Seals and walruses belong to the sub-order Pinnipeda. They are marine animals but still return to the shore to breed. Example *Odobenus* (10), the walrus.

The aardvark, *Orycteropus* (9), is the only member of the order **Tubulidentata.** It is found in Central Africa where it feed on termites which it obtains by breaking open their nests with its strong claws and rooting among them with its long snout. The order **Hyracoidea** contains the conies—small African animals which feed on low-growing vegetation. Example *Procavia* (12). The elephants, e.g. *Elephas* (13), occur in Africa and the Indian region. They belong to the order **Proboscidea.** The teeth are grinding plates suited to a vegetable diet although the two upper front ones are very large, forming the tusks. Order **Sirenia** contains the sea-cows which like the whales are completely aquatic. They are vegetarians feeding on sea-weed and river vegetation. Example *Dugong* (11).

The final two orders—**Perissodactyla** and **Artiodactyla**—are the 'hoofed mammals'. The first contains horses, zebras (*Equus,* 15) and rhinos. The horses walk on only one toe (16)—the others being reduced. The added length of the leg gives greater speed. The same effect is gained in the Artiodactyla but they walk on two toes (17)—they are the cloven-hoofed mammals and include cows, deer and pigs. Example *Cervus* (14).

See plate 123